PETROLEUM-238

PETROLEUM-238

Big Oil's Dangerous Secret
and the Grassroots Fight to Stop It

Justin Nobel

Karret Press | Hudson New York | 2024

KARRET PRESS

An imprint of MissKarret

723 Columbia Street, Hudson New York

https://karretagency.com/

Cover and Book Layout Design by Sabrina Bedford
Cover Photo by Julie Dermansky

Print Book ISBN: 979-8989546237

eBook ISBN: 979-8989546299

SCIENCE / Environmental Science ; POLITICAL SCIENCE / Public Policy / Environmental Policy ; NATURE / Natural Resources

1st Printing

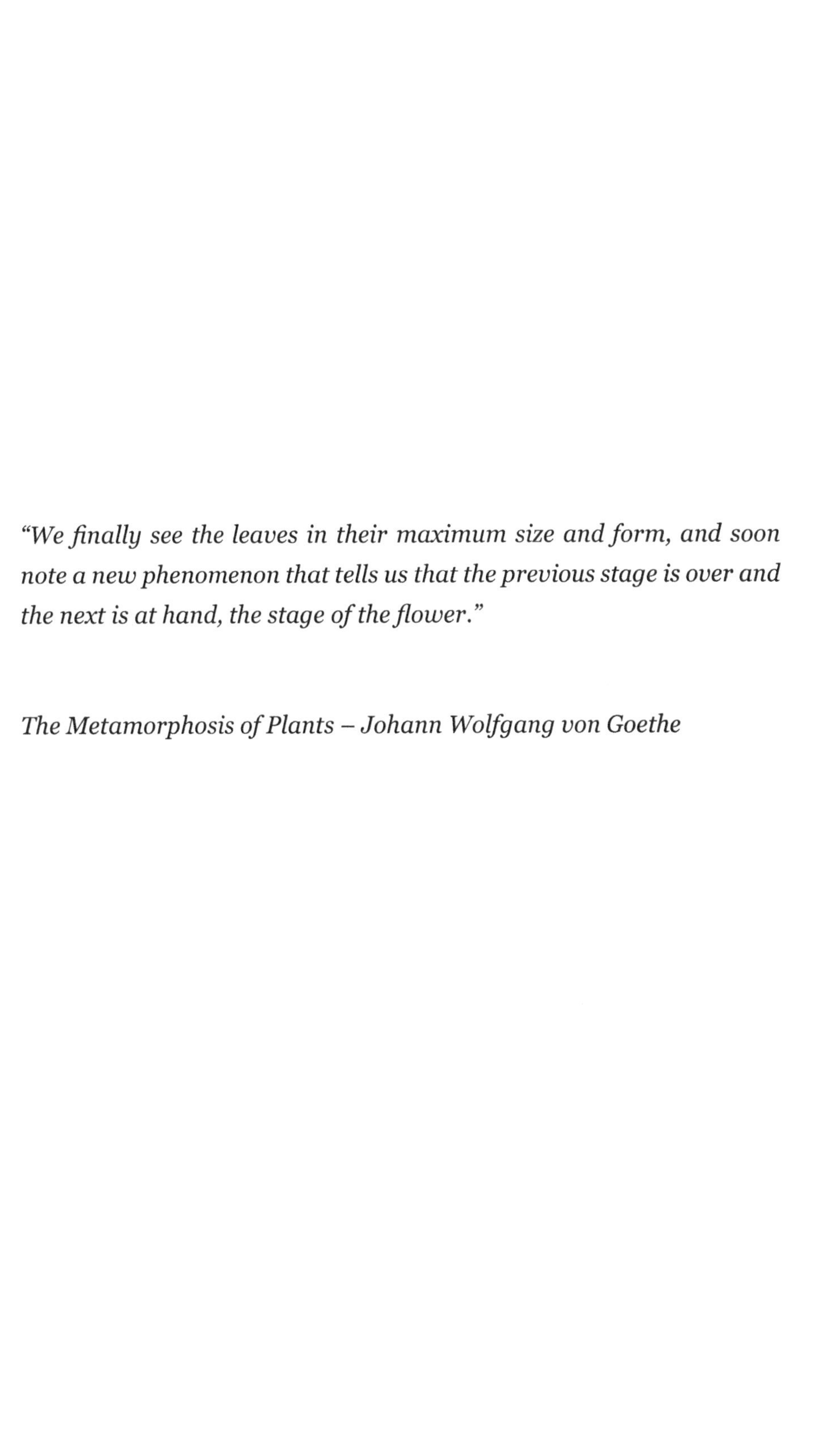

"We finally see the leaves in their maximum size and form, and soon note a new phenomenon that tells us that the previous stage is over and the next is at hand, the stage of the flower."

The Metamorphosis of Plants – Johann Wolfgang von Goethe

CONTENTS

There are a number of people whose words and stories are included in this book and informed my reporting yet passed away before the work could be completed. This book is dedicated to them:

Ray Beiersdorfer – Ohio geologist, educator & defender of community democracy

Shirley Palmer – Ohio sociologist, environmentalist and gardener

Stuart Smith – Louisiana environmental lawyer

Bill Hughes – West Virginia oilfield chronicler and educator

Mirijana Beram – West Virginia warrior and protector

Enrique Montañez – Brother of Ohio Taíno warrior Maria Montañez

April Pierson-Keating – West Virginia land protector & grassroots activism visionary, co-founder of POWHR Coalition

Teresa Mills – Self-taught environmental badass & relentless advocate for the people and the earth

Laurel Gulla – Wife of Pennsylvania community champion and educator

Ron Gulla – lived at site of state's second Marcellus shale gas well

Randy Moyer – Pennsylvania truck driver and oilfield brine hauler

¤ ¤ ¤

For Amy, who helped in more ways than you'll ever know. And all the others struggling against a fight that seems too big~

Author's Note

In Paris France there are fine cafés and famous landmarks but what nobody really knows is at the other end of a building known as *Le V*, on the northeast side of the city is a portal that leads to a secret pile of fracking waste in the woods of West Virginia. A lot more comes to the surface at an oil and gas well than just the oil and gas, including billions of pounds of waste every day across the US, much of it toxic and radioactive. My journey into this topic started when an Ohio community organizer told me someone made a liquid deicer out of radioactive oilfield waste for home driveways and patios that was supposedly "Safe for Pets" and had been selling it at Lowe's. As you will see, this indeed was the case. And unraveling how that came to be turned into a 20-month *Rolling Stone* magazine investigation, which won an award with thc National Association of Science Writers, and eventually became this book.

It almost doesn't seem real, you might deny it, but really all that has happened here is a powerful industry has spread harms across the land, its people, and more so than anyone, their very own workers, and did what they could to make sure no one ever put all the pieces together, and no one ever has—until now. Many people tell me there is nothing to see here, the levels aren't that bad, but unfortunately this is the same thing the oil and gas industry's shadow network of radioactive waste workers have often been told. So they work on, shoveling and scooping waste, mixing it with lime and coal ash and ground up corncobs in an attempt to try and lower the radioactivity levels, without appropriate protection, sometimes in just T-shirts, eating lunch and smoking cigarettes and occasionally having barbecue cookouts in this absurdly contaminated workspace. Sludge splattered all over their bodies, liquid waste splashing across their faces and into their eyes and mouths, inhaling radioactive dust, waste eating away their boots, soaking their socks, encrusting their clothes, which will often be brought home and washed in the family washing machine, or a local hotel, further spreading contamination. Oilfield waste has been spilled, spread, injected, dumped, and freely emitted across this nation. And contamination has been discharged—sometimes illegally, often legally—into the same rivers America's towns and cities draw their drinking water from.

Just the other month I visited an abandoned fracking waste treatment plant on a large US river where unknowing local kids had been partying. It was littered with beer cans and condoms and parts of it were more deeply contaminated with radioactivity than most of the Chernobyl Exclusion Zone. I was there with a former Department of Energy scientist and his Geiger counter issued a terrifying alarm—at around 2 milliroentgens per hour. He had samples tested at a radiological analysis lab and discovered the radioactive element radium to be 5,000 times general background levels.

It's all right there in the industry's own research and reports. And this is the beauty of science, an incredible record of our world and its ways laid out across time, and like a sacred language it moves through time, collecting new bits and building. One can go back to 1904, when a 25-year-old Canadian graduate student named Eli described "experiments with a highly radioactive gas obtained from crude petroleum." Or 1982, when a report of the American Petroleum Institute's Committee for Environmental Biology and Community Health stated: "Almost all materials of interest and use to the petroleum industry contain measurable quantities of radionuclides that reside finally in process equipment, product streams, or waste." Radium, they warned, was "a potent source of radiation exposure, both internal and external," while the radioactive gas radon and its polonium daughters "deliver significant population and occupational exposures." Radon is America's second leading cause of lung cancer deaths and naturally contaminates natural gas. Which means it is being emitted out of home stoves in parts of the country at levels high enough to generate public health risks, and over time, cancer and deaths. The 1982 American Petroleum Institute report concluded: "regulation of radionuclides could impose a severe burden on API member companies."

And they have triumphed, as the radioactivity brought to the surface in oil and gas development was never federally regulated and remains unregulated. The industry was granted a federal exemption in 1980 that legally defined their waste as nonhazardous, despite containing toxic chemicals, carcinogens, heavy metals and all the radioactivity. As the nuclear forensics scientist Dr. Marco Kaltofen has told me: "With fossil fuels, essentially what you are doing is taking an underground radioactive reservoir and bringing it up to the surface where it can interact with people and the environment." And he said this too: "Radiation is complex and difficult to understand but it leaves hundreds of clues."

Known to precious few people, the mineral scale and sludge that accumulates in our 321,000-plus miles of natural gas gathering and transmission pipelines can be filled with stunning levels of the same isotope of polonium assassins used in 2006 to murder former Russian security officer Alexander Litvinenko, by placing an amount smaller than a grain of sand in his tea at a London hotel bar. Natural gas pipeline sludge, reads a 1993 article on oilfield radioactivity published in the Society of Petroleum Engineers' *Journal of Petroleum Technology* can become so radioactive it requires "the same handling as low-level radioactive wastes." And yet, by US law, it is still considered nonhazardous. Unlike the cosmic radiation an airline passenger is exposed to, or the X-rays of a CT scan, moving around radioactive oilfield sludge or scale invariably creates dust and particles which an unprotected worker may easily inhale or ingest, thereby bringing radioactive elements inside their body, where they can decay and fire off radiation in the intimate and vulnerable space of the lungs, guts, bones or blood.

Then the real revelation, the oil and gas workers politicians regularly celebrate are getting their bodies and clothing covered in waste that can be toxic and radioactive but legally defined as nonhazardous. I ask these politicians now, as workers regularly ask me, is it still nonhazardous as they are breathing it in? Or tracking it through the door of their home and into their family? This same 1980 exemption allows radioactive oilfield waste to be transported from foreign countries seamlessly across America's borders and deposited in the desert of West Texas. I have been there.

This is a story about worker justice. This is a story about environmental justice. This is an astonishing scientific story. We live on a radioactive planet, and oil and gas happens to bring up some of Earth's most interesting, and notorious, radioactive elements. They can be concentrated in the formation below, and further concentrated by the industry's processes at the surface. From day one, which in the United States was 1859, the US oil and gas industry has had no good idea what to do with this waste. And so began an extraordinary campaign to get rid of it all. Modern fracking has only worsened the problem, by tapping into even more radioactive formations, bringing drilling closer to communities, and vastly increasing the amount of waste.

In a 1979 Congressional hearing, Texas oilfield regulators, using figures calculated by the American Petroleum Institute, provided a clue as to just what more rigorous regulations, ones that actually labeled the oilfield's most dangerous waste as hazardous, might mean for the industry: a "one time cost of over $34 billion to bring existing operations into compliance" and "as high as $10.8 billion per year." That number would be drastically higher today, but no one has done the math, in part because the full picture of costs and harms has remained unknown.

Whether it is a multinational company out of Paris, or the guy in rural Pennsylvania who stashed fracking waste beneath a courthouse, readers will be surprised at how deep this rabbit hole goes, and how close it may touch to the thing they call home, or the things they cherish. It is out of this unknowing, and deception, that this book can exist. My challenge to you is read it through to the end, and realize, this is not a book about despair—to say it, is to know it, is to change it.

SECTION I

1
Mississippi: Every Man May Lay His Hand to the Drill and Sink Wells

The story begins with James Earl Renfroe, a Black man whose eyes were eaten away by radioactive dust. Renfroe worked for a White man who operated an oilfield pipe-cleaning yard named James Case. Case is no longer around but his daughter Janice still is, and to reach her I travel a back road in rural Mississippi that leads into a pine forest. In a clearing are the charred remains of the James Case Grocery & Gas Station. It's a dramatic husk of a structure that appears to have just recently been engulfed in flames, with the word "Grocery" still visible on a burnt and crumbling outer wall. My initial thought was, I have arrived just a moment too late.

But the gas station is still in business, and for the time being run out of a small white building across the street and at the far end of a parking lot of pinkish stones. Gas is pumped directly to cars and trucks from large tanks, then customers pay inside, where utility shelves of motor oil stand beside a wooden mural of Jesus's Last Supper. Janice Case Britt is in back and out of view, although the sound can be heard of a coke being opened, and she comes forward with the drink in a tall frosted yellow glass, takes a seat at one of the plastic folding tables set out on the shop floor and says:

"Daddy had the lawsuit with Chevron because of the oilfield pipes that been contaminated, is that what you want to know?"

It is. And it is Christmas time. And Janice wears a sweater decorated in gold and silvery Christmas trees. People enter the shop for gas, everyone she knows by name. Small gossips and gatherings are shared, and Janice drinks her soda out of that fogged glass, the little ice cubes with holes slowly melting into cylinders then nothing, and she considers her past, and how much of it she will be able to tell, how much she even remembers. Seated in an office chair beside casually unspooling a roll of Christmas lights is her cousin Linda.

The Case clan is large, with various lines, and have owned land and run farms on the west side of Brookhaven, Mississippi for over 100 years. Never wealthy, but certainly a few steps above poor, and always hard-workers. Work, work, work, and never stopped working. They had cows, which could be milked, eaten, or sold. And timber, which could be made into homes and structures or sold. And pigs, which were usually just eaten. Also fields and a garden. And by and by, a life was made, a line continued, a culture carried forward. Except that during the beginning part of the 1900s, something extraordinary happened in these piney woods.

"I'll drink all the oil found east of the Mississippi River," a prominent geologist had said. Because until then no major oilfield had been discovered in the Southeast. But the oilmen suspected it was there, and during the early 1900s peppered Mississippi with holes. In the 1920s drillers found their way to the Jackson Gas Field, which happened to directly underlie Mississippi's capital city. The first well produced in 1930, and a frantic boom set in. Drilling occurred on the grounds of an insane asylum, in the lush bottomland of the Pearl River as it kinked through the city, and just a mile from the capitol building itself.

One city attorney, returning on horseback from a squirrel hunt, witnessed a drilling rig explode, disintegrate the derrick, shoot pipe, mud and rock into the air, blast open a crater. Another well near the city center blew little gas but lots of saltwater. A group of entrepreneurs constructed a swimming pool with wood sides and a sand floor, then filled it with "hot saltwater from the well" and called it Crystal Lake, according to the veteran southern oilman, Dudley Hughes, who wrote a book. The lake was "enjoyed by many Jacksonians for its balmy waters," although some complained of "the fumes, and the salt's burning children's eyes."

The boom was on, and a race commenced to find other gushers believed to be hidden across the state. "What Mississippi needs," said Governor Theodore Bilbo in 1930, is anywhere the geology seemed good for oil, "give to every man, whomsoever he may be, the right and full freedom to lay his hand to the drill and sink wells." But, every man in 1930 Mississippi was not free to lay his hand to the drill and sink wells.

It turns out, as is the case with many producing regions, Mississippi's oil formations were scattered across the state like popcorn kernels. In 1939, oil was struck outside Yazoo City, and during the early 1940s, drillers discovered other kernels, and boomtowns began popping up. Deposits were so localized that a single neighborhood or even a single street could have one side deeply in the formation, and the other side distinctly not. In this manner, oil emerged at Heidelberg, Hub, Soso, Flora, Cranfield, Cary, Eucutta, Pickens, Gwinville, Carthage Point, Baxterville, Langsdale, Fayette, Mallalieu, and on the west side of Brookhaven, where the Case clan was located.

"The whole state is swarming with geologists, roustabouts, scouts, roughnecks, tool pushers, riggers, drillers, lease hounds, wildcatters, speculators, lawyers, tipsters and gypsters," Collier's magazine reported in 1945. Soon enough, there was another job, one few locals, or anyone really, knew much about, but the Case's jumped to it. The task involved cleaning oilfield pipes and sounded simple.

Many oil and gas wells will end up producing much more of an extremely salty liquid, known as oilfield brine, than they ever will oil or gas. The industry also calls this waste produced water, or salt water, and in the 1820s in Kentucky and Tennessee they actually mined it, in order to make salt, with the oil considered an unwanted byproduct. Those roles were eventually reversed, and throughout the industry's history drillers directed the unwanted oilfield brine into pits dug beside the well, or intentionally dumped it into ditches, streams, swamps, quarries, bayous—or a wood-sided swimming pool for children. But there is more than just water and salt, brine typically contains benzene, a carcinogenic compound often associated with oil and gas deposits, and toxic heavy metals like arsenic, lead, strontium and barium. Brine can also be rich in the radioactive metal radium.

No one knows the rath of radium better than Dr. Harrison Martland, the Newark, New Jersey medical examiner who autopsied half a dozen *radium girls* and studied the ailing bodies of many more. These women worked in Midwest and Northeast factories during the 1910s and 1920s, applying a radium-based paint to the dials of watches and clocks. Radiation emitted by the radium excited zinc sulfide molecules in the paint, causing the timepieces to glow. The women ran their brushes between their lips to keep the tips firm, accidentally ingesting significant amounts of radium. Leading scientists doubted their illness, as did the radium industry, but Martland proved beyond a doubt radium contamination had sickened and killed them.

Radium and calcium are elements in the same column of the Periodic Table, and chemically-speaking, resemble one another. "Most of the paint swallowed passed rapidly through the gastrointestinal tract and was eliminated," Martland wrote, in a 1931 report in *The American Journal of Cancer*, but a small amount "was continually absorbed and eventually stored...in the bones" and "emitted their characteristic radiations day after day, month after month, and year after year." The radium girls developed painful tumors in the hip, leg, spine and skull, as well as various cancers of the blood, and experienced a condition called necrosis of the jaw, or radium jaw, in which parts of the mouth rotted so thoroughly they crumbled to pieces.

Radium has many forms, or isotopes, and the two most significant are radium-226, with a half-life of 1,600 years, and radium-228, with a roughly 6-year half-life. This refers to the general amount of time it will take a radioactive element to decay, blasting off a tiny piece of itself—radiation—to become another element, known as a daughter, which may also be radioactive. Only an "infinitesimal amount of radio-active substance" is "necessary to destroy life," Martland wrote. For example, a radium sample roughly ten million times smaller than a sand grain distributed throughout the bones can "produce a horrible death years after it has been ingested." And radium-226's long half-life meant the radium girls would remain radioactive long after death. "For instance in the year 3491 A.D.," Martland wrote, "the skeleton will still be giving off 185,000 alpha particles per second."

Harrison Martland has come to be known as one of the founders of occupational health medicine and had a New Jersey medical center named for him. From his experience with the radium girls he came away with several important revelations: radiation can cause cancer, we live on a radioactive planet so some cancer may be expected, and increasing our exposure to radioactivity by even minute amounts may increase the amount of cancer. "The radium cases should be looked upon as an unfortunate but valuable experiment," he wrote, "in which, through ignorance and lack of proper governmental supervision, human beings have been allowed to swallow, over long periods of time, radio-active substances."

What is astonishing about the oilfield pipe-cleaning operation James Case had set up in his family's backyard is a situation had been created in an entirely different profession, place and time, that nevertheless simulated the radium girls' exposure path. While the women ingested tiny drops of radioactive paint, the men in James Case's oilfield pipe-cleaning yard inhaled copious amounts of radioactive dust.

¤ ¤ ¤

The sound of a glass being put on a table. Janice has finished her coke, cousin Linda reads a local newspaper. They talk about a shop down the road called Funky Monkey, which sells flavored ice, flamingo yard art, shiny pottery from Mexico and where there has recently been a death in the family. Time drips forward at what presently remains of the James Case Grocery & Gas Station. The past is buried, rises to life, upon death gets back to being buried.

As oilfield brine journeys with the oil and gas to the surface temperature and pressure changes and certain metals, including barium, strontium and radium can accumulate on the inside of the piping as a hardened mineral deposit the industry calls pipe-scale. This scale may be white, like the middle part of an Oreo, and is very difficult to remove. In the US, radioactivity is often measured in picocuries per gram. Radioactive metals are natural in earth's soils and radium is regularly found at a level of around 1 picocurie per gram, referred to as background radiation. EPA is so concerned about radium that toxic waste sites contaminated with it typically must cleanup the topsoil to below 5 picocuries per gram above the background radiation levels, yet radium in pipe-scale averages around 500 picocuries per gram and can be as high as 750,000.

Oilfield pipes are typically about two to seven inches across, 30 feet long, and connect together from the surface down to the oil and gas-bearing formation, thousands of feet below. Over a matter of years pipe-scale can grow so thick it blocks the flow of oil and gas up these pipes to the surface. A now outdated EPA report from the early 1990s estimated 3.2 million cubic feet of radioactive oilfield pipe-scale are generated each year—37 dump trucks every hour. To remove it, piping must be pulled up piece by piece then cleaned, a task often performed away from the oilfield. James Case did it in his family's backyard.

"My daddy had a flatbed truck," says Janice, "and he would go around the oilfields of Mississippi, he used to go to Laurel, and Soso, and he would pick up loads of pipe and come back home." Case was not an oilman, he was a farmer, but he knew about machines and tools. Here was a specific job required by an industry with gobs of money that relied on inventing a clever way to clean the inside of a 30-foot-long steel pipe. The tools were not so different than what a dentist uses to clean teeth. A hydroblaster used a thin potent jet of water to blast off the scale, pushing a sloppy liquid discharge out the other end of the pipe. An air rattler used a drill bit driven by compressed air to chisel off the scale, creating tremendous amounts of dust.

The human work involved someone on one side who helped guide these cleaning tools through the pipe, then the person who caught them as they came out the other end, known as the catcher. Of the different jobs in a pipe-cleaning yard, catcher is the most dangerous. The slop of liquid radioactive waste shot through the pipe by the hydroblaster would splash at the catcher's feet, as would the radioactive dust generated by the air rattler. Protected by anything but a full hazmat suit and face mask with its own oxygen supply, a catcher would get contaminated. Their boots and socks would get soaked in the highly radioactive liquid, and they would accidentally inhale and ingest significant amounts of radioactive dust. Dust would coat their clothes, skin, eyes and lips too, leading to additional exposures. Gamma rays zinging up from the radioactive dust accumulated on the ground, groundshine, and radiation shooting back down from dust floating above the yard, cloudshine, would have locked the yard in an invisible radioactive firestorm, and be freely piercing the catcher's body.

All organs have their own radiation risks but an eye is one of the few places in a human body where a naked organ—one that is not the skin, protected by layers of dead cells—essentially sits on the surface and is uniquely vulnerable. Elements of the eye, reads an article in the medical textbook, *Radiotherapy of Intraocular and Orbital Tumors*, "are exquisitely sensitive to ionizing radiation." One reason is cells in certain parts of the eye do not rejuvenate, and if they are damaged by radioactivity have limited repair capabilities. And yet, other layers of the eye—cornea, conjunctiva, lens—contain cells that replicate regularly, making them especially vulnerable to chromosome-mutating blasts of radiation.

In 1987, the Society of Petroleum Engineers published an article that addressed radioactive oilfield pipes in their *Journal of Petroleum Technology*. The paper points out that stuck in the pipe the radioactivity is significantly less dangerous, but at pipe-cleaning yards the scale is crumbled into "flakes" by the cleaning tools then distributed across the yard. The radiation dose received by pipe-cleaners was high enough they would shoot past annual Nuclear Regulatory Commission limits for non-nuclear industry workers in three days. "Protective clothing should be worn by all personnel" and removed and washed before leaving the yard, the Society of Petroleum Engineers article reads. To prevent ingestion, the chewing of gum or tobacco should be prohibited in the work area, and "when the work has been completed, the controlled area should be decontaminated." At James Case's oilfield pipe-cleaning operation none of these measures occurred.

"The pipe would be on rollers," recalls Janice. "Daddy would have one man running the part of the machine that the drill bit or water jet chewed into, and another man at the other end of the pipe," the catcher. "My daddy, and both my brothers worked in it," she continues. "We had two or three Black men that worked in it too. And there certainly wasn't any protective gear for the workers—gloves and a hardhat. But my daddy was innocent, he didn't know he was exposing anyone. Daddy come to find out the oil companies knew about the contamination, but they never told us. The big boys swept it under the rug, our case proved it. We had a lawyer, I never thought I would forget his name..."

But she has. Although cousin Linda remembers: "Stuart Smith."

"That's right," says Janice, "Stuart Smith. Let me tell you something, he ate that Chevron lawyer up and down."

¤ ¤ ¤

Born in New Orleans, Stuart's father was a gambler, and he dropped out of high school at age 15 but encouraged by a hard-working mother eventually graduated law school. He was motivated for justice after a freak accident in which his younger brother was hit by a car then dropped on his head while being lifted into the ambulance. "I wanted to hold people accountable for hurting others," he wrote in *Crude Justice*, a book about his life, and "fight big corporations." His brother lay for several days brain-dead in the hospital before his mother decided to remove him from life support and donate his organs.

Stuart first fell into the world of oilfield radioactivity one day in 1989, at age 29, when he a took a cold call from a man named Winston Street running an oilfield pipe-cleaning operation in Laurel, Mississippi, 85 miles east of James Case. They had also taken pipes from Chevron, and Shell, and radioactive scale had contaminated the property, the worker's bodies, and even relatives and family members. "I had to roll the dice on this one," Stuart wrote. "You eat what you kill," his mentor Jack Harang, a well-known New Orleans trial attorney had told him. "If you don't kill, you don't eat."

Stuart would soon learn valuable knowledge. After the use of nuclear weapons in World War II radioactivity was to be regulated by the Atomic Energy Commission, and later the Nuclear Regulatory Commission. While radiation generated in nuclear energy and medicine were included in regulations, oilfield radioactivity never was. No one had tried an oilfield pipe-cleaning case before, but the harms appeared massive, and potentially there would be a lot to eat. Though up against two of the planet's most powerful corporations, the kill might be difficult.

"As I sat in our small downtown New Orleans office, building the case...became a nonstop obsession," Stuart wrote. Early on, Shell settled, but Chevron continued forward, practicing what Stuart called a "scorched earth policy," trying to break him financially and maybe even spiritually by dragging out the case. "It was a risky strategy," he wrote. "But if it worked, the oil giant would have squelched similar lawsuits from the other pipe-cleaning yards that it did business with." The truth was becoming apparent, this was a much bigger problem than a single pipe-cleaning yard in a single state. Stuart had discovered an extraordinary oilfield secret.

"The failure to properly protect workers or warn them of the health risks was instead a standard industry practice, carried out across the United States and all around the globe," he wrote. In the industry's wake one could expect a trail of radiation-sickened oilfield workers, and liability in the billions. Stuart wondered, "if the pipe-rattlers of Laurel, Mississippi" did not represent "the 'Radium Boys' of the latter twentieth century." He also learned that because radioactive pipe-scale was so difficult to remove the industry often gave up on the task and donated pipes, to ranchers across Louisiana and Texas, for building fences, and schools across Louisiana and Mississippi, to construct fences and playgrounds.

The trial for Winston Street's oilfield pipe-cleaners began in June 1992. "I'm extremely scared of cancer," one worker testified. "I don't think anyone knows what this stuff can really do to us." Another worker, wrote Stuart, said, "it had been the nastiest job he'd ever worked in his life, with thick scale coating his overalls and getting in his mouth." The man described how on some days his wife came to bring him lunch and brought their three kids, all toddlers. They chased each other around the yard and made sandcastles out of the radioactive pipe-scale dust. On one occasion, the man testified, he found his two-year-old daughter "sitting in a pile of it, eating it."

Meanwhile, Karen, the 26-year-old wife of one pipe-cleaner, sat on the edge of the bathtub while six months pregnant and her hip cracked in half. Pipes had been cleaned behind her home and tests showed the soil in their vegetable garden had become contaminated with radium. A doctor "confirmed that Karen was suffering from severe radium-induced bone necrosis," wrote Stuart, "undoubtedly linked to her exposure to the radioactive gunk that had traveled all the way from the oil patch to her backyard."

By the fall of 1992 the case was dragging. "Doubt was creeping in," Stuart wrote. "Had it all been a reckless mistake, taking that phone call from Winston and taking the case?" What if the dice came up snake eyes, he wondered.

The big break came when a law student on Stuart's "dream team" noticed Chevron's radiation expert, Henry T. Miller, had delivered two papers on radioactivity for an oil and gas conference in the Netherlands but Chevron hadn't disclosed that in court. Apparently, the company was keeping documents from Stuart. Late one night the Chevron attorney Ralph Johnson, a well-respected expert in the field of radiation law, knocked on Stuart's hotel room door. He carried files revealing Chevron had conducted extensive studies on oilfield pipe-cleaning and concluded there was a real radiation risk to workers. "It appeared he knew Chevron was in big trouble," Stuart wrote of Johnson, "and he was not going to take the fall." Not long after, Chevron settled.

The brash young attorney from New Orleans had defeated an oilfield giant and opened an entirely new field of environmental law. During the 1990s Stuart searched for other contamination and found, "a widespread pattern of highly unsafe dumping in which Big Oil companies," knew the risks, allowed local citizens to remain in the dark, and "littered these poor, rural communities with toxic and radioactive wastes," frequently in ways that contaminated their drinking water. The next case he took on was James Case's oilfield pipe-cleaning operation in Brookhaven, Mississippi. EPA investigators, visiting at the request of Mississippi's Division of Radiological Health, "found radium-226 in the grass in the Case cow pasture at levels 160 times above background," wrote Stuart.

"Proving once and for all that the poisonous radioactive material from the pipe scale will leach out and enter the food chain."

James Case's place, Stuart reckoned, since it had been in operation for longer, was even more wildly contaminated than Winston Street's operation. "The Cases actually lived out behind the pipe-rattling yard and the gas station," he wrote, "and their kids had frolicked in the radioactive dust."

¤ ¤ ¤

"God," says Linda, remembering back to 1957, when James Case first opened his pipe-cleaning operation, "that was 65 years ago." For the Case children and their cousins, a backyard family operation generating huge amounts of sand-like material and filled with pipes was like a gigantic playground. "We loved running along the pipes, and we would walk along them too," Linda recalls. "We were barefooted, too hot to wear shoes." And what came of such frolic? "My family had stomach, throat, breast and lung cancer," says Linda, "but we lived." Not everyone did.

"Mr. Renfroe worked for my daddy from the time he was 18," says Janice, "but he didn't just do pipe-cleaning, he milked cows and he bushhogged, and him and his family lived on my daddy's place. I used to tote their children on my hip when I was little, they had four."

The Renfroe children were David Earl, who died of cancer, two other brothers, both still around, and a daughter, Lisa Renfroe, who Janice says used to work for her right here at the gas station. The children's mother was Eva Mae Renfroe, and she's still alive. As for James Earl Renfroe, he was the catcher, entirely unprotected, and in a constant swirl of radioactive dust. One of Stuart's radioactivity experts told me Renfroe received a shocking dose. With all the dust his eyes had been particularly bombarded, and he eventually went blind. And "died with cancer," says Janice.

Eva Mae lives on the east side of Brookhaven. James Case Grocery & Gas is on the west side. Like many southern towns and cities, White and

Black, Black and White. I must travel back down the rural road, across the pine forest and through downtown. History books say Brookhaven was founded in 1818 by Samuel Jayne, who arrived from Long Island, New York and established a trading post and gristmill on what was Choctaw Indian land. But credit for the town's true blossoming is typically granted to Milton Whitworth, who in 1858 secured a railroad, milled the pine into lumber to build the town, founded a women's college, and owned a slave plantation.

"These pioneer planters," says a local history of Brookhaven's *Fine Families*. "Built their own homes, cultivated their land, raised their children, contributed to the vibrancy of the county." Even today, this is the happy story many Brookhaven residents tell themselves. And presently, in downtown modern Brookhaven it is Christmas to the hilt, with decorations in most shop windows. Streets lined with magnolia trees. Sidewalks bunched with their white and pink blossoms.

In a central plaza near the train tracks, and across a wealthy neighborhood of wedding cake-like homes with white columns and long green lawns, are nativity scenes. Father Joseph with a luminous lantern illuminates the world. Young mother Mary is innocence and purity. Baby Jesus represents salvation for all humankind. Shepherds keep the flock. The lambs, a symbol of innocent suffering. And so on, with the wise men, the pack animals, the angels, all beset in light.

Something I do not detect, is a publicly visible monument to slavery, to the bodies and faces who walked these early streets, worked these fields, made this land grow. Human beings like Charlie Moses, who was born into bondage and later, at the age of 84, told the Federal Writers' Project,

> "My marster was mean an' cruel...His name was Jim Rankin an' he lived out on a plantation over in Marion County. I was born an' raised on his place. I spec I was 'bout twelve year old at the time o' the war.

> Old man Rankin worked us like animals. He had a right smart plantation an' kep' all his Niggers, 'cept one house boy, out in the fiel' a-workin'. He'd say, 'Niggers is meant to work. That's what I paid my good money for 'em to do.'
>
> He had two daughters an' two sons. Them an' his poor wife had all the work in the house to do, 'cause he wouldn' waste no Nigger to help 'em out. His family was as scared o' him as we was. They lived all their lives under his whip. No Sir! No Sir! There warnt no meaner man in the world than old man Jim Rankin...The way us Niggers was treated was awful. Marster would beat, knock, kick, kill. He done ever'thing he could 'cept eat us. We was worked to death. We worked all Sunday, all day, all night. He whipped us 'til some jus' lay down to die. It was a poor life. I knows it aint right to have hate in the heart, but, God Almighty! It's hard to be forgivin' when I think of old man Rankin.
>
> ...I 'member a song we sung, then. It went kinda like this:
>
> Free at las',
> Free at las',
> Thank God Almighty
> I's free at las'.
> Mmmmm, mmmmm, mmmmm."

There is also nothing I can see to mark the violent lynchings that occurred right in downtown Brookhaven up through the 1950s. The Equal Justice Initiative, which maintains a verified list by county from 1877 to 1950 shows 10 lynchings occurred here in Lincoln County. Men shot on the courthouse lawn, like Lamar Smith, a World War I veteran, farmer and businessman working to register Black voters. Men hung from a telegraph pole, like Eli Pigot, accused of sexually assaulting the daughter of a prominent White family. Men like Stanley Bearden, involved in a fight with White service station owners over an unpaid bill of $6. According to the *Lincoln County Times*, he was tied to the back of a truck and dragged "through the streets of the city and through the negro quarters," then hung from a tree.

The fields are still there, the trees are still there, the same Mississippi skies are still there, the same wet earth, the same shiny metals and minerals, and fuels, but not everybody has been able to access them. "I just know that most of the wells are on White people's property, even though they are close to Black people's property," says James Crowell III, leading him to believe, "they drilled on White people's land to get to the oil on Black people's land." For 33 years Crowell served as the Biloxi, Mississippi Chapter President of the NAACP, with much of his time spent trying to secure good jobs for his community. "There have been efforts made to keep the Black community out of the riches of the oil and gas industry," he says, "and also the work." Photos of Mississippi oilfield workers show crew after crew of White men.

"At least one black citizen of Mississippi participated in the drilling boom," writes Dudley Hughes in *Oil in the Deep South*. His subject was Dr. S.D. Redmond, and the author devotes just four sentences to him. In reading them it is learned he built a derrick to drill a well that was destroyed by "lightning"—in Rankin County. Was it really? Perhaps we'll never know. But Redmond turned his lease over to Pioneer Oil and Gas Company, which drilled a highly profitable gas well, and that is that as far as the Black southern oil experience goes in the eyes of Dudley Hughes, and apparently also, his patrons at the Mississippi Geological Society, his publishers at University Press of Mississippi. Names, names, and names unknown—what is not written down in the history books, may never get known. But we do know, from the story of James Case's pipe-cleaning yard, there were other Black men in the oilfields of Mississippi.

To get to where one of them once lived I cross the railroad tracks on Monticello in downtown Brookhaven and turn left on North 2nd Street, passing Mama Ruby's, a popular soul food and southern barbecue spot. On the Monday before Christmas, meatloaf is being served, the sheriff is parked outside, and the place is packed. Continuing along a stretch of road leading out of the city center, a string of churches, a roller skating rink, and the little community of Pearlhaven and its pleasant greenspace of Bicentennial Park, where a furry green carpet of epiphytes covers the live oak tree trunks and branches. Onward by small shotgun homes, a man on a bicycle, a road littered with fallen beechnuts that spreads out into a neighborhood of mobile homes.

It is Christmas here too. At Eva Mae's place, clothes are drying in the sun on the wooden porch, and silver foil covers the two back windows. Nothing can be seen of the inside, but through the walls I hear a commercial advertising the TV show, *Walker, Texas Ranger*. The door opens. It is the daughter, Lisa, in a shower cap and pink and neon yellow pajamas. I ask if Eva Mae might be interested in speaking about her late husband James Earl Renfroe, and what happened so many years ago back at James Case's place, and Renfroe's job cleaning oilfield pipes, and just how he got sick, and just how he died.

"My mama is 77 years old," Lisa tells me, "and she don't remember that anymore."

"And what about you?" I ask Lisa. Lisa too, she doesn't remember.

And just why is it worth remembering? And just what is worth knowing?

The answer, of course, is that today, is tomorrow, is yesterday too.

2

On Park Avenue NYC All is Fine, Until it is Not

Clare Donohue is dressed in a black outfit with a colorful scarf and seated at a wooden table near the window in Bonjour Crepes & Wine, a block off Park Avenue in Manhattan. She is not a nuclear scientist, in fact, she is an interior designer. But as she cuts into her crepe and stares out at the street scene she poses an interesting research question: Is the dreaded radioactive element polonium accumulating in New York City apartments?

Polonium, mind you, is one of the most toxic substances on the planet. A single gram of polonium-210 could potentially kill fifty million people, meaning a quantity the size of 46 sugar packets could kill everyone on earth. When on November 1, 2006, assassins snuck from 50 to about 100 micrograms of polonium, less than a grain of sand, into the tea of former Russian security officer Alexander Litvinenko at a London hotel bar the poison swiftly absorbed into his bloodstream, decimated his bone marrow's ability to produce new blood cells, and accumulated in his brain, liver, kidneys and testicles. Within seven hours he was vomiting uncontrollably, and 22 days later Litvinenko's major organs failed and he was dead.

Marie Curie, who discovered polonium with her husband Pierre in 1898, named it for her homeland Poland, and earned two Nobel prizes for her groundbreaking radioactivity work, died at age 66 of aplastic anemia, a blood disease linked to radiation exposure. Her daughter Irène, who worked on radioactivity at the Radium Institute in Paris and also won a Nobel prize, died of leukemia. The stomach troubles, fatigue, and rapid hair loss experienced by the Curie lab chemist Sonia Cotelle were suggested to be from polonium evaporating out of solution and contaminating lab air. Sonia later died, after a vial of polonium shattered in her face.

Outside Bonjour Crepes & Wine it is a sparkly late winter New York City morning. A fresh inch of fluffy snow fallen the night before still clings to shrubs and banisters. Fur-clad women push sleek strollers. Backpacked schoolkids gather on street corners waiting for lights to change. Small dogs in sweaters trot proudly along the red brick apartment building canyons. And pressed up against glass windows panting at the passersby are other pets, already in their doggy daycare centers.

Along this spindle of real estate an apartment the size of a mobile home can cost $5 million. That the privileged humans, and dogs, walking by the window of the crêperie could unknowingly be getting dosed with even one wayward molecule of such a renegade element seems unthinkable. And yet.

¤ ¤ ¤

On December 28, 2009, Spectra Energy Corp, a Houston-based natural gas transmission company released plans to extend an existing pipeline network from Staten Island into Manhattan. The pipeline would be just 16 miles and involved an unusual trio. Natural gas would be coming from wells operated by Statoil, Norway's largely state-owned oil company (now called Equinor) and Chesapeake Energy, an oil and gas exploration and production company based in Oklahoma City. In New York City, the gas would be distributed by Con Edison to home stoves and gas boilers, gigantic units in many building basements that provide hot water and heat for residents. Chesapeake CEO Aubrey McClendon said he was pleased to help New Yorkers reduce their dependence on foreign oil by supplying them with his company's "clean-burning natural gas."

Con Edison is a name many New Yorkers know, because it's on their gas bills, and stems from a 1901 merger between Consolidated Gas and the famous American inventor Thomas Edison and his Edison Electric Illuminating Company. Chesapeake is not a name many New Yorkers know, though Aubrey McClendon may be one of the oil and gas industry's most notorious villains. He became a billionaire off the fracking boom, collected classic speedboats and antique maps, owned a share in a professional basketball team—the Oklahoma City Thunder—and had homes in Bermuda, Hawaii and Colorado.

"McClendon came to embody both the free-spirited wildcatter and the entitled CEO of the 21st century," *Bloomberg Businessweek* wrote, "who enriched himself while treating the public company he ran as his personal kingdom." In 2002, upon a financial gift to Duke University, McClendon and his wife Kathleen, both graduates of the school, were carved into the stone of a new dormitory as gargoyles. On March 1, 2016, McClendon was indicted by a federal grand jury for allegedly trying to fix oil prices. The following day he crashed his Chevy Tahoe at 78 miles per hour into an Oklahoma City highway embankment and the vehicle burst into flames.

It might seem like a volatile business partner to rely on for bringing an explosive gas into a crowded metropolis, but providing the necessary fuel for New Yorkers to cook their meals has always been complicated. In the 1700s and early 1800s much of the city cooked over open wood fires. With tenement houses in the early 1800s came potbelly stoves, and fuel was "scrounged up wherever it could be found," says New York City architectural historian Andrew Alpern. Used furniture, scraps from construction sites, discarded packing cases, fallen limbs pilfered from the woods of Central Park. By the late 1800s New Yorkers were cooking with coal.

In 1903, a *New York Times* correspondent visited the kitchen of a hotel restaurant where each day was consumed 200 gallons of soup, 350 to 400 pounds of beefsteak, 9 to 10 whole lambs, about 20 ducks, 170 pounds of butter and three barrels of potatoes, all cooked on roughly two dozen coal-fired ovens. "The heat emitted from this row of blazing furnaces is terrific," the article stated.

But there was a better way. When heated at extremely high temperatures, coal produces a gas that can also be used to cook food, called coal gas. Coal gas was manufactured in gasworks, pollutive plants often located in poor neighborhoods, stored in large circular tanks, then run through the city via a spiderweb of pipes. The gas that came up out of the earth, and was first harnessed commercially at a well in New York state in 1821, was called *natural gas*. By the mid-1900s this gas had become the favored fuel, and the thousands of miles of coal gas pipes that ran under New York City's streets were repurposed for it.

In 1947, a pipeline network used to shuttle oil from the Gulf Coast to the northeast during World War II was sold by the War Assets Administration for $143 million. The buyer was the Texas Eastern Transmission Corporation, who retrofitted the pipelines to supply natural gas from the Gulf region's gas fields to Philadelphia and into New Jersey. A pipeline to be completed in 1951, the Transcontinental, delivered gas from the Gulf to New York City. And New York would remain on that gas for over half a century, providing the heat that warmed generations of New Yorkers, and the flames that cooked their food.

Even come 2010, New Yorkers were still cooking with natural gas drawn from wells in Texas, Louisiana and offshore in the Gulf of Mexico, piped to them inside the Transcontinental Pipeline, or Transco. It entered the city's distribution system at what is called a city gate, flowed in main lines beneath streets and avenues, and tied into each building at a location in the basement, then was shuttled up to individual apartments in a set of much thinner lines, called risers. The final leg of the journey was to be released out of a home stove. In the evening, just after rush hour, momentarily dissolve the city's walls and you'd see millions of little blue flames burning across the metropolis, stacked one atop the other.

But the Spectra pipeline would change things. About 100 miles west of New York City begins the nation's most productive gas field—the Marcellus. It spans a vast section of rolling farms and woodlands, and rural towns and small cities, underlying much of Pennsylvania, northern West Virginia and eastern Ohio. Beneath the Marcellus lies an even deeper gas-rich formation, the Utica. Together, the U.S. Geological Survey stated in 2019, they contain about 214 trillion cubic feet of natural gas.

For much of the 20th century, most of it was inaccessible, trapped between the tightly packed mineral grains of these fuel-bearing formations. Conventional drillers had long shot water mixed with chemicals down a well in an effort to help draw out oil and gas, and attempts to shatter a formation with explosives and enhance production date back to at least 1865. The techniques of modern fracking, also known as unconventional oil and gas development, were pioneered in Texas during the 1980s and 1990s, and first deployed to Pennsylvania in the mid-2000s. They enabled drillers to drill down vertically to previously untappable formations like the Marcellus, then drill horizontally through them. Explosives placed in the horizontal part of the well are used to crack into the formation, and millions of gallons of water are injected down the well at high pressure, laced with chemicals, designed to lubricate and fracture the rock, and sand, to hold open the cracks and let the oil and gas flow out.

The Marcellus and Utica are black shales, geologic formations rich in organic material, hence the blackish color. Black shales contain so much uranium the country's Geological Survey, in a 1960 report for the Atomic Energy Commission, suggested mining them, with the oil considered "a possibly important byproduct." There is "a fair positive relation," the report states, "between oil yield and uranium content." As the Marcellus began booming, drillers knew this too.

By running a special type of Geiger counter down a drill hole they were able to locate the most fuel-rich parts of the Marcellus Shale formation. The best spots to look for gas, says a report on the Marcellus published in 2008 by the Pennsylvania Geological Survey, is not necessarily where the shale is thickest, but where levels returned by the Geiger counter are highest. "To put it simply," the report states. "RADIOACTIVITY = ORGANIC RICHNESS = GAS." If the Spectra pipeline were built, a large swath of New York City would for the first time be getting gas out of this formation.

¤ ¤ ¤

For some reason they never tell us in kindergarten, or high school, or any school really, but we live on a planet that can be dangerously radioactive, and it is actually killing some of us. While certain background radioactivity comes from things like cosmic radiation, high energy particles that rain down on earth from space, most comes from the planet itself. Rocks and soil contain uranium and thorium, radioactive elements which decay to different isotopes of radium, that decay to radon, and earth is continuously breathing up this radioactive gas, about six atoms for every thumbprint-sized square every second. Place an upside-down jar on the ground and you'll swiftly be capturing radon. And a home is like a big upside-down jar, trapping radon flowing up from tiny cracks and openings in the foundation. Any object in a house that sucks in air, such as an air filter, or human lungs, is inevitably going to pull in radioactivity.

"Radon is a cancer-causing, radioactive gas," says EPA's 2016 *A Citizen's Guide to Radon*. "You can't see radon. And you can't smell it or taste it." The agency estimates radon causes 21,000 lung cancer deaths annually, more people than die each year in home fires, 2,800, drownings, 3,900, or drunk driving accidents, 17,400. Only smoking causes more lung cancer deaths. The average home radon level across the US is about 1.3 picocuries per liter. The unit is named for Marie and Pierre Curie, and EPA recommends homes be remediated if radon is at or above 4 picocuries per liter. But even this can kill you.

An EPA graphic shows that if 100 people lived in a home with radon levels at 4 picocuries per liter for 70 years, roughly the length of a human life, about three would die of lung cancer. Turn radon levels up to 20 picocuries per liter, a level found in certain parts of Maine, Colorado, and Iowa, among other places, and after 70 years as many as 21 of the 100 residents would be dead from lung cancer. Cranking the radon knob up to 200 picocuries per liter for a lifespan could kill more than half of the home. You have done nothing wrong, the earth is simply murdering you for breathing.

In 1973, EPA analyzed the concentration of radon in natural gas to determine whether or not dangerous amounts of radioactivity was making it through the nation's natural gas pipeline system and into people's homes and lungs. It is an extraordinary report that confirms radon's presence in natural gas and "when this natural gas is used in unvented appliances, such as kitchen ranges and space heaters, the combustion products and radon are released within the home."

This unexpected source of radioactivity may be killing 95 Americans a year from cancer and "constitutes an additional source of radiation in the home which has not been adequately evaluated for potential health effects," the paper states. EPA calculated radon being emitted from natural gas stoves and space heaters would not just affect the lungs, it could cause lethal cancers of the bone and bone marrow and affect the gonads, and also contaminate the fetus, "exposed through placental transfer of radioactivity in maternal blood."

That radon can cause cancers other than lung cancer is a controversial topic. While studies have linked radon to stomach cancer in North Carolina, reproductive cancers in Maine, pancreatic cancer in Sweden, leukemia in Scotland and Canada and brain cancer in Denmark and Spain, other studies have differed. For example, a 1990 paper published in the respected British medical journal, *The Lancet*, by researchers at the University of Bristol found a significant association between a certain type of leukemia and radon. But a *Lancet* study published in 2000 by researchers at the University of Leeds looked at leukemia among adults in the UK and found, "no association." And on science argues, as science does.

"Nevertheless," writes Olav Axelson and Francesco Forastiere, in the journal, *Medical Oncology and Tumor Pharmacotherapy*, the idea that radon can cause tumors outside of the lung area "may warrant further studies, especially with regard to childhood exposure."

As for EPA's 1973 report on radon in natural gas, despite modern fracking having cracked open the earth in millions of new ways and tapped even more radioactive formations, the agency has not conducted a follow-up report.

Radon has several properties that end up having important consequences for the oil and gas industry. For one, it is a gas, which means it's free to waft up out of the earth and drift into the sky, or travel with natural gas across the country in a pipeline. Like most elements radon has many isotopes, and the primary one of concern is radon-222, with a half-life of 3.8 days.

Radon-222 will decay through a long chain of radioactive daughters that includes different isotopes of radioactive lead, bismuth, and polonium. Similar to the radium-rich scale that can build up in oilfield piping, inside a natural gas pipeline radioactive lead and polonium may stick to the inside of pipes, and also accumulate at points of flow or pressure change, such as filters, pumps and valves, as a dangerous radioactive sludge. This pipeline sludge, states a 1993 article on oilfield radioactivity published in the Society of Petroleum Engineers' *Journal of Petroleum Technology* can become so radioactive it requires "the same handling as low-level radioactive wastes." The longer natural gas spends in the pipeline system, the more radon is going to decay to its radioactive daughters, the more radioactive sludge and scale is going to accumulate.

While this waste is problematic for the workers who must clean it out, called piggers, it's not a risk to New York City residents. Their problem is radon that does not decay to radioactive lead, bismuth, and polonium and get stuck in the pipeline system is free to continue on through it, past the city gate, down distribution mains that run beneath streets and avenues, into a building, and up the risers, to be released out a home stove and into apartments. The switch from Gulf Coast to Marcellus gas brought on by the Sectra pipeline meant a more radioactive formation, and a quicker pipeline travel time. It would be expected that more radon would be making it through the pipeline system and into a New York City apartment, the question was, how much?

¤ ¤ ¤

There is the scent of sugary pastries, the sound of softly clattering cups. Clare Donohue, still seated at the wooden table near the window in Bonjour Crepes & Wine, has ordered tea and takes a sip. She went to high school in a mountainous part of upstate New York where teenagers fished for trout in rivers, everyone hunted deer, and people were suspicious of outsiders.

"There were 30 kids in my graduating class and I was salutatorian," she says. "It was typical America, real America. The emphasis was on sports, you shouldn't be too smart, you shouldn't speak up, you shouldn't be too different—and I didn't fit in." Still, she would never have called herself an environmentalist.

"I went to art school, studied graphic design, lived in New York City and had my own business," says Clare. "I was so the opposite of an activist. I would walk down the street and someone would try to get my attention with a flier and I'd cross to the other side. Activism just seemed like crazy people."

Then she realized the reservoir near her childhood home and where her brothers and father still fished would be surrounded by fracked gas wells. The Marcellus also underlies a belt of farming towns and mountain communities across the middle of New York state, where Clare had grown up. "They saw fracking as a way out of their poverty," she says. "They saw anyone opposed to fracking as getting in the way of them finally having a chance."

By this point, New York's environmental community was engaged in a bitter fight to ban fracking in the state. Two reasons, among many, involved showing the practice would pollute the upstate reservoirs the city relied on for water and the farmland it relied on for food. But Clare's job as an interior designer and knowledge of kitchen appliances gave her an inside look at a problem of fracking largely being ignored. Might natural gas stoves become conduits to bring the cancer-causing radioactive gas radon directly into the city's homes and kitchens?

The $850 million Spectra pipeline would travel under a heron rookery, skirt Jersey City then arch beneath the Hudson River and enter Manhattan at Gansevoort Peninsula, crossing a strip of parkland maintained by the Hudson River Park Trust—just 350 feet from a children's playground—and into Greenwich Village, a wealthy neighborhood where investment bankers and Hollywood stars live. From there, Spectra's gas would disappear into the Con Edison natural gas distribution system. "We concluded," stated the Federal Energy Regulatory Commission, which regulates interstate transmission of natural gas, in a March 2012 environmental report, "that the Project would be an environmentally acceptable action."

At a public meeting the commission organized in Manhattan a few years earlier, on August 5, 2010, only five people submitted comments. "The new pipeline" has drawn "barely a shrug from environmental groups," the *New York Times* reported in October 2011. The Environmental Defense Fund promoted natural gas as a way to eliminate the dirty heating oil burned in many New York City building boilers. "Spectra Energy's natural gas pipeline will go a long way in helping the city" meet its goal of providing cleaner, more reliable power for New York, said the New York League of Conservation Voters.

The main cheerleader for bringing fracked gas into the city was Mayor Michael Bloomberg. "He'd always been interested in science, so thinking about the environment was natural to him," wrote journalists in a book about his mayorship, *Bloomberg's Hidden Legacy: Climate Change and the Future of New York City*. Over Bloomberg's eleven years in office, says the book, he executed "an aggressive climate change action plan that would transform New York and the mayor into world leaders on global warming." Key to his policy was replacing heating oil with fracked gas.

"I'm an unrepentant capitalist," Bloomberg states in his own book, *Climate of Hope: How Cities, Businesses, and Citizens Can Save the Planet*. "But I also believe that government's most important duty is to protect public health and safety. When the push for profits endangers public health, I don't have much sympathy for industries whose products leave behind a trail of diseased and dead bodies." Bloomberg continues, "natural gas, when safely and responsibly extracted, has been a godsend for the environment and public health" and "fracking allows for the most efficient extraction of natural gas...as long as we need natural gas, it makes sense to frack."

Spectra, in Clare's eyes, had to be stopped. But with a powerful billionaire mayor pushing fracked gas, that was going to be difficult. Even among activists, few seemed to see the pipeline as a problem. "We walked around the West Village saying, please intervene in this pipeline," says Clare, "and people were like hold it with your pipeline stuff. Activist energy was being directed toward getting fracking banned in New York state, and the Spectra pipeline seemed like a distraction."

Then, in September 2011 Occupy Wall Street happened. Organizers from across New York City's activism community aligned to decry income inequality, and new alliances were forged. Clare met local artists and environmentalists who shared her concern of fracked gas and formed a group called Sane Energy. When the Federal Energy Regulatory Commission held a meeting in Greenwich Village in October 2011, this time more than 300 protestors filled the room. "You're about to mainline an ecological disaster for the rest of the state," stated the actor Mark Ruffalo, to standing ovation. "I'm begging you people to stand up."

That moment changed everything, says Clare, and helped generate an energetic grassroots resistance to the pipeline. "We have 15,000 to 17,000 people living in a square mile" and "the human damage and the real property damage if this thing were to explode would be almost incalculable," Derek Fanciullo, an official in Jersey City, near where the pipeline would pass, told the *Village Voice*. "It's not just the crater: the heat radiates out along the surface of the ground, and these explosions are so hot that if you try to bring emergency vehicles out to the area, those vehicles would melt."

Pipeline explosions do occur. The Texas Eastern Transmission Pipeline exploded in Salem Township, Pennsylvania, in 2016, generating a 50-foot-long crater. Three years later, in Noble County, Ohio, the Texas Eastern exploded again, producing a fireball that surged 120 feet into the air and engulfed the home of the Noll family, with 12-year-old son Nash inside—his grandfather whisked him out in the nick of time. Back in New York City, "a few hundred feet south of where the pipeline makes landfall—I am not making this up—is the Pier 51 playground, frequented by the sometimes adorable and always flammable children of the neighborhood," the *Village Voice* article reported. "How is this possible?"

Sane Energy pointed out gas entering New York City via Spectra would be harvested in Pennsylvania through the controversial techniques of modern fracking. Kim Fraczek, a jewelry designer and artist was Sane Energy's director and had grown up there. "A lot of people in my circle were really affected by the gas industry," she says. Solidarity with communities being fracked was a reason to oppose Spectra, but one of the main focuses of Sane Energy's activism was radioactivity.

They made an informational YouTube video about radon. They dressed up in hazmat suits and hosted dance parties in the lobbies of banks financing the project—Chase, Citibank, Wells Fargo. They painted their bodies a blotchy toxic green and walked, mostly naked, through the streets of Greenwich Village to the construction site. They locked themselves to construction equipment. And at one action, an activist named Lopi Laroe, wearing a black and white dress, walked from the wave splashed rocks along the Gansevoort Peninsula, where the pipeline would connect under the Hudson River to New Jersey, and to much cheering and chanting unfurled a handprinted sign that stated, "Danger Radioactive Pipeline." She was dragged away, stretcher-style, by a group of police officers and into a squad car.

Radon posed distinct threats for New York City. Unlike many other contaminants, it does not burn, passing through a flame unchanged. Small and often poorly ventilated apartments meant bad air circulation and radon emitted by a stove would be more likely to linger. In city restaurants, where half a dozen burners might be going at once, despite range hoods to vent the air, there could be the chance for a higher buildup. There was also the situation of people in buildings with inadequate heat that used their stove to warm-up their apartment. And the unstudied phenomenon of hundreds or even thousands of residents in a New York City high-rise coming home each evening and turning their gas stoves on at the same time to cook dinner.

"This fight," says Fraczek, "was about saving New York City."

¤ ¤ ¤

In July 2012, a Canada-based firm called Risk Sciences International published a report: "An Assessment of the Lung Cancer Risk Associated with the Presence of Radon in Natural Gas Used for Cooking in Homes in New York State." Risk Sciences, using Spectra's own data, confirmed radon levels in the pipeline as it approached New York City were more than four times EPA's recommended home radon remediation level. Although levels would dissipate as the gas traveled through the city then into buildings and out a stove, the report revealed that were New Yorkers to live their lives in an 800-square-foot apartment with 8-foot ceilings, reasonable ventilation, and a gas range with the stovetop used for two hours a day, the oven used for one, and four stovetop pilot lights that remain on, radon could cause about 2 lung cancers for every 100,000 people.

New York City's population is approximately 8.344 million people. Were every single one of them to use gas stoves for their entire life, about 167 New Yorkers would get lung cancer from the radon. Under a scenario with increased gas use and a smaller apartment, as many as 747 lung cancers from radon could be expected.

This all may seem like low odds, but the risk is high enough that in even the general scenario, under current California laws Marcellus gas would need to be labeled as a cancer-causing product. Lung cancer often kills, and so it seems like New Yorkers have a right to know that a lifetime of using Marcellus gas is expected to kill some number of them, and that number is not zero. But apparently no one has ever told them. And Con Edison, along with National Grid, New York City's other main natural gas utility company, and the New York State Public Service Commission, which regulates natural gas in the state, have not answered my questions on the topic.

Dr. Marvin Resnikoff, a Vermont-based nuclear physicist who has been working on issues of radioactive waste for 50 years, first connected to the nuclear industry then oil and gas, penned a report in 2012 on radon in Marcellus natural gas. He called the issue "a significant public health hazard" that "should be seriously investigated by" the EPA and warned of "the potential for large numbers of lung cancer among customers who use natural gas in unvented kitchen stoves and space heaters." Resnikoff concluded a lifetime of using Marcellus gas for cooking could lead to between 1,183 and 30,484 people across New York state getting lung cancer. Critics took issue with his math, which used some radon values far in excess of what has actually been reported for the Marcellus. Nonetheless, Resnikoff's conclusion that the issue "must be carefully assessed" seems valid.

Researchers at Carnegie Mellon University in Pittsburgh assessed the lung cancer risk from radon in Marcellus gas entering into homes across the Northeast and reported a detectable change in lung cancer death rates was "unlikely." But without more data on radon levels in natural gas distribution lines, the researchers stated, "it is difficult to dismiss public concerns." And they found an elevated risk for people living in homes with low ventilation rates, "especially those who use vent-free heaters or gas ranges to heat their living space."

Dr. David Carpenter, former dean of the School of Public Health at the State University of New York at Albany, and former chair of the neurobiology department of the Defense Nuclear Agency's Armed Forces Radiobiology Research Institute is part of a group of health experts who have followed the New York City natural gas radon issue with concern. An important point, he says, is that radon is not responsible for all the deaths, it is primarily the daughters of radon.

"Radon decays to various forms of lead, bismuth and polonium that are going to bond to the dust in the house and be deposited on your dishes, your tables, your cookware, your food and elevate the level of radioactivity in your home," says Carpenter. "You touch a contaminated surface, you bring your fingers to your mouth, or eat the food off the plate, and you are going to be bringing these radioactive elements into your body, and they will continue to decay and emit radiation. If you breathe them in, they can deposit in your lung tissue and lead to cancer, and if you ingest them they may settle somewhere in your digestive tract and pose problems there."

"One big concern in a New York City apartment," adds Carpenter, "would be pets, and especially small children, because they spend more time on the floor and have much more hand to mouth activity than the adults do."

Despite everything, Sane Energy's fight against the Spectra pipeline was doomed to fail. On March 28, 2012, the New York State Department of Environmental Conservation approved the project. A few months later, on May 21, 2012, the Federal Energy Regulatory Commission issued approval. "We did everything in our power," says Kim Fraczek, of Sane Energy. "We used our art, we used our geeky desire to dig into the radon issue, we used the legal system, we used civil disobedience." But they were unsuccessful. Other cities were set to receive natural gas from the Marcellus formation and New Yorkers, as Fraczek saw it, would be the guinea pigs.

There was one last chance to stop Spectra from entering the city. As the pipeline came ashore in Manhattan it crossed a strip of parkland maintained by the Hudson River Park Trust and an easement was needed. The group was governed by a thirteen-member board of directors, with five appointed by the governor of New York, five by the mayor, and three by the Manhattan borough president. At 11am Monday morning, June 18, 2012, the board was to meet in downtown Manhattan and vote on the easement.

At the time, board members included Pamela Frederick, an adjunct professor at Columbia University's Graduate School of Journalism, a Manhattan borough president appointee named Lawrence Goldberg, and Paul Ullman, managing partner at a firm that provided *hard money* loans to investors purchasing distressed real estate. The board's chair was Diana Taylor, a Wall Street executive and former official at KeySpan Energy, once the fifth largest natural gas distribution company in the United States. She was also Mayor Michael Bloomberg's romantic partner.

The pair met in the year 2000, when seated together at a civic luncheon and that evening coincidentally had dinner at the same restaurant. "He looked at me and came over and said, 'Would you like to have a drink after this?'" Taylor recounted to the Washington Post. The year before, Taylor had been named vice president at KeySpan, in charge of the natural gas company's Government & Regulatory Affairs division. One of Taylor's longtime friends, the business leader Kathryn

Wylde, told a reporter that when the couple met, “their interests were very much aligned.”

For the pipeline easement to be approved, according to bylaws of the Hudson River Park Trust, eight of the thirteen board members needed to vote yes. Mayor Bloomberg had made bringing fracked gas into the city a priority and his five picks would surely be on his side. The views of the other board members were less obvious. When the Trust had asked for the public’s opinion of the project they received 862 written comments, and more than 850 were opposed. The Hudson River Park Advisory Council, which advises the board on issues of environment and labor, opposed the pipeline. As did the local Manhattan community board representing the neighborhood where the pipeline would be entering, and Jerrold Nadler, the region’s US Congressman, who said he was “alarmed that natural gas” produced by fracking “will be consumed in New York City.”

But apparently, none of it was enough. Here the city was in the eleventh hour, with the Spectra pipeline on its doorstep, and its fate would be decided by a handful of members on a single board. The sole reporter at the June 18th meeting was Albert Amateau, a 79-year-old journalist who wrote for a weekly downtown Manhattan newspaper called *The Villager* with a circulation of about 6,000. Another record of the meeting was produced by Daniele Gerard, president of a community organization called Three Parks Independent Democrats, who attended the meeting as a public observer and sent her notes to Sane Energy.

As the meeting began, Spectra, the mayor’s office, and Con Edison all made presentations about the pipeline, all positive. The board’s most critical member was Ullman, the hard money lender. He asked the Spectra reps if they had conducted a risk assessment with respect to the park. They hadn’t. He pressed Spectra on their plans if the pipeline exploded in lower Manhattan. They said the pipeline would have “enhanced safety,” but mentioned no formal disaster plan, according to Daniele Gerard’s notes.

"No one presented any reasons to oppose the pipeline," the notes continue. "The public was not allowed to speak during the meeting." And "no one objected to the close relationship between the Chair of the board, Diana Taylor, and the Mayor (the latter being the main supporter of this pipeline and the former being his girlfriend)."

When Larry Goldberg brought up the point that community leaders and area environmental groups opposed the pipeline because it would encourage fracking of the Marcellus Shale, Diana Taylor shut down the conversation, saying, according to the journalist Albert Amateau's article, the fracking issue was not within the Trust's purview.

The stage seemed set for an interesting result. There were legitimate concerns, much of the public was against the project, and two board members had asked Spectra critical questions and received trivial replies. On the other hand, the mayor had five agents on the board and at the helm his romantic partner, a former natural gas vice president. But the vote's tally was clear—yes votes were only seven. There were not the sufficient eight votes to approve the pipeline. Both Ullman, Goldberg, and also Pamela Frederick, the journalism professor, had voted no.

What occurred next was "ridiculous," says Gerard. Her notes read: "Chair Diana Taylor realized what had happened and admonished the board about how serious this project is and then a roll call vote was requested." This would force each board member to publicly declare yes or no.

Albert Amateau's article, which ran later that week, says "Pamela Frederick...changed her mind at the roll call and was among the eight 'yes' votes." According to Gerard's notes, Taylor then "thanked" her. The necessary eight votes had materialized, and the easement for the Spectra pipeline had been approved. Despite most New Yorkers having any idea what had just occurred, radioactive fracked gas was set to enter New York City. And it would keep entering. The mayor's office released a report two months later that estimated by 2030, "over 80 percent of the physical gas going to New York City will be shale gas from nearby areas."

¤ ¤ ¤

About eight months after the Spectra easement was approved, on February 21, 2013, Mayor Bloomberg showed up at an event to promote natural gas with the 84-year-old Texas oilman T. Boone Pickens. The venue was a pizza food truck, and it was all about the photo op. To show the mayor performing a classic New Yorker activity, like scarfing down a slice of pizza, and also plug the novel type of food truck, which was run on natural gas and also contained a pizza oven run on natural gas.

When pressed by a journalist about fracking, Bloomberg reiterated his position. "Of all the things we can do, nothing's perfect, but natural gas certainly looks like it can make this country energy independent and reduce dramatically the pollutants going into the air," the mayor stated. "Does it have some risks? Everything has some risks. But unless you're willing to give up electricity and give up automobiles and trucks and airplanes and go back to living in a cave, you're going to get it from someplace."

"I've been on over 800,000 wells fracked in Oklahoma, Kansas and Texas," T. Boone chimed in. "And there have been no evidence of anything being damaged."

At last, it was time to roll the cameras and eat. Bloomberg dug in. "Mmm," said the mayor, "this is good pizza."

The Texas oilman had a slice too and said: "It's great."

3
A Day in Radioactive Ohio

Inside the kitchen on the second floor of Fire Station 1 in Youngstown, Ohio, a young lieutenant is dicing tomatoes and onions for a gigantic spaghetti dinner. Across from him Battalion Fire Chief Silverio Caggiano is brewing a pot of French vanilla coffee. He has a gray and white mustache, black Nike sneakers and a cross around his neck. The year is 2019. Caggiano has been fighting fires for nearly 40 years and is also a hazardous materials specialist and serves as technical advisor to Ohio's Hazardous Materials and Weapons of Mass Destruction Committee. "I'm the one FBI will call at 3 in the morning to a hazmat scene," he says. "I have their regional director on my speed dial."

Even out of uniform, like say when he's at the Indy 500 auto race, or a game for his daughter, a Youngstown State University cheerleader—getting degrees in biology and political science—he typically has a radiation detector stashed somewhere in his gear. As much as he can talk about auto racing, politics or cheerleading, it's difficult for him to discuss any of these topics without ending back on nerve agents, hemorrhagic fever viruses, or the uranium-238 decay chain. "I sleep," says Caggiano, "because I know there are people like me on the front lines who worry about shit."

When planes hit the World Trade Center on September 11, 2001, Caggiano, like first responders across the nation, embarked on a rigorous mission to assess threats. "We had access to all the information we needed to help protect the public," he says. Then, in 2011, came fracking. He was Battalion Chief of the Youngstown Fire Department, perched beside the Marcellus and Utica, two of the nation's richest new gas fields.

"I knew this had the potential to be big," says Caggiano. "As time passed, information came to us from areas already being fracked and most news was bad. It was like peeling layers off a rotted onion looking for any good parts. Through my training I knew about deposits of uranium and radium in Ohio's soil, so I cannot say I was surprised when I heard that fracking waste was contaminated with radioactivity. What did surprise me were the unusually high levels being recorded in the Marcellus." (Dr. Madalyn Blondes of the U.S. Geological Survey has examined the Utica and says levels are elevated, but not as high as the Marcellus.)

The industry's cunning surprised Caggiano too. In the decades and years preceding the fracking boom, Ohio legislators linked to a free market group called the American Legislative Exchange Council, or ALEC, sponsored bills that surgically removed state laws protecting air and water and also restricted funding for the state's health and environmental agencies. Most decisions of import were left to the industry-friendly Ohio Department of Natural Resources. Caggiano was used to dealing with the traditional oil and gas industry, Marathon Petroleum had a tank farm in Youngstown, and they were in regular contact on safety issues. But the fracking industry wanted nothing to do with his extensive knowledge on hazardous materials and radioactivity.

"We began hearing that model legislation drafted by ALEC was being enacted in fracking states across the country to circumvent the Emergency Planning and Community Right-to-Know Act," says Caggiano.

This came about after a disaster in Bhopal, India in 1984, when the Union Carbide pesticide plant leaked highly toxic methyl isocyanate gas into the night, killing at least 3,800 people. The act's goal was to prevent an event like Bhopal from ever occurring in the United States, by informing residents and first responders of facilities using hazardous chemicals in their communities. "Yet here comes the fracking industry spitting in the face of all that," says Caggiano. The contents of trucks, tanks, and vats of frack chemicals would, by order of state law, be kept secret from fire fighters and first responders.

"We quarterback scenarios," says Caggiano. "Throw them up on the board, prepare for the worst-case, so when the not worst-case pops up we got it. But to prevent me from being able to do my job to protect the citizens I've been sworn to protect—there is no greater feeling of helplessness."

By 2011, with the statehouse captured by industry lobbyists, regulatory agencies underfunded and defanged, and reactionary legislation on the books, the state was ready to be fracked. "Energy companies descended upon eastern Ohio like locust," says Caggiano. "The talk was of thousands of frack pads in my three county area alone."

Acting on a sense of duty instilled by an environmentalist mother who was raised on a farm during the Great Depression and spoke constantly of stewardship and leaving the earth better than you found it, and a father who was an intelligence officer in the U.S. Army Air Corps, spoke seven languages, had a master's degree in humanities and moved to America from Italy to become an educator, Caggiano refused to simply let the industry run him over. "I decided that no person was going to get away with turning back the clock on chemical safety," he says, "and put the public and my brothers and sisters in the first responder community at risk."

Remarkably, in the entire state of Ohio—and Pennsylvania and West Virginia—Caggiano is the only fire chief I am aware of who has publicly spoken out on fracking. "Most firefighters have zero understanding of what is going on," he says. "The tentacles on this are deep, and many of my brothers and sisters in the service are more centered on survival and financial well-being."

Caggiano tried to raise the alarm. But the state's big cities were not in the oilfield and largely unfamiliar with its ways and its waste. Rural volunteer fighters had jobs of their own and not enough time to comprehend the complex industry that, through allies in the statehouse, held their purse strings. And the state's legislators were entirely unresponsive. A tidal wave of radioactive oilfield waste was headed for Ohio, and few seemed to care, or even knew what was coming.

"We began to notice injection wells were multiplying across the state," says Caggiano. Here, oilfield brine and other toxic liquids brought to the surface in the oilfield are injected deep into the earth, where the belief is, at least according to EPA, whose laws govern the practice, that it will remain locked "almost indefinitely" within a specific deeply buried geologic layer. Injection wells are often located many miles from the oil and gas wells that produce the waste and can be located out of the oilfield entirely. Because of its favorable regulations and nearness to drilling hotspots in the Marcellus and Utica, Ohio has become a preferred location for oil and gas wastewater injection wells—Pennsylvania has 14, West Virginia has just over 50, Ohio has nearly 250.

"A truck carrying brine for injection is the worst of the worst," says Caggiano. "And it is going through your freeways, through your neighborhoods, through your streets, past your homes, past your school, past your grandparent's house, past everything, to get to these injection wells, and the drivers are not trained in hazmat and when their truck overturns have no papers to tell a fire chief like me what the hell they are carrying—it scares the fuck out of me."

Deep in the earth, radioactive elements like thorium, uranium and radium are in the formations that hold oil and gas, and water is present too. As oil and gas is tapped, this formation water flows to the surface as produced water, or oilfield brine. Uranium and thorium tend to remain in the formation, but radium can be moderately soluble, and generally, the saltier the formation water the more likely radium is to be displaced from the formation rocks, accumulate along with other metals in the brine, and travel with it up to the surface.

Due to a federal exemption known as the Bentsen and Bevill Amendments, brine trucks, no how matter how much radioactivity they contain, can travel without hazardous materials markings. There are Department of Transportation radioactivity limits that require trucks filled with radioactive waste of a sufficiently high concentration be labeled, or placarded, with a radioactivity symbol. And a Texas oilfield radioactivity expert has told me some Marcellus brine trucks may exceed these limits, because of the concentrated scale and sludge that can accumulate in a truck's tank. But, since the Department of Transportation has never required brine trucks be comprehensively tested for radioactivity they still run freely on the roads, without hazardous materials markings, without radioactivity placards.

"If you ever look at where the injection wells go," says Caggiano, "they don't go into the $500,000-home towns, they go into the neighborhoods like Youngstown and down in the Appalachian areas of southeastern Ohio, where people are piss-poor and can't fight this stuff. Industry preys on these communities, and Ohio has a lot of them."

In a 2014 crash in Lawrence Township, Ohio, a brine truck traveling south on Bear Run Road flipped over a guardrail, rolled down a steep bank, and struck the home of Pat and Patty Garrett. The couple, according to a local newspaper article, "heard an awful crunching, crackling, grinding noise," and ran outside to see the driver lying in their yard spitting up blood and brine leaking under their home. In 2016, in Barnesville, Ohio, a brine truck overturned on a bad curve and the contents flowed across a livestock field and entered a stream, carrying waste into a village reservoir.

Caggiano worries about people who live beside injection wells. In Vienna, a township north of Youngstown near the Pennsylvania border, a woman named Michele and her son live so close to an injection well they can watch trucks unload fracking waste from their front porch. In nearby Brookfield, the subsidiary of a Houston-based energy company attempted to construct a set of injection wells in woods behind a senior citizen mobile home community—the seniors protested, and the company hired a crew of former Army snipers to guard the operation. The activist Maria Montañez was among a group of concerned area residents who spent considerable time monitoring an injection well in the Coitsville area and showed me an incident caught on film in which copious amounts of brine spewed over a fence. She was concerned, because next door is a daycare center for adults with disabilities where skills like gardening and farming are fostered and goats and chickens are kept.

Ever since Caggiano started raising his voice, residents witnessing harms see him as an ally, and he gets calls. "We had a situation up here couple weeks ago where a fracking industry guy decided to clean his truck out at one of those coin operated car washes," he says. It occurred in a town west of Youngstown called Canfield. "All the shit," says Caggiano, "ended up getting into the sewer." Another call on the same issue came in recently from Coshocton. "Problem with these car washes is some of them recycle their own water," he says. "So a person comes to the carwash, and now they're washing their car with radioactive waste."

Caggiano is particularly concerned about Chief's Order facilities, where oilfield waste is *down-blended* with other materials like lime or ground up corncobs in an attempt to lower radioactivity levels enough so waste can be taken to a local landfill, rather than transported to radioactive waste disposal facilities out West that can be vastly more expensive. A list of rules for operating a food truck in Ohio is 14 pages long. But with the treatment of radioactive oilfield waste, interested companies merely answer questions on a one-page application and a special order from the chief of the oil and gas division of the Ohio Department of Natural Resources allows them to operate.

At one Ohio company operating under Chief's Order, EnviroClean Services, inspectors with the Department of Health's Bureau of Radiation Protection visited in 2014 and discovered a staff clueless of basic radiation safety, operating without protective gear, with no records or documentation for the waste they were receiving, and no instrument to measure it except a pocket Geiger counter that appeared to have never been used. One entry on the form documenting the inspection asks for an "Evaluation of individuals' understanding of radiation safety procedures." The inspector noted: "Unable to evaluate — no radiation safety procedures being used." There were no fines issued, the facility went on operating and eventually went out of business.

In February 2014, a company called Austin Master Services received permission from the Ohio Department of Natural Resources to process radioactive oil and gas waste in a large industrial building on the northwest side of Youngstown. "We run trucks through, analyze them, and then they go away," the company had told a local newspaper. Austin Master indicated their special technology could test the entire radioactivity contents of a load without it ever "coming out of the box," but Caggiano was skeptical and went to check out the site with the administrative chief of the Youngstown Fire Department.

"They had their nuke guy there and thought they were going to have two dumb firemen," he says. "I took a look around, spoke to them about rads, and the administrative chief explained we would be inspecting regularly. You could see the look on these guys' faces. I told the chief, they are going to get the fuck out of town, and that is exactly what happened. They set up shop in southeastern Ohio, where firefighters are less informed."

"The big question," says Caggiano, "is are these companies abiding by what little regulations there are on accepting this waste?"

But it is a question Caggiano has already answered. He points behind the fire house, where the Mahoning River weaves through industrial Youngstown. "We know the river has problems and we've been trying to fix it up," he says. "Then along comes Lupo."

He means Benedict Lupo, whose company, Hardrock Excavating LLC, hauled and stored fracking waste. Sometime in late 2012, Lupo directed employees to empty waste tanks under the cover of darkness through a hose and into a storm drain. Tens of thousands of gallons of brine and drilling mud were dumped on dozens of different occasions. The storm drain emptied the waste into a creek that the assistant US attorney on the case described as having become, "void of life."

"The problem," says Caggiano, "is that while some of the contamination was easily visible, "I am sure Mr. Lupo never monitored for any rads." Which would be invisible. And that creek leads to the Mahoning River, which eventually empties into the Ohio River.

"You have created an environment ripe for corruption," says Caggiano. "If we caught some ISIS terrorist cells dumping this into our waterways they would be tried for terrorism and the use of a WMD on US Citizens, however the frack industry is given a pass on all of this."

He believes that like cockroaches, for every Benedict Lupo you find there are 50 you don't. And incidents like the one with Lupo show his concerns on health and the environment are not just academic, there is reason to be worried about flesh and blood. "Just look at the radium levels being brought up in the brine," says Caggiano. "Here we have a bone seeking rad that was once safely locked deep in the earth, now it's on the surface thanks to fracking and potentially entering the food chain."

There's a list of worries. "With illegal dumping into creeks," he says, "what about the crayfish and freshwater mussels that live there, and the fish that eat them? Is stuff working its way up the food chain to where you go deer hunting one day and end up with contaminated meat? When shit hits the fan, 90 percent of the time it's the farmers, so what happens when the farmer whose field got contaminated sells his wheat to a rancher who feeds it to his cows? Is it getting into our hamburgers? Is it getting into us? Is anyone really monitoring the radiation levels or the long-term effects on the environment?"

Caggiano has a special connection to the farmers, because they grow his food and work the land, and are the heroes of the ecosystem his mother instructed him to respect and protect. As a child she bought him a school notebook that pictured a bulldozer bearing down on a farm of fleeing animals. It's also from the farmer's ranks that firefighters often spring, especially in rural America. In Caggiano's eyes, no one has been duped worse. "Many 150-year-old family farms have been driven to the edge of bankruptcy," he says. "The same politicians who sold them out to big corporate ag are now selling them out to the frack industry, and we have hurt the farmers so bad they are willing to take the risk."

"Money offered by the drillers means they can keep their land and source of family pride," he says. "But these companies are throwing money around without properly informing people what their rights are and what they are exposing people to. The farmers have no idea that over the years contamination may condemn their families to cancer, birth defects and other physical maladies. It is sinister, they are fucking killing people and our own government is allowing it. The public needs to know what is happening but the fracking industry's way of operating is throw this magic Harry Potter invisible cloak over themselves and say, you stand the fuck over there, stay the fuck out of the way, and hopefully nobody will die."

"My worst fear," he continues, "is that it's uncontained now and there's no follow-up, and 30 years from now farmer Jim's kids all have non-Hodgkin lymphoma and liver cancer and bladder cancer. People are already complaining of more leukemia. Are we going to see a spike in bone cancers in the future? Twenty, thirty, fifty years from now are your grandkids going to have brain cancer because they live next to one of these things? Is it worth it, do you give a shit?"

Caggiano examines his almost empty coffee cup. The lieutenant in the firehouse kitchen is opening massive cans of Cento tomato sauce with a can opener and rolling meatballs, making the sauce for the spaghetti meal. Caggiano ponders putting on a new batch of coffee. "I would love," he says, "to say everyone in the world is a good person, but not everyone in the world is a good person. There is not just one bad apple, because that one bad apple is making a lot of money, and it snowballs and before you know it everyone is making a lot of money, and everyone is a bad apple."

As much as creeks are getting contaminated, and farmers are getting screwed, and there are risks to the public, no one is more immediately at risk than the workers. "Radioactivity is the easiest thing to jake people over on, because they don't understand a bit of it," Caggiano says. "Have the risks for workers in the Marcellus and Utica been appropriately studied?" He shakes his head. "These people exist in the margins."

"At a frack site," he says, "we have everything we would anticipate finding when looking for WMD deployment capability. There is chemical and radioactive material, large scale contamination capability, aerosolization capability, dispersal capability. Every time you move the stuff rads are going up into the air. Virtually none of these workers have masks or respirators or any idea what they are doing is dangerous, and they're eating, drinking and smoking without washing their hands, and their hands are smothered in this shit."

"The real tragedy is they are not just contaminating themselves, they are bringing this stuff home to their kids," Caggiano continues. "And the younger they are the more at risk they are, because cell reproduction is more rapid in kids. You go from a lump of flesh to a fully grown baby in nine months. And if you fuck this up, I mean one mistake, and you are birthing something from *The Hills Have Eyes*"—a 1970s horror film featuring a band of atomically mutated cannibals preying on lost tourists—"do I even have to tell you about radium in the bones of babies? When you are bringing an alpha-emitting element like radium home you are dooming children to forever carry this radioactive timebomb in their system."

"Workers have been reaching out to me, but there is nothing I can really do for these guys," says Caggiano. "I try and help them sort it out. I tell them to hose themselves off and keep their clothes in a bag. I say, find a spot in your yard, use the same spot each time, wash clothes there and make sure your kids don't play in that spot. I tell them, buy an old washing machine and only use that one to wash your stuff, and keep it separate from the rest of the family. And make sure you wash yourself down before climbing into bed with your spouse."

"I am trying to find these guys medical help," Caggiano says. "I work my way up the ladder. The hospital says they can only pay with an employer mandate. The city of Youngstown's health department says they can't help. Ohio Health Department doesn't even return calls. I have even spoken with family practitioners, they won't see these guys because they're worried about them sitting there in the office and contaminating their practice. And the politicians don't want anything to do with these guys and hope it eventually goes away. But it won't."

It's a lot of heavy talk for one morning, and Caggiano needs to be getting back to work. "You are dealing with a shameless bunch of individuals who think they can do whatever they want," he sighs. "What the fuck ever happened to the Hippocratic Oath?"

He decides to brew a second pot of coffee after all, and the smell of French vanilla re-envelopes the firehouse kitchen. "Make no mistake, this is a radioactive fire," says Caggiano, "and they are saying, let it burn."

In 2021, Caggiano retired from the Youngstown Fire Department and is presently working with communities across Ohio to raise awareness on the dangers of radioactive oilfield waste.

"When I close my eyes and meet my maker," he tells me. "I want to know I have made a difference, I don't give a shit if it makes me a dime. But more importantly, I want to be able to walk up to my dad, look him in the eye, and say—hey, did I do right?"

¤ ¤ ¤

Just over one hundred miles from Caggiano, at a Taco Bell located in a shopping plaza in the eastern Ohio city of Cambridge, Tom McKnight sits down with a burrito at a table beside a window. The year is 2020, and it could be a shopping plaza anywhere in America. There is Chipotle, Starbucks, Burger King, Dollar Tree and a Verizon store. But this plaza is unique. It's located beside two interstates that run out of the Marcellus/Utica. Directly behind Verizon, and visible from the dining tables inside Taco Bell is an injection well. It's operated by Silcor Oilfield Services and caters to a continuously arriving brigade of brine trucks.

Every day across America about 3 billion gallons of brine comes to the surface with the oil and gas. Equipment at the wellhead—separators and heater treaters—separate it all out. Gathering lines pipe the gas away, the oil is directed into oil tanks, and the brine into brine tanks, which sit together at wells like gigantic green or beige soup cans. A tanker truck will empty the oil tanks then head to a pipeline or refinery, and like an oilfield garbageman, it's often the job of a brine hauler to drive around to different wells and empty the brine tanks. Approximately 96 percent of the brine generated in America's oil and gas fields will be disposed of at an injection well, although this is the only one I know of on the edge of a shopping plaza.

As Tom eats his burrito, trucks coming from the Marcellus/Utica back up to tall tan tanks and someone at the disposal site connects what looks like an oversized fire hose so drivers can discharge their waste. The trucks resemble septic trucks. They have no markings to indicate their contents may be hazardous or radioactive. Radium levels are typically presented by combining together radium-226 and radium-228 values and can vary greatly across oil and gas formations, and even within the same field. The Pennsylvania Department of Environmental Protection found Marcellus brine to average 9,330 picocuries per liter, and be as high as 28,500 picocuries per liter. These values are hundreds of times above EPA's level for defining liquid waste as "radioactive," and also hundreds of times above limits the Nuclear Regulatory Commission has for discharging waste to the environment. Yet Ohioans can watch just that happen while they eat chalupas.

Drivers typically wear a simple blue work uniform called FRs, consisting of jeans or long pants and a long sleeve shirt made of *flame-resistant* fabrics. From Taco Bell one can see these blue men, pumping waste from their trucks into the tanks. Oil will float to the top and can be resold, solids will settle at the bottom, and what remains will be shot down the injection well and deep into the earth. Most of the people moving about the shopping plaza likely have no idea what is happening at this odd industrial facility in the corner, but Tom does.

"Back in 2012 the oilfield was coming on strong and I was selling John Deere tractors and trying to get my kids raised," he says. "Then I got fired at John Deere and went to selling used cars. I was hating my life more and more, meanwhile I was looking at these hillbillies in cowboy hats and cowboy boots coming in with big-ass pay stubs and buying these expensive trucks, and I was thinking, I want one of those big-ass checks."

"I was out for a ride with my wife on a Sunday afternoon and drove through the parking lot of one company. There was a guy working in back and he asked what I was doing there and I said, I heard this is a good place to work, and he shed his coveralls and took me into the general manager's office. Turned out he was the general manager, and we sat down right then and did the interview. No phone calls, no introductions, no points of reference, no nothing. He had to get people working fast so they could handle all the business they were getting. And there I was—a brine hauler. That was maybe June 2014."

"I had a lot of fun with it. There were so many brine trucks out there and so much inexperience and so much of a, damn the torpedoes, full speed ahead attitude. Guys are fracking the hell out of the place, and there are literally thousands of us brine haulers, working for dozens of different trucking companies. There was just so much need. Occasionally, I worked 36 hours straight. I was always happy, with a big smile on my face. We hauled mostly from oil and gas wells in southwestern Pennsylvania and eastern Ohio, then dipped down and did a little bit along the corridor of Highway 50 in West Virginia. It was insane the amount of waste that got trucked out of those places."

"I made $86,000 one year and took a month off, it was too good to be true. I paid off my Visa that I never had paid off since like 1982. We could buy our own house. All my children were coming up in age and now I could help put them through college. I could peel 'em off a couple hundred bucks for groceries, or fill a car with groceries and go visit them. The carrot out there was really big, and I sure appreciated it. A lot of guys like me struggling for work took jobs as brine haulers and now we had money, it was a breath of life in this community."

Tom worked at a company called CS Trucking and was under the impression he had received good training. "It was a comprehensive weeklong course in a classroom, and I paid attention. Everything they said I needed to do, I did. I thought I was going in with my eyes open. Radioactivity was presented to us as not an issue, so I didn't ever consider the risks. I specifically remember someone in our orientation class bringing up radiation and the guy putting on the class held up his cellphone and said, you will never get more radiation in this job than you're getting off one of these right here. We all thought, great, nothing to worry about there."

To load up a brine truck with oilfield waste, drivers fetch the hose from where it's kept hung on the side of their truck, connect it to a fitting near the base of the brine tank, open a set of valves, and vacuum the waste into their truck.

"In retrospect, I sure wish I would have had some training," says Tom. "Brine splashes up on you constantly. We have all tasted it. I will tell you, and to be honest I was probably guilty of it more than others, but when I was working and it was time to eat, I wouldn't wash my hands, a lot of times it was just a pants wipe. I would be going down the road and had a cooler full of sandwiches and I'd try to reach in with one hand and roll the baggy over my hand and never touch the sandwich. With potato chips it was harder, every chip you ate you touched. While I was loading up with brine, I might grab an apple."

"The dirtiest stuff that I hauled on a regular basis was flowback," says Tom. "As they frack the well is plugged, and all of the water, sand and chemicals used in the fracking process are held down in the borehole and under pressure. When they bring a well online they drill through that plug and everything surges back to the surface, and sometimes fountains into the sky and falls down on the workers at the well pad like rain. Flowback is frigging dirty, and it can be hot, like bathwater hot."

Oil and gas companies try to capture flowback by piping it into a set of large and often colorful—red, blue, yellow, green—frac tanks. These resemble shipping containers and are on wheels so after use at one well they can be towed behind trucks and moved to the next. A full frac tank is too heavy to tow, and before being moved must be cleaned. It's a nasty job, as the tanks can be filled with toxic sludge settled out of the flowback, and a hydrovac will be called in. These look like brine trucks but have a powerful pump for sucking sludge, and they are expensive. To save time and money brine haulers like Tom may be asked to suck up any liquid lying on top of the sludge.

"I opened the manhole and stuck my head in," says Tom, remembering one time cleaning out frac tanks. He needed to guide a two-inch hose down to the bottom of the tank. "The end of that day, my head underneath the hard hat and above the neckline looked like I been down in Florida out in the sun," Tom says, "and the little spot between my gloves and where my shirt started, the only other part of my skin that was directly exposed to the tank, was all red like a sunburn."

An even worse job falls to *swampers*, who must crawl down into tanks. "Let's say your hauling brine for a month," says Tom. "Sludge builds up in the bottom of your truck's tank, and every time you haul it gets a little thicker. Back at our shop they'd pop the manhole and send these guys in with a shovel and pressure washer. Shovel the waste to the middle, then use the pressure washer to scrape down the sides and scour the bottom. A guy on the outside would be holding a bucket or big pan, you shovel the waste in there, then he would take that over and dump it in a hopper."

"Them guys on the inside would be exposed to anything in that brine or flowback. And you know how it is with some guys, they want to be tough, and could easily be in there over an hour, it was a challenge to them. Someone would get out, sit down and say, fuck it's killing me, and someone else would be like, you pussy. If you complain to the boss they'll say, shut up, don't like it go home. And you do shut up, because you need that job. Don't forget, it is crappy and gross, but none of us knew that sludge was radioactive."

Tom says swampers are supposed to wear standard oilfield PPE, FR's, steel toe boots and a hard hat. Some were supplied with, "these little yellow neoprene rain suits," a face mask, and a respirator. "But most of them don't wear the respirator," he says. "I seen guys go in there just a face mask, blue jeans, and a T-shirt, and they're made to do their own laundry. At home, in the hotel, or wherever. They're also instructed to bathe in Dawn dish soap, just like when the Exxon Valdez went down and the volunteers were cleaning off the little ducks, same deal."

People connected to the oil and gas industry will often point out that even bananas are naturally radioactive, but the statement is designed to mislead, and helps cloak the dangers posed by oilfield radioactivity. A banana's radioactivity comes from a radioactive isotope of potassium which has a half-life of over a billion years and in decay gives off a beta particle to become nonradioactive elements. The radioactive isotopes brought to the surface in oil and gas production decay to other radioactive isotopes, which decay relatively quickly to other radioactive isotopes, which continue to decay through a long list of other radioactive isotopes, blasting off radiation each time.

Sludge sitting in the bottom of a brine truck or tank, or scale stuck to the inside of an oilfield pipe would be giving off radiation in the form of gamma rays, beta particles and alpha particles. Gamma rays can travel several hundred feet through the air, go right through a human body, and even go through concrete and steel. Beta are minuscule particles and can go several feet through the air and penetrate human flesh. But of greatest concern are alpha particles, which are many thousands of times heavier than a beta particle and travel at a speed of 12,430 miles per second. The outer layers of human skin or a piece of paper are dead and act as shielding, absorbing an alpha particle's incredible energy. But the soft lining of an organ, the marrow of a bone, or the delicate tissue of the lung is very much alive. An alpha particle fired off here will smash about the cellular space, colliding with tens of thousands of different things. Any hit to the nucleus can break strands of DNA, usually killing the cell, or worse, leaving it genetically mutated, damage that can lead to cancer.

Oilfield waste happens to contain a number of radioactive isotopes that emit alpha particles as they decay, including radium-226, radon-222, and five different isotopes of polonium. Working in a contaminated workspace littered with piles of sludge or open pits of brine provides several pathways for workers to inhale or inadvertently ingest these elements. Even wearing some protective gear, workers cleaning out a tank can get their underclothes, faces, boots and bodies splattered in sludge, and also their hands. Because workers are uninformed, easily preventable actions can still lead to exposures, such as drinking a soda, smoking a cigarette, or not washing their hands then eating lunch.

In 2017, Tom stopped hauling brine. In 2019 he had a weird experience where a banana didn't go down right. His chest hurt and thinking a heart attack he drove himself to the emergency room, but the doctor said there was nothing wrong with his heart. Then they did a CT scan, he had a softball-sized tumor in his upper chest. It was thymoma cancer, and had spread to other organs. Survival rates Tom found on the American Cancer Society's website are scary. He had a one in four chance of making it to 2024.

Tom doesn't believe the cancer is linked to his oil and gas work. Although, he says when he asked his radiologist whether radiation he may have received in this work could have been the cause, she just stared into her computer, "kind of like when you are buying a used car and ask if the warranty is bad, and they just look away."

The shopping plaza is humming. Out the window of the Taco Bell, at the Silcor Oilfield Services injection well, the continuously arriving brigade of brine trucks continues. As one driver leaves the facility, rather than exit and get back on the highway, he motors deeper into the shopping plaza, parks his brine truck, and heads toward Starbucks.

Meanwhile, brine haulers remain a ghost fleet. And the Department of Transportation has not replied to my questions regarding how many drivers like Tom are out there, how much oilfield brine is being transported daily on America's roads, and why the agency has not conducted an investigation into the issue of brine trucks operating without radioactivity placards despite at times potentially containing levels high enough to require them. Estimates from Ted Auch at the environmental advocacy group FracTracker Alliance indicate there are at least 8,400 certified trucks hauling brine across the Marcellus/Utica. CS Trucking, Tom's brine hauling company, has not replied to questions.

¤ ¤ ¤

South and east from Cambridge the low rolling hills become steeper, the forests thicker, and near the foothills of the Appalachian Mountains in Noble County appears a glittering body of water. Seneca Lake. It's one of Ohio's largest inland lakes. Nestled along the woodsy shore are cabins, campsites and swim docks. Bald eagles soar above. Striped bass cruise beneath. At the marina's Dockside Restaurant, one can order a sirloin steak supper with *redneck fries* and watch a water-skier paint a wake through the perfect summer light. But look harder, and the stain of the fracking industry becomes visible.

Steep valleys hide fracked oil and gas wells—called frack pads—on the hills above. Each pad can have multiple wells, and wells have been drilled within 2,000 feet of the lake's shoreline, and also laterally out beneath to tap oil and gas buried below. In the first decade of the boom, from around 2011 to 2021, the oil and gas industry sucked approximately 600 million gallons of water from Seneca Lake to use in fracking operations, decisions approved by the Muskingum Watershed Conservancy District, which is responsible for water conservation and recreation. Jonathan

Mizer, the lead attorney for the group, says they have made more than a quarter of a billion dollars leasing watershed land for fracking. And what has this great sale of the public good produced?

A few ridges out from the lake, on a farm that once held chickens and sheep, Kerri Bond stands on a hillside like a neon beacon, wearing a lime green and creamsicle orange dress with pink plastic sandals. Her son sits on the stoop smoking a cigarette. Grandson Grayson is nearby, he is thin, shy, shirtless, and seems fragile. Both father and son have just returned from the barber with buzzcuts.

"I am concerned about my grandchildren," says Kerri. "Grayson has been having asthma attacks." They got worse when his older brother Christian went to the military and Grayson took his bedroom, on the side of the house facing the frack pad. She has to put a mask over his face and blow a mist down into his lungs that lets him take in more air. About a year ago Grayson fell from the school playground monkey bars and broke his arm. Although the break may have been expected, Kerri is suspicious her grandson's bones are brittle from the buildup of some oilfield contaminant in his system—such as radium. There are dark circles under his eyes too, she says, from the pollution.

"Two girls in the preschool have brain cancer," she continues, "and for the first time ever we have a cancer doctor at the local physician." She wants her family to leave but knows they can't. Her son, a Marine and veteran of the US wars in Iraq and Afghanistan recently got a good-paying oil and gas job. But Noble County, Ohio, has become its own war zone. "Living here," says Kerri, "is like having a loaded gun pointed at your head. Someone needs to expose the truth." And while sitting on her Ohio hillside in the late afternoon summer heat, she does.

When fracking hit Ohio in 2011 and 2012 Kerri and her sister Jodi were working as home health nurses. They took the most difficult patients. Feeding tubes, ventilators, quadriplegics, babies born with rare disorders. One patient was paralyzed from the chest down after a sledding accident in which he got runover by a car. Another would seizure without stop. "Her diaphragm goes into spasm, she can't breathe, and she will go, Hhhhh!, and look at you like, Do something to help me!" says Kerri. "That means she is dying on you. Oxygen stops going to the brain and you have to attach her to life support and give her Valium and an emergency rectal gel. Her name was Amanda."

At the time Kerri and her husband Jeff were living here above Seneca Lake on a 104-acre farm with around two dozen sheep, chickens, cats, dogs and a rooster. Kerri did her nursing work, and Jeff, who once told her, "you haven't lived until you feel every blade of grass," ran the farm. Her son's family had built a home on the land, and her sister Jodi visited regularly.

In 2012, a leasing company held a meeting at a Methodist church in the town of Mt Ephraim, just down the road from their farm. It was a chance for residents to quickly sign documents enabling a Denver-based oil and gas extraction company called Antero Resources to begin fracking on their land. "They told everyone they were going to be millionaires," says Kerri. "People were high-fiving." Still, Kerri and Jeff weren't interested. "We thought we could say no," she says. "We were foolish."

In Ohio, as in many US states, it's often impossible to say no to fracking. Munroe Falls, a small city south of Cleveland tried to ban the practice but in 2015 the Ohio Supreme Court, in a 4-3 decision, ruled cities were prohibited from exercising powers in a manner that "impedes, or obstructs oil and gas activities."

Even on their own land, Ohioans are helpless. State law requires drilling to occur in units of a certain size and shape, and companies work hard to acquire the land necessary to form one. If a drilling company gets 65 percent of landowners in a prospective unit to agree to lease their mineral rights, they can request the state to force in resistant landowners against their wishes, a process called unitization. The resisters can demand a unitization hearing, but the state has no authority to consider environmental concerns, all they can legally consider is the project's profitability.

"We kept hearing this noise every night coming toward us," says Kerri. It was drilling and fracking, inching their way across the landscape. Residents who didn't sign up received visits from the notoriously slick door-to-door oilfield salespeople called landmen. Their goal is to convince landowners to sign papers so their property can be fracked, and get as good a deal as possible for the company. In Belmont County, 50 miles northeast of Kerri, there is the story of Jos Miller, an illiterate Amish farmer with seven children who leased his 170-acre farm to Chesapeake Energy at the rate of $50 an acre—some of his neighbors got $6,000. "Industry profiles you when they send the landmen," explains Kerri. "The girls across the road from me were in a lesbian relationship, and they sent a lesbian woman to talk with them. My son was in the Marines, and they sent a young Marine to talk to us." Eventually, Kerri says her and Jeff signed, "what we thought was an environmentally friendly lease."

"One morning," says Kerri, "we came home and the woods had been cut down." Trees were put through a chipper and made into bags used to build a wall around the frack pad. "Every branch that was cut I felt, my husband did too," she says, "but they laughed at us and called us tree-huggers."

For fracking to occur, first the land must be made level. On Kerri and Jeff's farm, the energy company cut off the top of a hill, a technique used across the steep Marcellus/Utica oil and gas country terrain of Ohio, West Virginia and Pennsylvania to create the flat ground necessary for a frack pad. Then, massive drill rigs are hauled in by truck, along with a dozen or more hydraulic fracturing pumps, each the size of an 18-wheeler, enormous vats of frack chemicals, gigantic blender trucks that enable the mixing of fracking fluids, tanker trucks filled with hydrochloric acid, trucks loaded with fracking sand, called sand cans, mammoth tanks for maneuvering sand called sand kings, a small factory of conveyer belts and hoppers to move and mix all the sand, and a labyrinth of pipes and hoses to connect everything together. Impoundments are dug into the landscape to hold the millions of gallons of fresh water that will be used to frack the wells, and later these same impoundments or different ones may be used to temporarily store the highly toxic flowback. All of this will be happening in a backyard, the edge of a farmer's field, or the woods just beyond your front door.

"You start feeling bad," says Kerri, "like it is affecting your neurological system, like you are someone who has not had food, like things are not right in your body. You are sleep-deprived, as if you're sleeping next to a jet engine, night after night, month after month." Like many people in fracking country, Kerri kept a diary.

> *July 24, 2015: Woke up this am to two more dead trees in my yard...The trees are dying at an alarming rate.*
>
> *July 30, 2015, 11am: Sandra Colegrove environmental specialist with Ohio EPA arrives...Soon as she gets out of her car her yellow monitor she uses for air quality starts to beep.*
>
> *October 23, 2015: Fracking begins...on the Bond pad. Terrible rotten egg smell in the air...loud noises, vibration and a constant hum that never goes away. Makes you irritable and shaky.*
>
> *October 26, 2015: Sand trucks on the pad. Loud noise kicks up at night keeps everyone awake all night and makes it difficult to think clearly. Bright lights and looks like dust clouds of sand visible in the air and coming from the pad.*
>
> *October 30, 2015: Noise, smell, bright lights. This is slow torturous death by fracking.*
>
> *December 5, 2015: Bloody noses, coughing, shortness of breath, dizziness and unexplained rashes on us and our animals. It's just a shame that we have to run for our lives, like refuges from an industry who is destroying our air, water and soil. How can they do this without any recourse?? Don't we have any rights as*

landowners and tax payers in this fight?? I can only assume that we don't...We are going to abandoned our home and run for our lives, we have no choice!! This will affect everyone someday we all need clean air, water and food to survive!!! You really should take up this fight for your children or the governor is going to ruin Ohio. They are dumping and injecting waste everywhere!!!!!

December 9, 2015: Everyone is scared to death !! Who do you call??...Living in fear in America, in our own home! I could have never dreamed this could happen in this country!!

The die-off of the animals was particularly disturbing. Snails and frogs were the first to go. Songbirds thinned out. Butterflies and fireflies disappeared. Kerri had Great Pyrenees whose job was to stay outside and guard the sheep. Suddenly, Rockie, the male, was at the front door scratching frantically with his paws, and Snowy, the female, was banging on the door with her head. Kerri noticed their bodies had become speckled with tumors, and their teeth were falling out, and also the fur around their eyes. Then her cats, sick with what she described as, "a sneezy little sinus infection," died. And a vile white sand, Kerri believed to be used sand from fracking operations, bubbled up into her cow pond.

"One day, Larry the chicken just dropped over dead," she says. "My rooster, perfectly healthy one day, dropped dead the next. I had a fish tank and always put water in it from the sink—they died. Then my sheep started prolapsing, the uterus would fall out of the vagina. Once a sheep starts prolapsing you can't put the uterus back in, there is nothing you can do. Another sheep birthed babies with the heads fused together, that was the red herring for me." Kerri and Jeff sold off the rest of the sheep to save their lives.

The earliest documentation of oilfield waste contaminating farm animals may come from a 1926 research bulletin of the West Virginia Agricultural and Forestry Experiment Station. "Deep-seated brines" in West Virginia, Ohio, Michigan and other places were made into salt for cattle. Those that consumed it experienced, "frothing at the mouth, diarrhea and purging, convulsions and death in 10 to 24 hours."

Many years later, in a 2012 scientific paper published in *New Solutions: A Journal of Environmental and Occupational Health Policy*, veterinarian Michelle Bamberger and pharmacologist Robert Oswald reported on pet and farm animal sickness across fracked America. "Because animals often are exposed continually to air, soil, and groundwater and have more frequent reproductive cycles," the authors wrote, they "can be used as sentinels to monitor impacts to human health."

The stories the researchers discovered were harrowing. In one case, hydraulic fracturing fluids were released into a cow pasture—within an hour 17 cows were dead. On a farm besieged by gas wells beef cattle drank water from a creek suspected to be contaminated from the illegal dumping of wastewater, over a three-month period 16 adult cows died, with dead fetuses still inside of them, while other cows produced stillborn calves with unusual eye colors. In another case, farmers learned a tear in an impoundment's liner had caused fracking waste to leak into their cow pasture, "six of the exposed cows eventually went on to slaughter, and, according to the farmers, there was no testing." Bamberger and Oswald pointed out this meat becomes food for not just humans, but other farm animals and also our pets, as rendering plants transform cow parts into feed for pigs, horses, chickens, and cats and dogs. "The gas drilling boom sweeping the world," the paper concludes, "will remain an uncontrolled health experiment on an enormous scale."

One night Kerri awoke to see a nearby hillside cloaked in fire. It was the Crum Compressor Station, purging pipeline contaminants into the night air in what was apparently a perfectly legal blowdown event. "It really hit home for me that night," she says. "Do we call 911, do we call the county, or do we just run?"

The natural gas of this region is collected in thinner pipelines called gathering lines. These lead to natural gas processing plants that clean the gas stream and separate it into different types of fuel, such as ethane, propane and methane. Methane, the main component in natural gas, goes into larger pipelines destined for cities across America. Because the nature of a gas is to naturally expand, every 40 to 100 miles a compressor station is needed along a pipeline to compress the gas and move it along. Kerri knows the farmer who sold land for the Crum Compressor Station to be built. His name was Bobby.

"He did cattle and hay and didn't know what he was getting into," she says. "One day I saw him up there mowing and I said, Bobby please wear a mask and protect yourself." When she saw him again, Kerri says, "he looked like someone had dipped him in scalding water. He had a raised red peppery rash all over his body, and he just lowered his head and started crying. And he apologized, he didn't know all this was going to happen." About a week after that, she says, "he dropped dead."

The Louisiana environmental toxicologist Wilma Subra, who in 1999 was awarded the MacArthur "genius grant" for her work defending communities against radioactive oilfield waste and other industrial pollution, said Hurricane Katrina brought a brew of toxic materials into the New Orleans area which settled with the floodwaters in yards. When waters receded, she says there was a distinct spate of illnesses connected to lawn mowing, and the mechanism of exposure made sense to her. Toxic contaminants in the air and also storm floodwaters naturally settle out on grass and soil. When stirred by a lawn mower these contaminants can blow back into the face of the person doing the mowing, creating the pathway for a unique exposure.

Dr. Michael McCawley, at West Virginia University's School of Public Health, says compressor stations, whose EPA air permits legally enables them to annually lace the air with tens of thousands of pounds of carcinogens, are, when it comes to emissions, the worst type of oil and gas industry facility to live beside. And "the worst emissions," says Kerri, "are always vented at night, and they would settle like a giant cloud in our valley and over our house."

The natural gas pipelines being installed across the region also posed distinct risks for Kerri's son. In the military he worked as an explosives expert, and his oil and gas job involved much of the same. Kerri recalls when a large natural gas pipeline exploded on Smithberger Road outside Summerfield, "he was in his underwear, a pair of boots and a leather coat, everyone else was driving away and he was driving into it."

Everything changed one evening when Kerri and her sister Jodi saw a show about Chernobyl's radioactive forests and Kerri says she recognized Ohio. That night she spent hours researching radioactivity and purchased a hand-held radiation detector on Amazon Prime called the Gamma Scout. "As nurses we are trained to assess and document, and when fracking happened we took our documentation and started asking questions," says Kerri. "When we didn't find answers, we began searching for them on our own."

At first the sisters only used the device in the backyard, where they recorded radiation more than seven times typical background levels for southeastern Ohio. By standards of the National Institute for Occupational Safety and Health, this characterized Kerri's home as a "hot spot." In May 2016, David Lipp, a supervisor in the Ohio Department of Health's Bureau of Environment Health and Radiation Protection visited Kerri's home. Her diary entry for May 11 reads:

"David Lipp, from Ohio Dept of Health comes to our house, along with two other helpers and the Noble Co Dept Health. He walks about the property and takes several levels. They were consistent with what we had been getting...He never at any time told us it was safe!!! We are living here 24-7 and my grandsons are 4 years old and 16 years old. They are only 850 ft from this site!!!"

Kerri says Lipp told her not to worry, as long as the family wasn't exposed to such levels on a regular basis. "Hey dude," Kerri informed him, "we are living here!" But Lipp left, and nothing was done. The Ohio

Department of Health has not replied to any of my questions on this incident. "If you live in Ohio and you want to have, or you have children, you should really push to find the answers," Kerri's diary entry for May 11 continues. "These guys are exempt from all the laws the rest of us have to go by. We are in the way of the gold."

The sisters eventually grew bolder with their snooping around, which they dubbed frack-tracking. After their nursing rounds were complete, curious where the fracking waste trucks they saw constantly crisscrossing the region's roads were going, they followed them into the night. They say they observed men burying a red shipping container in the woods, found containers of waste lying in a remote field, witnessed brine trucks injecting waste through a hose into a creek, and located injection wells hidden in Wayne National Forest beside pits filled with a liquid glowing green like Mountain Dew. Virtually everywhere they looked were harms, going completely unaccounted for.

One afternoon Kerri was at a gas station in the town of Sarahsville when her radiation detector spiked. A brine truck had just passed, and she followed it past the local elementary school and high school, down a dirt road, and toward a massive pit in the woods. "I had a feeling it was secret," she says. The reality was worse, it was a lake of fracking waste called the Cowgill Impoundment, hidden in the forest but legally permitted by the Ohio Department of Natural Resources. "They have dumped something really nasty here," Kerri recorded that day. "It is leaching out of the hill and is white looking like milk and smells like a dead body."

Cowgill was legal, even though the Ohio Department of Natural Resources had no clear idea what was in the impoundment or seemed at all concerned that after the site was done holding fracking waste a future housing development or school could be built there. "There are no oil and gas restrictions that would prevent future development of the site," a spokesperson tells me, and "no soil remediation" would be necessary. And when the Cowgill Impoundment was closed up, the plastic impoundment liner was going to be scanned for radioactivity by a contracted Ohio radiation remediation contractor, according to the spokesperson, then sent to Ultra-Poly Corporation, a plastics recycling firm near the Pennsylvania-New Jersey border. "Countless items for sale at any big box store," says Ultra-Poly's website, "are made from our plastics"—the company has not answered any of my questions.

In Noble County, evening is coming on. Kerri goes inside her son's house, the garage door opens, and she roars out on a camouflaged four wheeler, having replaced the pink sandals with muck boots. I hop on, Jodi follows on her own four wheeler, and we set off toward the Bond pad.

The sisters must cross the valley then go through the yard of their neighbor Jean, who is wearing jean overalls and has a ponytail swinging out from beneath a John Deere cap and boots caked in mud. "He has had all kinds of trouble with his cows," says Kerri. Jean leads the sisters across his property on a buggy with a bumper sticker that reads, *Every Farmer Needs a Hoe*. He opens a farm gate, allowing passage through another belt of woods, then clinks it shut and heads back down the hill to his farm. Kerri tears the four wheeler into the woods, swiftly getting stuck in mud, Jodi swiftly helping her get unstuck. Another route is tried, mud kicked up into the sky and splattered across the vehicles, though somehow the sisters are still perfectly clean in their dayglo dresses.

At the top of the severed hill is the enormous Bond frack pad, with 9 wells. The noise, the emissions, the strange clouds of sand and dust hanging over the valley in the night, the bloody noses, nausea, white sand in her cow pond, tumors on her dogs, sick and dead cats, dead chickens, prolapsing sheep, compressor station blowdowns, pipeline explosions, the disintegration of her farm, her family, her entire community, was, allegedly, for this.

Above the pad the evening wind builds and rushes. One cannot quite see it, but Seneca Lake is there, has always been there. "We grew up right next door," says Kerri. "In the winter ice skating, in the summer we literally ate out of the lake. The whole time was spent in nature. I was called a tomboy, and used to climb a tree and sit and read books. And I used to love to sit and watch the birds, we had blue heron, cranes. Jodi too, and our younger sister Lisa. We camped, we boated, raked up leaves, every tree had every color. We were three sisters, we didn't go to the theater or bowling, we built forts, and we built campfires, and we made smores and told stories and whispered in each other's ears, we thought it was Shangri-La. And we always felt blessed, I always felt I lived in the greatest place in the world. You can go west, you can go south, but you won't find these big oak trees, walnut trees, buckeyes—there is no place as beautiful as Ohio."

4
How to Dispose of Men, A Tale in Three Acts

Act I – The Story of Jesse Lombardi

I fear nothing as far as recourse. I am not worried about intimidation. It is not even a word that bothers me. I got security like no one's business. I am known around here as a quite intimidating dude who doesn't take any shit. Legally they can't try anything, I never signed a non-disclosure. And illegally, they are not going to try anything, I will drop them where they stand. In my driveway is a sign that says, *If you can see this you're in range.* You come to my house welcomed and that is the only way you come. This is my sanctuary.

My other half says, tell them. Tell the people what they need to know. It's not a money thing. It's not a revenge thing. I'll back it up with science. I'll back it up with examples. I'll back it up with facts. What I got to do is jack the e-brake, take a look back, and figure, what can I do to right some of the wrongs. Help balance the ledger. Because you're going so fast in life and sometimes you need to take a break. Now, I am sitting on a nice chunk of land, and I'm thinking on my legacy, so to speak, and getting my ducks in order. Everybody does something for some reason. I got three kids. And I don't really want to leave my kids, and their kids, to lack a better word, a world of shit.

I grew up down in Proctor, West Virginia. And Bellaire, Ohio, at my grandparent's house out in the country. There were big factories up and down the Ohio River. My dad worked at Consolidated Aluminum and I wanted to work in a factory too, that was the dream. At 17 I left high school and went to the barges. Scrap metal, coal, lime. Really good money. I was a young guy going down the river like Huck Finn. Ohio on the right, West Virginia on the left and I am cruising right smack dab in the middle. After the barges I did contracting around the country. I built military vehicles in Cincinnati. I built helicopters in Connecticut. I worked in silver mines in Montana, and a copper mine right outside of Phoenix, Arizona. In Nebraska, I worked at Cargill, dealing with corn and grains. The mischief probably started in Iowa.

That was a 14-month contract building front-end loaders and forklifts. It was work as many hours as possible, because that's what I'm there to do, and get as much money as possible, because that's what I'm there to do. So I started experimenting with coke. I use a little bit of this powder and I can work more hours. That is where the cycle started. Do more coke, work more hours, do more coke, work more hours. In Arizona it graduated into harder drugs, and I got pretty strung out. I'm a little farm kid, working 84 to 96 hours a week and making $10 to 12,000 a paycheck and there are strip clubs. Of course, I had to see every stripper in the state.

Naturally, I ended up getting fired. I took a small contract job in California. Eureka and Arcata, up in Humboldt County. And you know what I'm doing up there. Dealing, using. I end up in Ohio with a stripper back at my father's house. A whole lot of drugs. I was there about a month. Fucking angry. Mad at the world. My dad was not proud of me. Then my mischievousness got the best of me. I thought I pulled it off once, I'm going to commit a crime, and I did. I robbed a bank. This time when they came looking for me, my dad turned me in. He knew I was strung out and in a bad way. He never knew me to be so careless. But I wasn't going to let them catch me, so I went on the run.

I committed another crime, bought a vehicle, I'm out. Basically, I drove until I ran out of money. I was up on Route 3 in Montana, trying to cross into Canada. I was in Buffalo, New York. At one point I was down in Kentucky. I was all over the place. I ended up in Winchester, Virginia. I called home, they said, Our phones are tapped, the FBI wants you pretty bad. So I went down the road to a casino, watched the cops swarm the place. Hit the road again, stole gas if I had to, committed a crime if I had to, worked day jobs, worked with a lot of illegal immigrants, got paid in cash, and that is how I was getting by for a while. Then I messed up.

I got a job at a paper mill. I knew something was up one day because it was two in the morning and the boss was in. I went to take a break. Had a Mountain Dew and Reese's cups in my hand and I see all these SWAT dogs and black shirts. I'm screwed. Naturally, I try to make a run for it. I ran through the factory, through the back door, through a field. Then I got taken down by a couple dogs and tasered and that was the end of that fiasco.

I went on a vacation to federal prison and did some stupid stuff and I'm not going to say I'm proud but I wouldn't change it because it made me who I am. I did eight and a half months in the hole. That will fuck with you. You have a metal sink, metal toilet, metal shower. I slept on a cold floor, LED light on 24 hours a day. After a month you figure out that you need to take that thing you have, your brain, and dump it out like it's a tote. You go through everything in your filing system and you recharge. If my dad hadn't turned me in, I probably would have killed someone, or killed myself.

I came out of prison and back to Ohio. I didn't have anything but the clothes on my back. I got a job installing conveyor belts at mines, steel mills, power plants, Walmart. As the frack boom came on, I had a job at a facility down by the Ohio River. I said, What do you need a conveyor belt for, and they said, Moving sand, and I said, Well then you need a covered belt, what is called a tube belt, because you are going to have sand blowing all over the place. But they didn't want a covered belt, because that was more expensive. So I put in the regular belt, and sand blew all over the place, and I got silicosis, which is when your lungs get scarred and inflamed from breathing in silica dust. Right now, it's just this little dot, nothing that looks like it's going to kill you, but eventually it's going to be a big issue. We had no clue that the extra fine sand they used in the frack could eat up your lungs if you breathed it in. So we just sat there, breathing it all in.

The first time I got called out to a frack pad was upstate New York, before fracking was banned there. The job's coordinates are in the middle of a farm field. It was very picturesque. You got these 100-year-old apple trees and cows and all these beautiful buildings, and this old stone wall on either side as you enter the farm. It was just gorgeous, and it went on forever. We're talking a mile, two miles, a stone wall like a work of art. It really doesn't serve any purpose, it is just beautiful. I'm coming from a farm background and I am thinking this is the prettiest fucking farm I ever been on.

Then I'm at a security shack and suddenly it's like I'm at an industrial facility. In the middle of this beautiful farm you have flames shooting up and all these drillers and every company known to man and I'm like what the fuck did I just pull up to? That was my introduction to fracking. I got out of the truck on this massive well pad and there are trucks and tanks and shit everywhere, and waste everywhere, just chilling in puddles, and they had their hoses, what we call noodles, lying all over the pad.

My job was to run the conveyor belt from a sand king truck into the hoppers so the sand could be mixed with chemicals then shot down the hole for the frack. I did that all over the Marcellus for five years. Halliburton, Baker Hughes. I was the area's lead expert on conveyor belt systems for the oil and gas industry. But it physically beat me to death and destroyed my back and I decided, it is time to do something else. In 2015 I saw a dispatch job with Recon Oilfield Services in Bridgeport, Ohio at $16 an hour. They hired me instantaneously. I got bumped up to facility manager pretty quick and was making $165,000 a year. Then

I worked for a company called Atlantic, and that is where I learned the fucked-up world of oilfield waste.

There are three main pathways companies take in getting into the oilfield waste business. One is just a matter of taking your business cards, scratching something out and putting something else in. That is how septic companies got into hauling brine. If he's sucking the shit out of a porta-john or he's sucking the shit out of an oilfield brine tank he don't care, nobody cares. He doesn't know about any contamination or radioactivity. They just suck stuff. And they see an opportunity in an industry with some shit that needs sucking.

Then there are the gypsy companies. They follow the oil wherever it goes. Guys from Texas move into an area and call their buddies and are like, Hey dude if you get 15 trucks over here we will make some money. I don't know what they do to organize the money, but outside money comes in and these companies are up and running, hauling waste, or processing waste, or doing something shady to try and dispose of it and make it go away.

Then there are the mom and pops. Companies that dealt with other industrial waste services and saw the need in oilfield waste and transitioned into that. Atlantic was a mom and pop into industrial cleanup for steel mills and power plants. When oil and gas hit big in this area these companies were like, you know what let's take it on. And they get a couple guys and look at one, You know how to turn a wrench, right? Yeah. Then to the other, You know how to turn a wrench, right? Yeah. Let's go, we got a pad cleanup job.

It is 100 percent about making money. You put your morals in your back pocket. Drill baby drill. There is no regulation. There is no way to regulate this shit. No way to make it work safe. It is a ticking time bomb. When you build a business out of corruptness, how do you ever expect it to be clean? I thought I was doing a great job, thought I was helping save the world. Thought I was helping American industry. Man—we polluted the living fuck out of this place.

What is happening here is the government has made an exemption to call oilfield waste nonhazardous even though it is filled with radioactive waste and all sorts of other hazardous shit, and then these workers are getting this shit slopped all over their chests, their hands, their feet, their toes, their faces, and they are breathing this in, and ingesting it, and drinking their sodas and eating their sandwiches and smoking their cigarettes and chewing their dip all while covered in hazardous waste that the government and the oil and gas industry has put a pretty little label on to call nonhazardous—do you see what I mean?

In every single oilfield you will find these oilfield waste treatment centers churning radioactive waste around like pancake mix, trying to down-blend it and lower the radioactivity. They call these places different things in each oilfield state. In Ohio they are Chief's Order facilities, in Pennsylvania they are centralized waste treatment facilities, in North Dakota they are solids disposal facilities. In no oilfield I have ever been to or heard of do these guys know what the fuck they are doing, do they have any training, and is any sort of concern given for their health and safety and the environment, ever.

For a Chief's Order site, you want a good sharp hill. Then you can back stuff over the top, dump it down the hill and push dirt over. At the bottom of the hill will be a creek, the same creek that kids fish from and downstream people may be drinking from. If you are not on a hill you are at least on the creek. There might be a spot on the creek where trucks can back up to and clean-out their tanks after dumping off waste. On the site itself everything gets pressure washed, and where does that go? Everything flows down the hill, everything goes into the creek.

If you are by a river, then you are able to back down to a boat launch and suck water out of the river for your water usage. You are right there by the river, you got all these fluids, you are trying to save money. Hey Jim, you been here for 20 years, dump that in there, I'll kick you 500 bucks. Oh yeah no problem. Splurt. Shits in the river. It's not like typing in special numbers then you hit the launch codes at the same time. It's not like I have to contact the president to get this okayed. It's a matter of, I'm a fucking moron and I got some beer to drink and now I got 500 bucks in my pocket and I can buy more beer. Thanks for that safety bonus boss.

We are dealing with high pressure lines in this industry. Most of us don't even know anything about them. We don't know about most of the stuff on site. What is this bud? It's a ring gasket. Where's it go? Right there. Okay cool. No specifications, no torque specs, no nothing. But later on somebody is going to be pushing 15,000 pounds of fluid through there and it's probably going to leak. Nobody gives a shit. And what happened to all that stuff that spilled on the ground? Nobody cares. Do you know someone with a semi? Good, bring in some gravel. You take that skid steer and back drag that for me. EPA guy comes in, sits in his car, *Notes: 12 o'clock noon, guys are on site cleaning up.*

Ask the EPA guy, what time you leave bud? I'm out of here at 4. Cool, we'll be finished up by 4. Then to your crew, Guys start wrapping up. And they are like, It's only four o'clock, we work till 8. And I go, *Start cleaning it up.* It's like mom coming to clean your room, fuck throw everything in the closet. EPA guy sees us cleaning up, he's in his car and gone. Then me to my guys, Okay unload everything and get back to work, we got a thing we need to cleanup. When's the gravel going to be here? 6 o'clock. Gravel is here at 6, click, dump, I'm back dragging, and the whole place has a foot of gravel over everything. EPA guy comes back in the morning to take his sample, pulls up, takes out his little test strip, *You're within level.* Hah, no we're not! I am not in level, the neighbors aren't in level, nobody around here's in level anymore. And six inches under that gravel, when it rains tomorrow, shit is going to be seeping out. But the EPA guy thinks everything is good and that's all that matters.

Guys will pressure wash the waste off their vehicle and all that goes in the storm drain and that storm drain ends up in that creek and now I just poisoned my neighbors. Nobody gives a shit. When you have sludge and oil-based drilling fluid you can't clean off they will use these industrial cleaners, like White Lightning and Purple Power. Everybody I know has scars from this stuff. You mix it with water and spray it out your pressure washer. It's badass scary stuff. It will eat rubber. They use it to clean their rigs, they use it everywhere, and it runs off everywhere. I have seen guys use White Lightning right in the parking lot. Where is it going? Into the pond? Into the park where the kids play basketball or baseball? I don't know.

There is a spill every day. It doesn't matter what site you go to in this county, this state, across the country, there is a spill every single day of at least five gallons on bare naked ground. Say I am on your farmland and I have a spill. I'm not going to come to you and say, Farmer John I had a spill. I am going to come to you and say, Farmer John I planted some new grass.

I might know what happened on that pad, couple other people might know what happened, but the farmers who live out there don't know anything about what happened on that pad. Let's do the math—what does a spill of five gallons of radioactive material do to your groundwater? Whose cows are dying? Whose fucking deer have three heads? There is not one person on this earth that can tell you all the streams and all the groundwater and all the ponds and all the fields that have been contaminated by this industry, because there is not one person on this earth that knows.

I know about swampers and I'll tell you how that comes to be. I taught a confined space training. What I do is give information I get off YouTube. I don't really know what the hell I'm doing. I'm not certified. I would fake training documents. I got a whole bunch of guys who I know have never done this before, and I got a whole bunch of pretty documents and I know PowerPoint and so I create a training. I worked with people who didn't know how to read and write. These aren't the brightest crayons in the box, these are guys who need to work, need that job, need to provide for their families. And they do not absorb what they are being trained on. The training is not done properly to tell the risks. There is no quiz. There is no chance to confirm. No one thinks of radioactivity. But if an audit comes and someone says, did you receive any training about radiation, they can say yes. Hopefully, I gave you enough information so that you are not going to go in there and die.

None of these companies are ever going to say, is that guy certified, don't send him. You are going to say, is that guy certified, send him if you need, keep an extra eye. And if it's a young guy who has shown he has a really strong back and listens well, it doesn't matter if he's not confined space trained, we send him on the next job too. And you're going to run that until someone catches it. You want the worker who doesn't complain. The one who will fill up three trucks of waste per hour compared to other guys who are filling up two. Man this guy didn't complain, he didn't need a break, he knows the job, sucks it up, puts the waste in my truck, that's a good worker. And that is the guy you'll give the job of hauling illegal stuff, because he is not asking any questions. People think brine trucks just haul oilfield brine, no, a brine truck hauls whatever the fuck they want off that pad. And we haven't even gotten into tank cleaning.

Imagine going into a tiny room with a six-foot tall ceiling and these claustrophobic dividers and it's packed full of brine or used fracking sand or sludge and the smell is horrible, and now they need to pressure wash that out so they can make that tank clean and send it back to the vendor. And the guys who go in there might be wearing their little paper yellow suits and rubber gloves and even if they have a face shield, it is probably not a full face shield, and they shovel waste out of tanks and pressure wash and it's in their mouth and they're eating it, breathing it in, all over the ground, scooping it up, they are absolutely covered head to toe, and they come out with the stink on them, and they pull their Tyveks off and their regular work clothes are absolutely filthy, stuff all over his face, face black with waste, and it's going into the atmosphere and the air, and it's flowing down the hill. Has anyone checked that guy for radioactivity? No. And that guy wouldn't have a clue.

I love a guy who just came out of prison. If I were to be presented with someone clean cut, knows a lot, worked in the industry for 20 years, and your guy who has just gotten out of prison I'm hiring him. A guy who has just gotten out of prison is broke and has got to pay his bills and I got no problems. I want him. I love him. I take him. He's going to be my star worker. Everyone wants that person. He doesn't know what the word EPA means. He doesn't know what workers' comp means, and no one's going to miss this dude if we fucking kill him.

Some guy who owns his own house I can't go knock on his door and wake his ass out of bed and drag him in. He'll say, get off my porch or I'm calling the cops. With a guy coming out of prison I know you been sleeping on a fucking floor and I am going to get you in company housing, and I'm going to get you the nicest bed. In fact, I go out and get you the deluxe mattress too. I give you my best flash. I buy you a new phone, latest model with all the bells and whistles. You need new boots, I don't just get you some crummy pair, I get you a nice pair of boots. I provide for you. And now I've got you back in prison. Now I own you. Multiply this guy by 100 and multiply him by another 100 and that's your oilfield.

I would talk to the adult correction officer where they do parole. I'm a confidence man and I tell him some bullshit. I would say, I'm an ex-felon myself and my life has really been changed, this is the company that did it for me and we like to hire local guys. Now the probation officer is landing more guys jobs and they are going to be like a superstar. And their department is getting more grants from the community and the commissioner is getting more grants from the state and the state is getting more grants from the federal government and the money is flowing and everyone is doing well.

Now, say Dave Yoho gets injured on the job. I go and bonus him out, let me get you some cash Dave. I go to the ATM, pull out of my own personal account, 500 bucks, here you go. And I'll make you right Dave, I'll pay your medical bills. You are going to get some good drugs. I am going to let you do light duty stuff at work, answer the phone for dispatch. Or sit in the fucking house. And I'm still going to pay you 60 hours a week. Dave is like, this is a no-brainer. I don't have to wait for workers' compensation, I don't have to wait for anything. Yeah absolutely.

Three weeks go by, Dave's good. I already have the hospital bills, everything's squared away. Dave, you want to come back to work? I need you for an ASAP job. Dave is confused. He is like, well I'm hurt. I say, I don't know how you got hurt, I don't know anything about you being hurt. Dave: But my hand hurts. Me: Dave you are going to need to hit this ASAP job and you are going to need to hit it now, or I'm going to have to terminate you for refusal to work. Boom. Gunned him down. Dave Yoho is gone from this company.

The oil and gas industry preys on the undereducated and people who live in poverty. You are being dangled a carrot and you're like holy shit, that's a carrot. And you come up all the way here, and it's a muddy carrot. It takes someone willing to abandon morality and decency to come work in this industry as a manager. It is shameful to admit but that's what it takes. Everything through the oil and gas industry is coercion. In this industry it is thanks for the information, now leave, and please Jesus Christ, let's not ask too many questions. I wrote SOPs, Standard Operating Procedures, which are instructions for a worker on how a job is to be done. I purchase ordered equipment. I did every aspect of running a company that deals in oil and gas waste. And I am here to tell you that not once, not once did anyone ever mention the word radiation. Never.

The energy companies like EQT or Ascent would come in and audit us. But all they were really there for was to get the free snacks and hear us say some fancy words like, capabilities, capabilities, capabilities, no injuries. And if we give them copies of our capability insurance and our training manuals they say, oh it is good enough and file away. No one is really reading this stuff. It is all superficial. These are publicly traded companies, they are under scrutiny, they have a board of investors, they have to be by the book. But if I can push off my dirty work to this third-party oilfield waste company who may or may not abide by the rules but appears as if they do because they are really good at covering their tracks, absolutely let's run with that. They are putting all this money out to third party companies to avoid having to pay litigation risks down the line. In 20 years, we can't sue EQT because Joe Schmoe worked for a dozen different waste companies and who the hell are any of these companies, and who the hell is Joe?

I'm a high school dropout. I'm an ex-federal felon. I never was the best kid. There ain't two ways about it. But I look like a saint compared to these oil and gas companies. At Atlantic we had someone working in the office full on pregnant, and every day for the full day she would be there. Your office personnel aren't being trained, she is just there to do the books. Why would you train a secretary in radioactivity? But the truck drivers and tank cleaners are bringing in their paperwork and they are covered in this stuff. And even their paperwork is covered, it has it all over. And these guys in their boots are sitting in chairs in the office talking on the phone and the mud and waste is drying out and turning to dust. Is that pregnant woman being exposed to harmful levels? No one is checking. No one gives a fuck.

And the workers, the type of guys I hired, will eventually and inevitably get sick. You are never going to find them later, and you are never going to be able to hold anyone accountable. It's part of the trick of the industry. The waste company they worked for will be gone and they will die in agony in the trailer park they came from and no one will give a fuck. I came, I conquered, I got what I wanted, I'm out. Basically, just kill them off, because no one has a fucking clue. Imagine a gazillion Jesse Lombardi's out there with my thought process and not really morals or ethics and strung out on drugs. That's your oil patch.

The word you are looking for is desperation, you prey on someone's desperation. No one has a clue they are being exposed. No one is informed. There's collateral damage all over. I'm not a bible guy, that is just not my cup of tea. But I was raised Catholic and I am familiar with it, I can quote you scripture all day long. Gluttony is a sin. We are killing everything. We are fucking polluting the oceans. We are destroying national reserves. We are fucking up people's backyards. Twenty years down the line there is going to be a catastrophic fallout from this. I mean the amount of people that are going to be dying is insane. And I was a part. I got paid for destroying Mother Earth.

But let me tell you something. My family worked our fingers to the bone for industry. My dad had cancer three different times. They cut out his pancreas, they cut out this, they cut out that, he got mesothelioma, he died. Virtually every single person in my family has died of cancer. The cancer lobby is doing well off those of us who live along the Ohio. My thoughts are this, I believe that I can make a change. My kids are not going to die of cancer. I know someone who pulled their daughter out of a preschool in St. Clairsville because they built a frack pad right next to it. Wrap your head around that one, kids playing in the backyard and next door they are fracking and have an open-air brine pit. Everyone has their trigger in life. That was my trigger.

Now, I live on an old farm that has been in the family since the 1930s. We have 49 acres, and that is my inner sanctum. I got my other half, and we got three kids, Adelyn, 5, Jarren, 11, and Sophia, 13. We grow our own food. Built a chicken coop, a garden, getting ready to do cows. I put in a wood boiler and got the water wells working, our next step is put in solar arrays. My other half, Cortnee, wants to go vegan. This is my life now. When you take the time to appreciate what you've been given and make it work for you and build a legacy and leave a legacy, then I think you put a pin in it.

I want to say that my daughter is a cardiologist, my son is a lawyer, and we live off the land and we work the land and we have our own water and food. And someone might ask my kids, well why do you do that, why do you live like this? And they will say, because my dad worked in the oil and gas industry and died a miserable death from cancer. And if I have to be that martyr I will. Because things need to change. My grandfather wasn't able to do it. My father wasn't able to do it. Now it's my turn, and I'm going to hit a home run.

Act II – Flipping Pancakes of Radioactive Waste in North Dakota's Bakken Oilfield

North Dakota experienced its first oil boom in the early 1950s but was never really a major oilfield player. For decades, petroleum geologists had been longing to comprehensively tap the Bakken, a geologic formation made of layers of sandstone and organic-rich black shales located two miles deep beneath the rural western part of the state. But no one knew how to fully crack out this formation's tightly-held oil and gas. Then, in 2005, came modern fracking and oil development exploded across the state. By 2012 the Bakken had surpassed Alaska and North Dakota was producing more oil than anywhere else in America but Texas.

The state's boom coincided with the recession, and workers from other parts of the country made their way to one of America's coldest and most remote states in search of work. One of them was Rob Kanack. He lives in an apartment complex in Dickinson, North Dakota and pays $874 a month in rent and has gotten used to the winters, and the work, but that doesn't mean he is going to sit quiet and let his story disappear like so many others into the cold Dakota night. He takes a breath and goes back to the beginning, back to Wisconsin.

"A guy I knew came out to North Dakota in 2012," says Rob. "At the time I had two jobs, working as a manager and security at a bar, and later at a factory making solid surface materials. Bakken? Never heard of it, why would I want to go out there? Then in 2012 I lost my job. I had a place to live but that's about all I had. And I was hanging out in Milwaukee trying to find decent work, going from temp service to temp service, and I thought, screw it."

From Wisconsin to the oilfield is a 900-mile trip. Rob packed his life into a camper trailer, drove out with his dad, and in August 2014 set up home at Watford Indoor RV Park, in Watford City and the heart of the boom. "I honestly didn't know what to think coming out here," he says. "I just wanted to get hired and have a potential career."

Within a week he was working in the town of Arnegard for a company called Cypress Energy at a saltwater disposal well—the term used out West for what in the East is called an injection well. One of Rob's jobs was to clean out the filter pod system, which contains the filter socks, filters that resemble a gigantic mesh condom. Oilfield brine has a lot of solid particles suspended in it, and before brine is shot down an injection well filter socks trap these sediments, which could otherwise clog the well. Among things they filter out are the radioactive metals inherent to brine, and as a result filter socks can contain elevated levels of radium, and also radioactive lead, and are regarded as some of the oilfield's more highly radioactive waste. North Dakota, according to the 2014 estimate of one health official, produces 27 tons of dirty filter socks every single day.

They have ended up stashed inside black trash bags at an abandoned Mobil gas station and dumped in ditches, city dumpsters, and littered across the Fort Berthold Indian Reservation. They have also been illegally snuck into county landfills. In 2014 the state crafted rules to try and fix the problem. Contaminated filter socks were to be kept in leak-proof containers at the injection wells where they were produced and picked up like bins of dirty laundry by drivers properly trained in handling hazardous and radioactive materials.

At Cypress Energy it was Rob's job to take the filter socks out of the filter pods and deposit them in these bins. "I would be wearing rubber gloves, the ones that go up past your wrist, no mask or respirator," he says. "I was never taught any safety precautions. All I know is brine is just salt water. Stuff would be dripping out of the filter sock and all over you, and if you opened the chamber too fast you got sprayed. I have gotten it in my eyes, even with safety glasses on. I have had brine in my mouth on many occasions too, it doesn't really taste good."

It was Rob's first introduction to the sloppy world of oilfield waste, but not his last. After a couple other jobs, in January 2016, Rob was hired at a facility in Keene, North Dakota, operated by a Canadian company called Secure Energy. They dealt in the disposal of oilfield brine, or as it's simply called in North Dakota, *salt water*, and also did solid oilfield waste disposal. Rob was getting paid around $23 an hour.

Secure has headquarters in Calgary, Alberta, assets in Canada's notorious tar sands, and is traded on the Toronto stock exchange. In North Dakota they run solid oilfield waste processing facilities, saltwater disposal wells, and oilfield waste landfills. At a 2019 public meeting in Williams County, North Dakota, Secure representative Kurt Rhea demonstrated the use of a Tracerco radiation monitor on a box of Master Paws kitty litter. "I received minimal training on the Tracerco," says Rob.

Sludgy oilfield waste is often hauled in a truck called a hydrovac. On some, the rear end lifts up like a dump truck, allowing waste to slide out. Other trucks push material out with a plunger-like device. Contaminated soil might come in a side dump, a long sleek truck that flips its container to the side to unload. Waste splats onto the pad and forms a pile and Rob's job was to check radiation levels with the Tracerco then call the readings into the office, and also collect a sample in a mason jar, to be kept on site as a reference. He then maneuvered the waste around the pad with a front-end loader, the classic yellow heavy construction equipment, or a skid steer, a smaller scooping machine.

One goal at a solids disposal facility is to dry out the waste, which makes it lighter and therefore cheaper to dispose of. Tubes with antifreeze ran beneath the concrete pad to keep it heated and fly ash, a hazardous byproduct of coal production, was used too. Rob recalls it came in bags, and he would mix them into the waste like packets of yeast into bread dough and a chemical reaction occurred that generated heat, though he noticed fly ash had trouble drying out the higher-level radioactive waste. For this material, Rob says, "you would take the loader and have to constantly keep flipping the waste around on the pad like a pancake."

The Tracerco measures radiation in microroentgens per hour, a unit abbreviated μR/hr. Rob says he would take background radiation readings at a location off the pad at the start of each shift, and they were typically between 8 and 12 μR/hr.

"Anything double background is considered radioactive," says Rob. This runs in line with government health agencies, and also the International Association of Oil & Gas Producers, which considers an area to be contaminated if radioactivity levels are more than twice background.

At Rob's work site, he says readings of 100 to 200 μR/hr occurred regularly, and levels occasionally approached 1,000 μR/hr. He was surprised to find radioactivity levels above background inside the small office building, where he says there was a coffeemaker, vending machine, rotisserie for cooking hot dogs, and a freezer with food like frozen burritos, available to Secure workers and also truck drivers delivering waste. "You would pull out a rad counter in there and it was hot, maybe three to five times background," says Rob. One woman who worked in the office would cook food up in a crock pot.

"At the time I worked there, no one in the office ever mentioned anything about radiation," he says. "Any hazard, radiation or fly ash or whatever, if I asked about it, was always downplayed—according to the bosses, nothing that happened on that pad was ever considered hazardous."

How the Secure office might have become contaminated with radioactivity is something Rob has spent some time thinking about. A regular flux of drivers wearing clothing splashed with waste inside the small poorly ventilated office dealing with paperwork or waiting for their hotdog to cook on the company rotisserie is one possible route. There was also a saltwater disposal well at the facility and Rob believes the office's nearness to the brine tanks, which would naturally accumulate radioactive sludge, may have contributed too. But it's impossible to know for sure, because Rob never carried out a full assessment of the entire facility with his radiation detector, and neither, he says, did anyone else.

Once liquids were removed, based on the levels Rob recorded, a decision was made on where to send the waste. He says waste that was less than two times background would go to a North Dakota landfill specifically for oil and gas waste called 13 Mile, located about 80 miles away, near Williston, and also operated by Secure. Waste that was more than twice background went to a landfill in the remote ranch country of eastern Montana called Oaks Disposal. "At some point there was a cutoff," says Rob, "and really hot material would go to a site in Texas."

He was unsure the name of the Texas facility, and just how much waste ended up there. What he does recall is sending waste to Texas was very expensive, sending waste to Oaks Disposal in Montana was less expensive, and sending waste to Secure's own 13 Mile landfill near Williston was the least expensive option.

"The practice of blending radioactive material with non-radioactive material so it could go to Secure's own landfill or Oaks was occurring when I got there," says Rob. He had issues with this practice, but ones that came later concerned him even more. North Dakota landfills, he says, may use a handheld radiation detector similar to the Tracerco to check for radioactivity, and also may have large portal monitors that generate a reading as trucks pass through. Rob says toward the end of his employment, in 2016, he was instructed by his bosses to load trucks in a way that made it difficult for this equipment to detect the radioactivity in the loads. For example, fill the middle of the dump truck with the most radioactive waste and line the top and sides with non-radioactive material—like a radioactive waste Twinkie. Or, line a certain side of the truck with radioactive waste, knowing only the other side would be checked with a handheld detector at the landfill. The apparent goal, he realized, was simple enough. The more radioactive oilfield waste Secure could sneak into its own North Dakota landfill, the less money the company would have to spend hauling it long distances to the higher-level disposal sites in other states.

"I expressed...that this was % 100 not legal and they were pushing the boundaries with sending these trucks to 13 mile," Rob wrote in a letter he sent in the summer of 2016 to one of his bosses. "All of this was done knowingly, and under duress as we all thought if we didn't comply with this we could lose our jobs," his letter continues.

He says no one at Secure acted on his concerns, so Rob tipped off the North Dakota Department of Health. On July 24, 2016, the agency stopped by the site where Rob worked and also Secure's 13 Mile landfill for unannounced visits. They reportedly found 10 loads of illegally dumped material, and more illegally dumped waste at two other North Dakota oilfield waste landfills. Even though this violated landfill permits, no fines were issued. Rob had risked his neck to raise the alarm on a practice that put workers, the environment, and North Dakota communities at risk, and the state hardly offered a slap on the wrist. "I quit shortly after that," he says. "I walked into the office at the end of my shift and said, fuck this place, and never came back."

North Dakota regulators defend their rules, and in 2024 pass along to me a "Radioactive Material License" for Secure's landfill near Williston, which mandates radioactivity be strictly monitored in the groundwater, the air, the liquid that runs off the landfill, called leachate, and the perimeter of the facility.

Another North Dakota winter storm is coming, and Rob needs to do some errands before it hits. He is still working in the oil patch, because it's the only work he can find that pays decent, and the only work he knows, and going back to Wisconsin would be too difficult at this point. His latest job involves operating a hydrovac truck, the same kind that used to empty waste onto his pad when he worked at Secure.

"I feel like I am just chasing my own tail," he says. "With what I'm doing now I get covered in sludge and am probably exposed to a lot of radiation, but like anything else, you get used to it." But he hasn't given in.

"The moral code out here is garbage," says Rob. "Everything gets swept under the carpet. Seems like everywhere you turn in the oilfield it is just a lie upon a lie upon a lie to cover up another lie. What do you teach your kids? How do you run a society? The only thing they care about is how many more billions they can take out of here. And the environment goes to hell, and the culture goes to hell, and everything goes to hell, and that has become the culture of North Dakota. And the state doesn't give a fuck, because there is too much money involved."

Rob connects me to one of his colleagues, who recounts a story of how he was made to clean-out filter tubes, which are similar to filter socks and can become heavily gunked with toxic sludge. This worker was instructed to regularly spray them off with a pressure washer so the company could reuse them rather than spend the money to buy new ones. Waste would fly out all over his face. "I was literally so sick after that incident that I shit myself," the worker tells me.

This worker won't give his name, worried it would prevent him from getting future work in the industry. Rob isn't worried.

"You are supposed to shut your mouth and do as you are told and believe what they tell you, otherwise you won't have a job," he says. "And when you say something about the shit going on you become the scapegoat because they don't want a guy who is hurting their pocketbook. And it comes at the cost of people's health, and it comes at the cost of doing things illegally. In the oilfield, if you speak up to protect your fellow workers, dude, you are so done. But fuck it, what they are doing is wrong. If it keeps people from getting hurt or dying, I am going to speak up. I will poke the beehive."

Secure has not replied to my questions regarding practices at their North Dakota facilities.

Act III – The End of the Line

In November 2021 Bill Torbett began working at an Ohio oilfield waste treatment center located in an old steel mill on the Ohio River. It was in the town of Martins Ferry and run by a company called Austin Master Services. Inside is a big warehouse-like space and drivers who haul fracking waste across the Marcellus/Utica tell me when they have nasty loads, things like filter socks or particularly sloppy and radioactive sludge, they take it here. Austin Master, I learn, is authorized by the state of Ohio to receive 120 million pounds of radioactive oilfield waste a year. In a different world, one might expect a shipshape place, operated by an appropriately trained and protected crew of workers.

"That place was a hoot," says Bill. "I was working 3 to 11pm, so halfway through my shift, boom, it was on. Seven o'clock them night shift guys would come on, and one guy sold reefer and the first thing we would do is we'd sit there and open up the door and smoke a big joint. Then we hang out and smoke a couple more."

"When I got the night shift is when I seen the bigger picture," he says. "It seemed like virtually every single operator, every guy I met, was in some sort of rehab. I'm from the '70's, I'm just a pothead. These young kids are all on Suboxone, what they call subs, methadone, and of course, if you got the actual pills they are worth their weight in gold, Percocet, OxyContin, any of that opioid based stuff. Almost like they were recruiting addicts. This is the type of guy who has just come out of prison and is not really going to question the radioactivity of some sludge, he's just happy to be making money, and this is better than anything he can get in fast food or retail. A dude like that will be one of the hardest workers, confined space entry, going into tanks, all the shittiest jobs, you hand them a power washer, pay them $15 an hour and they jump right in."

"It's a good situation for the parolee or the newly released from prison. If they are looking at a guy fresh out of prison and a guy who is not out of prison, they are going to take the guy out of prison and the reason is they become extremely loyal. It's not like they were entered into any kind of formal rehabilitation program. I think it was more like, some guy got out of prison and somehow found Austin Master and was in touch with guys on the inside basically saying, Hey when you get out I have a job for you. If your parole officer says you need a job and your buddy is like, I got a job, you make decent money, you can start right away, and you can continue to get high, well fuck the job service, I'm going with that guy's job."

"The shop was a mess," Bill continues. "Sludge was everywhere, everywhere, and I didn't know the extent of what was in that sludge. There was a lot of cleaning, hosing down the press used to dry out the waste, or hosing down what they call the snake pit, and stuff would just splash up on you. Waste was always splashing around. In disconnecting lines sometimes it would squirt out. We were literally ankle deep in sludge, and a lot of times knee deep. All that shit is dripping down on you, you're saturated in it, your hands are covered in it. The denim of the FR uniforms would hold the wetness, and the moisture would soak right through into your skin, like if you got caught outside in the rain without an umbrella. It was not uncommon to see an operator change out of his jumpsuit halfway through his shift because it was soaked through with sludge. There was a shower in the locker room, but I never saw anyone use it. There was also a washing machine, always getting broken because there was so much sludge."

In February 2022, after just three months of working at Austin Master, disturbed by the lack of concern for health and safety, Bill left. I first visited Austin Master with a group of Ohio scientists and community members in 2018 and was appalled a facility processing thousands of tons of radioactive oilfield waste sat right on a public road, just down the street from the Martins Ferry high school football stadium, and 1,000 feet from wells that supplied the city's drinking water. The Ohio Department of Natural Resources had been inspecting Austin Master for years, and although they never mentioned the alleged drug use or practice of taking advantage of formerly incarcerated individuals, their reports were damning.

An early inspection, from September 16, 2015, reads, “the facility is now in operation...no issues to report.” But by April 2017, “the floors appeared to be dirty with oilfield wastes” and the roof was leaking during rain events. “The potential exists for radioactive and other wastes to be tracked out of the warehouse by trucks,” inspectors noted in July 2017. Later inspection reports found waste splattered on the floor, walls, and around electrical panels. Photos taken by inspectors show massive oozing piles of leaking black, brown, and yellow sludge on the warehouse floor, tire tracks leading waste directly out of the facility, and employees in inappropriate PPE, including one man who appears to be in a T-shirt, pushing around waste with a push broom. In September 2018, the roof was still leaking and inspectors observed, a “frac tank being removed from the facility” and waste “falling off the truck” and onto the public roadway. Filter socks were being shredded with a tree shredder, and later, a piece of equipment called “Muffin Monster.”

In November 2018, the Ohio Department of Natural Resources assessed radioactivity at Austin Master and found some waste containers at 60 times background. Another assessment, in February 2019, found levels 73 times background “on a large ‘burrito’ bag of waste waiting to be loaded into a gondola rail car.”

Despite all of this, the state had issued the company no fines. When I ask Austin Master questions I receive a reply from spokesperson Christopher Martin, who tells me there is nothing “unusual or harmful” about their operations. “Austin Master Services takes a responsible approach to providing valuable waste remediation services and jobs in the Martins Ferry community,” says Martin. “There are no known complaints from AMS employees concerning work conditions.” He does not reply to questions on the alleged practice of hiring formerly incarcerated individuals, although I find a July 2022 post from Austin Master Services on the employment website Indeed.com looking to hire people eligible for “Second Chance Employment.” Meaning, individuals with a criminal record.

Bill Torbett tells me radioactivity was never mentioned to him through the hiring process, but he eventually learned that assessing it was a critical part of the plant's operations. "These waste trucks come in and a guy out there has this radiation meter, and he goes around and gives them a number and according to this number, that determines where this waste gets dumped," says Bill. "Bins 1, 2, and 3 was supposed to be low dosage, 4 was waste that had to be pressed, and 5, 6 and 7 was the high doses. I found out later the shit in 5, 6, 7 would be blended down with the low dose stuff or blended down with lime, which creates lots of dust, to try and lower the levels. Kind of like, to give you a street analogy, a drug dealer cutting down cocaine."

I find out the waste with lower radioactivity levels was leaving Austin Master and headed to five different Pennsylvania landfills, including Imperial Landfill, in Imperial, Westmoreland Sanitary Landfill, in Belle Vernon, and Arden Landfill, in Washington, just 30 miles southwest of Pittsburgh. An important question remained, if the mission of Austin Master was to separate out the more highly radioactive oilfield waste for special disposal, where exactly was that material headed?

In correspondence with Tim Orton, technical officer at a radioactive waste disposal site in the Utah desert operated by a company called Energy*Solutions*, I learn that from March 2015 through March 2020, more than 76 million pounds of oilfield waste, too radioactive for local landfills, were shipped in railcars from Austin Master's Ohio facility across the country to Energy*Solutions*. And on five occasions Energy*Solutions* staff found those railcars to be leaking. "There is a potential that the waste had leaked all the way across the country," says Tim. Though, he says his company analyzed the spilled waste in each instance and "did not find any radioactivity."

Tim tells me, "waste was transported by CSX Transportation and arrived on the Union Pacific rail line." CSX tells me they "work closely with customers, first responders and local communities to manage the safe movement of hazardous materials on our rail network" and "have not had a documented release of product associated with Austin Master Services." I go to Kansas, along the likely rail line the material would have traveled, and in Salina, learn from two women at a knitting supply store that trains containing toxic waste often traveled through their community in the middle of the night, including, they believed, trains containing fracking waste. I go on to the Energy*Solutions* radioactive waste disposal site in the Utah desert and stare through the fence in the dark of night, realizing that somewhere out there was 76 million pounds of radioactive fracking waste from the Marcellus/Utica. And this is where the trail stops—until I am led to David.

Concerned Ohio River Residents, a local advocacy group, working with Dr. Yuri Gorby, a native West Virginian and former Department of Energy scientist who spent 15 years studying how radioactive and chemical contaminants move through the environment, took two different sets of samples along the public roadway and discovered a growing trail of radioactivity led right to Austin Master's door. Concerned Ohio River Residents alerted town officials and were largely ignored, but they eventually received an extraordinary piece of scientific evidence. The boots, headlamp and hardhat worn by one worker. The items were covered in sludge, which they also had tested for radioactivity, at Eberline Analytical, a radiological analysis lab in Oak Ridge, Tennessee. Combined radium-226 and radium-228 levels on the worker's clothing items were 85 picocuries per gram, 17 times limits set by EPA for cleaning up toxic dumps and nuclear sites like uranium mills. Yet here it was, globbed onto this worker's body. Or, more specifically, the body of David Duvall.

I meet him in 2022 at a gas station coffeeshop in southwest Pennsylvania, about an hour east of the Austin Master radioactive oilfield waste treatment plant where he once worked. He emerges from a gigantic pickup truck, a wiry and intense man with what looks like a broken nose and takes a seat at one of the coffeeshop tables then asks me what I want to know.

David has been dealt a tough hand, and his work as a laborer at Austin Master from June 2020 through April 2021 fell right in line with a long list of difficulties he has experienced in life. As we speak he constantly seems just a step away from slipping out the door and back into the safety of his gigantic pickup truck, but what he eventually reveals corroborates the stories of others.

Much of it by this point is familiar. Such as the treatment of workers—"They treat you like garbage and work you like a slave," says David. The unprotective clothing—"The suits they give you tear easily, and the crotch gets ripped, a lot of times I just wore a wife beater, I was really getting covered in that shit." The failure to inform of even basic risks—"Workers would eat, drink, and smoke cigarettes one after the other with dirty hands, I did the same thing." The health concerns—"Since I been there my teeth have been falling apart." The drug use—"Meth, weed, a lot of weed, Suboxone. I heard them talking about doing acid, I never saw that though I seen them passing it around in the locker room, one guy would sell it to another guy, right on a little strip. I've seen them snort crystal meth right in the locker room too, one worker who left before me was smoking meth in the locker room, and smoking crack in the bathroom."

I learn new things too. Contamination I hadn't considered before—"Waste gets in your ears, in your nose, eyes sometimes, I've had it in my mouth, and we're always banging ourselves open, so it's probably getting in our bloodstream too through our cuts and sores." The way things were kept from inspectors with the Ohio Department of Natural Resources—"We always knew when ODNR was coming and would hide hot stuff in back of the steel mill." And the details of just how they loaded the railcars that went to the Utah radioactive waste disposal site—"We'd spend days under those railcars with foam and Flex Seal plugging up holes so they wouldn't leak, once they get out of there who the hell cares, anything to get it out the door." David says three trucks a day went from Austin Master to a local landfill, and like Rob in North Dakota, he conveys that the practice of loading them up with waste was not an exact science—"A lot of trucks got screwed up, a lot of trucks got sent out hot."

I am regularly relaying to state and federal regulators what I am finding out from workers like David concerning oilfield waste treatment facilities, and regularly asking them detailed questions. Some of their answers:

"While the Ohio Department of Health has been designated as the Ohio radiation control agency, there are certain instances where ODH's authority is exceeded by other statutory authorities. One of these instances includes regulation of the oil and gas industry in Ohio." – Ohio Department of Health

"The Division does not have the authority to levy fines, none the less, the Division strives to ensure regulated entities are complying with Chief's Orders, Ohio law and rule." – Ohio Department of Natural Resources

"We went from a rural agrarian society to a rural industrial society overnight, we didn't know what we didn't know." – North Dakota Department of Environmental Quality

"The waste products from the oil and gas drilling operations you describe are referred to as technologically enhanced naturally occurring radioactive material, or TENORM…*We do not regulate or license this material.* My understanding is that the Environmental Protection Agency is the federal regulator of TENORM for oil and gas wastes." – Nuclear Regulatory Commission

"EPA does not regulate radioactivity in oil and gas production, processing and transport systems. EPA does not regulate the radioactive content of sludge, scale, drill cuttings, and fracking sands, and so does not collect data on radioactive content or estimates of volumes generated… There is no one federal Agency that specifically regulates the radioactivity brought to the surface by oil and gas development." – EPA

"We don't track brine hauling, we are only able to apply our regulations to materials that fit the definition of hazardous materials and that isn't considered a hazardous material." – U.S. Department of Transportation

There is "little potential for harm to workers or the public from radiation exposure due to oil and gas development." – U.S. Occupational Safety and Health Administration (OSHA)

What sticks with me most about David's story is what it reveals about oilfield waste regulations. In 1976, Congress passed the Resource Conservation and Recovery Act, an attempt to deal with the nation's hazardous waste crisis by creating rules to properly transport and dispose of it. But the Bentsen and Bevill Amendments exemption, passed in 1980, provided the oil and gas industry with a remarkable gift by legally defining oilfield waste, despite being potentially loaded with radioactivity and a host of other carcinogens, as nonhazardous. And here this waste was being plastered across these worker's boots, clothes, skin, faces, and inevitably making its way into their bodies. Where, of course, it is not the oil and gas industry's exemption that prevails, but the laws of science.

David tells me, before we depart the gas station coffeeshop and go our separate ways, how hard it is to get a job coming out of prison, with a felony, and no driver's license. At Austin Master they didn't drug test, which he cites as a plus, and they paid guys like him $15 an hour, which he says was good money for the area. "They gave people like me opportunity," David explains. But he admits workers like him didn't really know what they were getting into, and Austin Master told them they had nothing to worry about.

"I think what's happening," says David, "is they see we're so desperate for work, and by the time we get in there—it's too late."

5
Washington, D.C. and the "Breath of Satan"

In January 2020 I receive a call out of the blue from somebody who has spent years working at a federal agency as a staff health physicist—that is, they study how radiation interacts with the human body. This person has vital information to share, and after a number of phone calls we finally meet at a table in a crowded sports bar just blocks from the U.S. capitol.

"Our opinion of mother nature as benevolent and everyone is butterflies and marshmallows is wrong," the source begins. "Mother nature is insidious and will kill you at any opportunity. Just because something is natural does not mean it is safe, see arsenic, see botulism."

To them, one of the most interesting and alarming natural contaminants on earth is the radioactive gas radon. "Radon," they say, "is the real deal. I call it the breath of Satan."

In the silver-rich Erz Mountains, along the border of Germany and the Czech Republic, Medieval miners suffered from an unexplainable mountain sickness they referred to as *Bergsucht*. "The dust has corrosive qualities, it eats away the lungs" and leads to "premature death," the Saxon scholar Georgius Agricola wrote in his epic illustrated book on mining, *De Re Metallica*, published in 1556. There were many theories on what killed these men, we now know it was radon. These 500-year-old miners are considered the radioactive element's first victims, although it surely killed before.

The US story began during World War II, says the source. In order to make the nuclear bombs test-dropped over the Nevada desert and held in ready for launching at Soviet Russia, America dug uranium out of mines across the West. "Back in 1948 the first couple whistleblowers started raising issues that radon was causing lung cancer in the miners," the source explains. "The Public Health Service put teams out in the field and X-rayed miner's lungs but were not allowed to tell the miners what they were looking for or finding. They knew these guys were going to be dead in ten years but couldn't say it to their face. Then the body counts added up and the feds still blew it off. It took 17 years until the government acted and made them vent the mines. Over 1,500 died from lung cancer unnecessarily."

"It's the original sin of our profession," the source continues, "not stamping our feet harder, letting those uranium miners get all that dose. Because of the Cold War they needed the uranium more than they needed to protect a couple miners, many of whom were Native American."

And now a new industry has emerged, or rather, a new set of challenges to an old industry. "Fracking," the source says, "is changing the geopolitics of the world." Meaning, we need the oil and gas more than we need to protect a couple oil and gas workers.

Radon's presence in oil and gas appears to have been first detected in 1904, by a 25-year-old Canadian graduate student named Eli Franklin Burton, who described "experiments with a highly radioactive gas obtained from crude petroleum." But "there is night and day differences between radioactivity protections received by a worker in the nuclear industry and that of an oilfield worker, and it is not fair," says the source.

"On natural gas pipelines, often you don't see this radioactivity, it's scary shit, like a thin film, chalk maybe if there's any color. Any time you bust open the system, say you want to change out filters at a compressor station, that is when exposures can happen. Workers lick their hands, smoke a cigarette, eat a sandwich, and next thing they're ingesting lead and polonium and they have no idea. Lead-210 is lead, it will impact your blood and IQ regardless of the radiation. The greater hazard, though, is the polonium."

The bar thins out but the source stays on, there is another issue they want to discuss. "I'm worried about radon at the wellhead. When you are drilling unconventionally into black shale formations higher in radioactivity and you have a methane leak, you inevitably have a radon leak. Flaring is a big problem, and if they are flaring off methane they are also flaring off radon, but radon can't burn. People will say radon at the wellhead just dissipates into the air, yeah at standard temperature and pressure. But what happens when radon comes up at high temperatures and pressures and is being shot in the direction of a house? That's what we're worried about, but we need data, and the industry considers their data confidential."

How much radioactivity is coming up at the wellhead, and how much is accumulating downwind? And is that radon simply dissipating into the air and not of concern? Radon's daughters are metals and will attach to other particles in the air and fall out. In some hilly parts of Appalachia, where the wellheads and compressor stations and gas plants are often constructed on hills and people live in steep valleys below where air commonly settles, is this radioactivity collecting in the human environment to a point where levels are significant? "In West Texas, you have hundreds of wells in a small area," the source continues, "and people are living down inside of that, what is the collective dose of all those sources? In health physics, we don't even have a term of art for that type of distributive industrial source. And that is just emissions, never mind all the radium left behind."

"There are research questions I would like to ask if I had time," sighs the source, "but politics is driven by the crisis du jour and right now among politicians there is no outrage for oil and gas radioactivity. It doesn't have a bumper sticker. It doesn't have a mascot. It doesn't have a cute phrase. It doesn't have a politician carrying it in a briefcase—there is not one politician out there carrying water on this."

We pay our separate bills and I prepare to walk out of the bar.

"Listen," the source says. "You are on the right track, just keep digging."

SECTION II

6
Maps in Red, White, Blue and Black

North Dakota unfurls. A land of sugar beets, flax, wheat, beans, barley, and locked inside sunset-colored buttes, the bones of dinosaurs perished on the shores of an ancient sea. The Mandan, Hidatsa, Arikara, Yanktonia, Sisseton, Wahpeton, Hunkpapa, Lakota, Pembina Chippewa, Cree, Metis all lived here. Still live here. And their names and places are still here too. Creases and folds in the farm fields are sacred. Turtle Mountains, Makinak Wudjiw. Killdeer Mountains, Tahkahokuty. Badlands, Makȟóšiča. Missouri River, Ouemessourita. "One does not sell the earth," said Crazy Horse, Tasunke Witko, "upon which the people walk." And yet, the earth has been sold.

There are two ways to look at North Dakota, a testament to the American way of capitalism, farming, and energy. Or a land where an Indigenous way of life and land-tending was trampled, stolen, extracted. Something great built, or something great broken.

In 1862, the Homestead Act enabled White settlers to claim "unappropriated public lands" for a filing fee of $10. Roughly 10 percent of the United States was settled under this act, and 41 percent of South and North Dakota. The Indian Appropriation Act of 1871 stripped Native American tribes of their right to negotiate in treaties with the United

States and granted Congress power to change policy without their consent. The theft was further enabled by the General Allotment Act of 1887, better known as the Dawes Act, which allotted Native Americans parcels of their own land, then transferred the surplus and any land tribal members didn't properly occupy back to the US government to be sold to settlers. "The real aim of this bill," stated Congressman Russell Errett of Pennsylvania, "is to get at the Indian lands."

But Errett was an outlier. The US government was gladly for Dawes, which Secretary of the Interior Carl Schurz said would "open to settlement by white men the large tracts of land now belonging to the reservations." A 1911 US government poster advertised: "INDIAN LAND FOR SALE" – "GET A HOME OF YOUR OWN" – "PERFECT TITLE" – "POSSESSION WITHIN THIRTY DAYS".

A multifront war was on hand. Just as North Dakota was being parceled and snatched from above, a different force was parceling and snatching from below. "Are you a stockholder?" asks an ad published on April 15, 1919, in the Minot, North Dakota *Business Bulletin*. "Are you a pioneer? Are you showing your patriotism to your home state by helping to put down the first oil well in North Dakota?"

America's oil boom started in the East, with the Seneca Oil Company's find at Titusville, Pennsylvania, in 1859, when Edwin Drake famously struck "black gold" at the shallow depth of 69 feet, and oil flowed forth in the Pennsylvania countryside, to be crudely captured in barrels, tubs, and jars. By the early 1900s discoveries shifted westward. Texas's boom began at Spindletop, in 1901. In Oklahoma at Glenn Pool, 1905. In Kansas at Stapleton, 1915. After natural gas was discovered in North Dakota in 1892 there came a frantic quest for the oil many imagined would follow. On a summer day in 1925 a man stops at a well in Robinson to fill his radiator with water. The liquid he pumps has a sheen and when a match is lit bursts into flame. Townspeople bring their cream cans and pails—North Dakota's boom is on. But a sample sent to a state geologist found it to be refined gasoline, perhaps from a nearby spill. Or intentionally dumped in the well to start a frenzy.

Not long after that A.C. Townley arrives, who had been looking for oil in Kansas. He claims to have chauffeured a God-like man called a doodlebug around Texas in a car strung with black curtains. Armed with a special and mysterious instrument, and without even being able to see, the doodlebug could find oil and decipher exactly how much a well was able to produce. There was an Indigenous way of distinctly knowing the earth, and here a new sham magic had been born. “If we strike oil it will make us all rich,” Townley told onlookers. “There will be plenty of money to pay off mortgages and all other debts.”

At last, on April 4, 1951, true oil was discovered 11,640 feet beneath Clarence Iverson’s farm near Tioga, North Dakota. Within two months, nearly 30 million acres were leased. But the family name that would live on in history was not Iverson. On September 5, 1951, oil was discovered on the Henry O. Bakken farm from the geologic layer that sixty years later would seed the state’s fracking boom. “His family name has become synonymous with oil and opportunity,” reads a December 2, 2012, article in the *Mitchell Republic*. And just who is Bakken’s family?

Originally from Norway, moved first to Minnesota, then in 1907 located land in North Dakota.

Layers, over layers. This is North Dakota.

¤ ¤ ¤

The layers are on display outside the western North Dakota town of Alexander, on a bluff high above the Missouri River, Ouemessourita, as a raw May wind still wet with snowflakes blows over the fields of BJ and Wes Lindvig. The couple has been kind enough to provide a tour of their 5,000-acre ranch, a rolling tableau of spring-filled pastures, glens and knolls where roam more than 200 cows, 32 Suffolk sheep and they grow sudangrass, oats, barley and wheat. From a spectacular ridgeline the rolling land folds down into the rushing muddy river, wild with snowmelt from upstream mountains. BJ nods at the torrent. "I'm a rags to riches sort of story," she says, having grown up occasionally wearing plastic bread bags for shoes and using kerosene lamps for light and heat.

Times are better now, thanks in part to her husband Wes, whose family originally came from Norway and homesteaded on this lush spread above the river. But their rural Dakota ranch life has become an outdoor museum to the oil and gas industry's intrusion. Ranch roads have become haul roads, to carry in drilling rig units, mobile chemical containers, frac tanks, acid vats, sand cans, and all the other incredible accessories. Not to mention the dozens of unknown men who arrive each day in pickup trucks, because the Lindvig ranch is now their place of work to drill and frack.

Over the crest of one hill becomes visible an active and bustling frack pad, like a windowed view onto a foreign moonscape, the thing down there does not even seem real. A complex factory for the intensive extraction of petroleum carved right out of their cow fields. Visible is the rig, the line-up of frac tanks, the machinery for mixing and delivering the frack sand, the labyrinth of pipes and hoses, and perhaps 60 workers milling about. On the gray green foggy land, they work by day and they work by night.

And the flares are visible even by day. Some formations contain mostly oil, some contain mostly gas, and some, like the Bakken, contain a good bit of both, but despite efforts to pipe the gas away, much is simply burned off at the well pad, a low-pitched foul-smelling jet scream that in daytime resembles a squiggled fiery haze and may contain, as the health physicist source from the DC sports bar had told me, copious amounts of the radioactive gas radon. Although right here on their ranchland, one imagines it would be shot into the breezes and dissipated away by wind. But no one knows for sure—I ask the North Dakota Department of Environmental Quality if they require testing for radon at the wellhead and homes nearby, they do not.

Meanwhile, the oil being produced is stored on the Lindvig's land in groups of large tanks, called tank batteries, which at any one time may hold enough fuel to run a small city. It has not always gone smoothly. And as the Lindvig's tour their land, around each new bend is part of the story. A set of trash bags in the road, most likely hurled from a pickup truck window by one of the workers. The spot where a heater treater blew out, this being the unit that separates oil from brine and is known to buildup radioactive sludge and scale. Then there is the ravine where the couple learned operators had intentionally been dumping oilfield brine. "Right over the berm and into the coulee," says BJ. At first the couple didn't notice, but "the next spring," she says, "trees started dying."

BJ believes the industry was just too lazy to haul away the brine, and she has also witnessed brine trucks open valves and dump their waste right onto public roads. She takes some comfort in the new pipes installed under their land to run brine directly to a set of nearby injection wells, thus replacing the job of the brine trucks. But running oilfield brine through an underground pipeline poses additional risks. Many have been made of fiberglass-based materials, and these pipes can rupture and leak hundreds of thousands of gallons into the landscape before anyone notices.

Indeed, millions of gallons of brine have leaked from pipes across the state since the Bakken boom began. Bakken oilfield brine is among the nation's most radium rich. The Energy & Environmental Research Center at the University of North Dakota examined 20 Bakken samples and found radium levels, in picocuries per liter, to average near 3,600 and be as high as 6,490. Meaning Bakken oilfield brine is so radioactive it would be illegal for a nuclear power plant to spill it into the environment. And yet, in North Dakota, oilfield brine spills, and spills, and spills.

One investigation revealed that from 2006 to the middle of October 2014, 11.8 million gallons of brine spilled in North Dakota, an average rate of almost 3 gallons a minute. It is rather worrisome, as nearly 90 percent of the state is farm and ranchland. Brine spills in North Dakota go back decades, to the oil boom of the 1950s, and have laid lingering scars and dead zones across the land, as I learn firsthand when I tour Daryl and Christine Peterson's 2,500 acres of grains, soybeans, and corn near the Canadian border. "The oil industry controls politics in North Dakota," says Daryl, "and long-term consequences to our precious land, air, and water resources are being ignored." When spills happen, there is often little or no fine. North Dakota regulators have a habit of downplaying Bakken spills. Like the massive one outside Watford City in 2015 the North Dakota Department of Health officially listed as 10 gallons, but was actually, at 11 million gallons, the size of the 1989 *Exxon Valdez* spill in Alaska.

A 2014 report of the U.S. Geological Survey found that across the ecologically important "Prairie Pothole" region of western North Dakota two out of three surface water and groundwater systems they sampled were "moderately or extremely contaminated with brine." In nearby eastern Montana, on the Fort Peck Indian Reservation, oilfield brine from oil development during the 1990s has contaminated private wells and also the city of Poplar's public water supply, and the lens of contamination appears to be growing.

Even if all of North Dakota's brine makes it to injection wells, the designated place of disposal, there are problems. An exemption to the Safe Drinking Water Act allows aquifers—underground zones of freshwater—to have oilfield waste injected into them. EPA has exempted thousands of aquifers across the country from protection, says a report by the environmental group Earthworks, including a swath of North Dakota's Dakota aquifer, which is larger than Portugal.

Here on Lindvig land, so many wells have been drilled and fracked that BJ and Wes have lost count. They explain that because of the lease terms Wes's father agreed to about half a century ago, when the Bakken boom began they had no choice but to allow frackers onto their land. "His father's generation signed the leases in the 1970s and 1980s," says BJ, "and now we have to live with the consequences," a yearly rental payment for each well of about $1,000. Scott Skokos, executive director of Dakota Resource Council, an advocacy group dedicated to preserving family farms against corporate agriculture, says, in North Dakota, "it's somewhat common to see this happen, you're stuck with the lease your parents signed despite the economics being totally out of whack."

Skokos tells me something else important in explaining the culture of the state. "You have a history of being second fiddle to everyone, and when you become first in something you don't want that to go away, it's an inferiority complex, and now with the Bakken is our chance in the sun, you can't say anything bad about it."

But why has the state's conservation ethic folded in the face of the boom, I ask.

"The idea that the thing that is helping keep your farm more solvent and supplement your income is also the thing destroying your farmland creates a cognitive dissonance," says Skokos, "and you don't know what to think."

BJ has short hair and black glasses. Wes has a white beard. If they are resentful or mad about the lease arrangement, they don't really show it. But BJ is a bit sour.

"This is how it's going to be and we have done the best we can," she says. "They have the legal right." And besides, none of it is worth fighting, because the fight is too big. "Everything you think of, they've thought of something different, you've got a little bit of say in it, but basically you don't."

"The whole of western North Dakota was dying," BJ continues. "Now, it is so revitalized, and I feel like my grandkids will have a job instead of going out of state."

"Everyone in this town was broke in the '80s," says Wes, "and now people have money."

"It isn't ever going to be back to what it was," adds BJ.

"The thing is, now the oil companies have more conscience," says Wes.

"I'm all for everyone making money, but there does have to be rules and regulations," says BJ.

"And I know we have to progress, but this was just a blank canvas, and to see that beauty destroyed is tough," she continues. "And they do good, but it's hard, it's hard to see that change. And you got to talk about it, and see a middle ground to it, and there are goods and bads, and I don't mind the drilling, but I hate it, I absolutely hate it, but I do love it... So there you go."

"If you take anything away, please take this," says BJ, pushing one more thought. "Once it is here—you can't stop it."

The tour ends back at the Missouri River, Ouemessourita, where Wes has something he'd like to show off.

"You don't have to be an archaeologist to see," he says, and points out a circle of lichen-covered stones. "This was probably the fire pit."

These Indigenous stone circles are all over this part of western North Dakota and, according to Wes, "thousands if not millions have been plowed up" and lost forever. "But there's no way of knowing," he says, "because they were just another rock to the settlers."

Still, to him they are much more. And Wes explains that he has made sure the frackers stay away from this area, because, as he explains it, "you want to keep something."

¤ ¤ ¤

Beneath that very same circle of stones on the Lindvig's land, in April 1805, the American explorers Lewis and Clark traveled upstream on Ouemessourita with their famous tour guide Sakakawea. Just about 30 years later, in 1833, coming the other way, was the gentleman explorer and German prince, Maximilian of Wied. According to his journals, he intended to explore "the natural face of North America."

The trip was essentially an extravagant though rugged hunting expedition in which the men sucked in the glorious landscape and gathered freely whatever game they fancied. "When I came to the riverbank I saw a beautiful wild swan swimming in the river," Wied writes. "I crept up and shot it." They shot and ate everything, deer, elk, wolves, bighorn sheep, prairie dogs, buffalo, and carried with them a small bear they had trapped in a crate, with nails pointed inwards as a deterrent against its escape. At night the men smoked pipes and identified plant specimens.

Near what is now the Montana-North Dakota border, on Assiniboine land, Wied observed, "every evening for three to four days, the medicine drum could be heard being beaten in an Indian tipi for a sick child." The parents asked Wied's expedition for medicine, they refused. In western North Dakota, just beyond the sunset-colored buttes of the badlands begins a rich prairie region, where the expeditioners met the Mandan Chief Four Bears, Mató-Tópe. Wied described him as a generous, "proud and gallant man," and the travelers were invited to a feast inside a Mandan earth lodge. It was "spacious, rather bright," wrote Wied. "We sat down on buffalo robes and received a wooden bowl with cooked corn and beans," and black berries. "After we ate, our host lit a pipe" and handed it around.

Just a few years later, a smallpox epidemic wiped out much of the tribe, including Chief Four Bears. The Fort Laramie Treaty of 1851 granted the Mandan, Hidatsa and Arikara, known together as the Three Affiliated Tribes, an area of more than 12 million acres, extending from present-day North Dakota southwest into Montana and Wyoming. The space would be whittled down, then whittled again. First through an 1870 executive order that slashed at the southern boundary. And again in 1880, with an executive order designed to create a right-of-way for the Northern Pacific Railroad. In 1910, the northeastern section of the reservation was opened to homesteaders, who parceled away most of it. The original 12-million-acre territory had become less than 3 million, and it would become less.

"Still, the population had rebounded by the early 1900s, and the buffalo culture was replaced by the horse and cattle culture" and "the people were living quite well since the land itself was so productive," stated Marilyn Cross Hudson, director of the Three Affiliated Tribes Museum in New Town, the big city center on the reservation. She spoke as part of a presentation on what some people still recall as the Great Flood. In 1944, Congress had authorized the development of dozens of dams on western rivers to increase irrigation and energy. One project, the Garrison Dam, would flood the village of Elbowoods and force the relocation of more than 340 Mandan, Hidatsa and Arikara families, taking over 90 percent of the tribes' productive farmland. They had been pushed and squeezed and backed onto a thin slice of land but made it bloom, and now they would once again have to abandon and migrate. The lake formed behind the dam was named Lake Sakakawea.

Despite all this and much more, the people of the Three Affiliated Tribes still occupy part of their homeland in western North Dakota, the Fort Berthold Indian Reservation, a small nation within the greater nation of the United States. But there has been an odd twist. It turns out the undesirable plot of land the tribes were backed onto is underlain by a sweet spot of the Bakken formation, and now finds itself in the middle of a major oil boom. One of the most heavily drilled communities is Mandaree, a grid of small homes on the vast brown-green plain. In a house flanked by wind chimes and bird feeders live Lisa and Walter DeVille. The couple runs Fort Berthold's most prominent grassroots environmental organization, the Fort Berthold Protectors of Water & Earth Rights—POWER.

Lisa has two master's degrees in business and returned to school to get a bachelor's degree in environmental science so she could better understand how to protect the environment from oil and gas. The couple has also helped to found emergency management and firefighting services in the community. On the fine May day I visit, in 2019, Lisa wears a shirt that says, "Wonder Woman." Walter is a big man, in a T-shirt with a white bison and four rainbow hands. They have found the easiest way to grow their environmental movement is recruit their children into it, one son is a biologist, another has a degree in environmental science, and their daughter is soon to graduate with a degree in the same. The family's kitchen table has become an environmental crimes war room, covered with papers and maps.

"Every day we have a spill," says Lisa. "Whether it is frack sand spilled, trucks that stall out and drop their oil, trucks wrecking and spilling oil and gas waste, or our invisible spill, the methane released into the air from flaring and venting, which can make the snow here yellow."

Like happens in Appalachia, Lisa's people are not properly informed about projects in their own community, and often have little clue who is operating them, and what the health risks are. And so, her little family environmental unit, along with a few other allies, have had to take things into their own hands, educating themselves on oilfield waste, capturing the harms on film, and trying to entice researchers at distant universities to come and take samples.

"My people, the Mandan, Hidatsa, and Arikara Nation have been here for centuries, our purpose as Indigenous people is to protect Mother Earth," says Lisa. But with the oil boom, that has not happened. "Our tribes have allowed industry to come in and run all over us," she says. "We want to make sure our water is safe to drink. We want to make sure our air is safe to breathe. We want to make sure our soil is okay to plant crops. We want laws."

"My wife has always been an advocate for Mother Nature," says Walter, "and I myself am an advocate for Mother Nature. But it comes to the point where it falls on deaf ears, because here in North Dakota the regulations don't seem to matter. You have all these regulators, but who is out there doing the studies to make sure all of this is safe?"

When the Bakken oil boom came on, "there was a lot of talk about job opportunity," he continues. "But there was no one at our door saying, hey we got a refinery here, we want to train you." Instead, he says, "everyone from Wyoming, Louisiana, Oklahoma, Arkansas, everyone from every goddamn oil state in the country was up here chomping on the bit to take advantage."

He points to one map, which shows all the land that used to belong to the Mandan and Hidatsa people. "This here is what was taken from us," says Walter. "Our territory was huge."

Lisa produces a different map, of the region's pipelines. It is completely crisscrossed. "I don't want anymore pipelines near the water," she says, expressing concern for, among other things, a tiny endangered butterfly called the Dakota skipper. But there is indeed another project on the table, the Sacagawea Pipeline. It would cut right through the reservation, cross under Lake Sakakawea, and transport crude oil. A map of the pipeline, being developed by a group of partners that includes Phillips 66, fails to even show Fort Berthold Indian Reservation. These companies do give back, in their own way. Crestwood Equity Partners, based in Texas, operates a vast pipeline system on the reservation and in 2019 donated $2 million for a new Head Start facility in Mandaree. "They helped create a dream for our babies," the director told the *Bismarck Tribune*.

Lisa is not swayed by such gifts. "The upsetting thing," she says, "is our people are not fighting as loud as they should."

There has been, says the couple, a decay.

Tex Hall, the tribe's former chairman, grew up in Mandaree, was fond of cowboy hats, and welcomed oil and gas companies onto the reservation to drill. He promoted a policy he called, "sovereignty by the barrel" and founded his own company, Maheshu Energy. In 2013, Tex slid into Lake Sakakawea a 96-foot, $2.5 million yacht called *Island Girl*, "intended to be a floating casino for high rollers," noted the *New York Times*. "The dream starts here," Tex told attendees in April 2014 at the tribe's Oil and Gas Expo. By that time well over 1,000 oil wells had been drilled on the reservation and $200 million had been set aside in a trust called the People's Fund, though little had been distributed to the people.

But even worst news had already begun to break. In 2012, Tex had allowed a five-time convicted felon named James Henrikson, who moved to the Bakken to cash in on the boom, to operate a trucking company called Blackstone out of his garage. Henrikson and his wife vacationed with Tex and his girlfriend in Hawaii. Then, in 2013, a Washington state oil developer was murdered in his own kitchen and the killing, along with the suspected murder of a fellow Blackstone worker named Kristopher, was linked to Henrikson. Tex was never connected to these crimes, but his image as an honest oil broker was tainted.

"Our own tribal government is not seeing, not listening," says Walter. "Myself, I'm sitting here wondering now how much more Mother Earth can take?"

Lisa and Walter climb into a red Dodge Laramie with tinted windows and head out for a ride, eager to point out to me the detritus the boom has left them.

"Everywhere you looked there was trash," says Lisa. Buckets and pipes and parts falling from the bed of oilfield trucks. And bottles of piss lining the roads from oilfield truckers who chucked them out the window. And billiard table-sized potholes created by all the industry traffic. And anti-Native graffiti, things like "Fuck Indians!" scrawled on the objects of their community. And comments hurled at them from the speeding trucks, which regularly crashed and killed people. Her sister found filter socks littered about the reservation, and Lisa says oilfield brine has been regularly dumped into fields and onto roads.

According to a lengthy newspaper investigation, in the summer of 2013, Edmund Baker, the tribe's environmental director, was called out to Tex Hall's home and found more than 200 filter socks strewn over the tribal chairman's land. Although Baker recognized the ethical dilemma, he initially didn't go public with the episode. "There have been other instances where individuals have spoken up and they have been kicked out of their homes," he told the reporters. Tex said the more oil produced on the reservation, the more revenue there would be for environmental regulations.

Walter and Lisa scoff at this. "We have our own regulatory agency," he says, "but there's no regulation."

Case in point is the Bear Den Bay spill. From around July 3 to July 8, 2014, a million gallons of oilfield brine leaked out of a pipeline on a hillside outside Mandaree and ran into a ravine that funnels into Lake Sakakawea, which provides drinking water to the reservation. The spill laid a path across the landscape nearly a mile and a half long. EPA visited and said most of the waste pooled on the ground, soaked into the soil, and was held behind beaver dams, though around a quarter million gallons reached an unnamed creek, and about 10,500 gallons reached the lake. The pipeline belonged to Crestwood, who would eventually pay EPA a fine for the spill of $49,000.

As the DeVille's navigate their red Dodge across the reservation to the spill site, Lisa makes Walter a sandwich on wheat bread with lunch meats and passes it across to him on a paper plate. She explains that part of the problem is tribal leadership never fully appreciated the harms the Bakken boom posed, or took appropriate steps, or any steps really, to prepare for spills and the various other disasters and crookery common to the industry. "We have no protocols," she says. And although tribal, county, state, and federal government officials all have some jurisdiction to this land, no one has taken the lead on environmental issues, and priorities are skewed. The North Dakota Industrial Commission, which oversees oil and gas development has jurisdiction on the reservation, but the North Dakota Department of Environmental Quality does not.

"No one knows the amount of spills on Fort Berthold because industry will lie to our tribal leaders, and there is no data for the public to see," says Lisa. "There are no studies, research, or analysis, which is what we would need to create laws or codes for environmental justice." The new chairman, Mark Fox, according to statements he has made, believes, "more development, more drilling, more jobs." But he has not responded to my questions on what environmental improvements his administration has made over the last few years, the shocking nearness of some Fort Berthold residents to emissions-spewing oil and gas wells, and how he is ensuring radioactive oilfield waste on the reservation is being handled safely.

Driving along a wash with pretty oak and ash trees, well pads still visible everywhere, flares roaring, Lisa says, "we are losing our way, we are losing our language, with every hole that is put in. I focus on preparing my children and grandchildren for the aftermath that is going to be left them."

As the couple arrives at the site, Lake Sakakawea shimmers below. The ravine where the brine ran down is clearly visible, and they head off toward it on foot, a tough scramble down a twisting rocky slope, then slashing through underbrush. The spill killed plants, bushes, and trees, which cleanup crews contracted by Crestwood "mulched," says Walter. But neither Lisa, Walter, or any of the reservation's ordinary residents had access to the spill site or knowledge of what was going on. At a meeting the following month, Edmund Baker, the tribe's environmental director, said the spill was located a quarter mile from the water intake system, "which supplies the reservation its drinking water." Still, even he had not been able to obtain test results or proof there had been no contamination. Crestwood, for their part, has not replied to my questions on how they assessed, and continue to assess, the radiological threats posed by the spill.

Coming down toward the base of the ravine that carried the brine spill into the lake, Lisa shows me that five years later the trickling stream is still stained with waste, and there are a series of stagnant orange puddles. Hoof-marks in the mud indicate a deer has been through. Oilfield brine is rich in salt, and the phenomenon of wild animals licking up spills has been noted. "Everything that is in there," says Walter, pointing up the hill toward the origin of the spill, "is seeping down and coming back up here."

In July 2015, a year after the spill, the Duke University geochemist Dr. Avner Vengosh, renown for investigations around the world on natural contaminants like arsenic, chromium and radium, visited North

Dakota and collected samples from this ravine, and other brine spill sites across the state. His arrival in Fort Berthold was a big deal, and meant a topnotch research team would be assessing their land to determine just what had been spilled across it.

The resulting paper Vengosh and two Duke colleagues published in 2016 revealed the Bear Den Bay brine spill had contaminated the land with salt, heavy metals and also radium. The radioactive element attached to certain soil components, the Duke researchers reported, and because radium-226 has a half-life of 1,600 years, "will remain for thousands of years." They suggested that to fully understand the impacts of brine spills in North Dakota, "a comprehensive assessment of long-term ecological and possible human health impacts" be conducted.

For Lisa and Walter, the report was solid scientific evidence which showed that the millions of gallons of brine spilled across Fort Berthold was indeed contaminating their land with radioactivity. "To call this a saltwater spill is misleading," says Lisa. Which is what it has been called in numerous local and national news stories. "This," she says, "is a radioactive spill."

Despite the significance of the Duke research, in 2019 when I mentioned it to Dave Glatt, Director of North Dakota's Department of Environmental Quality, in an interview conducted in the department's offices in the Gold Seal Building in Bismarck, he told me he hadn't seen the report. He added, about the researcher Avner Vengosh, "I question his initial premise coming in there and looking for the worst-case scenario on all of these sites. The worst-case scenario may be very factual and very true, but can you make that assertion for every spill in the Bakken?" Glatt told me his department could have pointed Vengosh to a lot of different spills where he could have done "all the studies" he wanted, and that the Duke team's study demonstrated, "a biased view."

No matter, the research continues to flow in, whether the North Dakota Department of Environmental Quality is going to believe in it or not, or act on it or not.

In 2021, a team of scientists with the U.S. Geological Survey that had assessed a Bakken brine spill in Blacktail Creek, about 100 miles northwest of Fort Berthold, published their research, revealing contamination had traveled 4.5 miles downstream from the spill site, and built up in creek sediments and also the floodplain, at levels "significantly above the U.S. EPA action level for" radium-226 in surface soils. Radium in the creek sediment "is of particular concern," the authors noted, and presented "a route of exposure to aquatic organisms," while radium on the floodplain could be blown about by the wind and marked "a potential for animal exposures." Radium, the authors reminded, is "similar to calcium and therefore can be deposited in bone and connective tissues surrounding organs." They identified 41 other brine spill-prone watersheds across North Dakota that could be subject to a similar situation.

"This actually proves that they didn't get rid of it," says Lisa, continuing to examine the orange puddle. "It's still in the soil. So, it's a cancer zone, and it's going to spread."

Walking back up the ravine and toward their vehicle Walter is bit by a mosquito. "That damn mosquito bit me," he says, "now he's got my DNA."

"Now," Lisa jokes, "you've got the brine in you."

7
Trespassers with Guns, and the Invisible Trespassers

A Saturday evening in February, the tiny Fort Berthold Indian Reservation community of Four Bears, temperature about 15 degrees Fahrenheit, sun has gone down, wind is light, stars are out. Following farm roads south and west outside town through a landscape of winter-frozen wheat and pea fields is a compound of small homes. In the kitchen of one is the young Native father, James Brugh, who has just received a package.

"It's not like it's just boohoo poor James, something really bad happened here, and it is just sitting there," he says. "I can't go on like this. I thought about covering myself in oil and setting myself on fire, like a monk. I just don't know what else I can do right now. I am sorry, I apologize. I am getting worked up. There is a lot of history that comes with it. There is a lot of unresolved feelings that come up, and I really hate dealing with that—the history."

James steps into the living room. There are sectional couches, a large recliner. "I have my plants, and I have my ferns," he says. They sit by the window. Beside them is a bookshelf with little candles, photos of his children, and on the top shelf, one of his father-in-law, who was supposed to live next door but passed away before he could move.

"He was a tough guy," says James, "and often I wish he was here, because he would have known how to handle things. He had a tough-ass approach, I didn't always go for that. He was a Marine, and I think he realized after dealing with many different types of people there is always a fine line between when they listen to you, and when they don't, and it all boils down to posturing. Something happened one day and I asked him what would you have done, because I was worried I had gone too far. He told me, No, don't ever second guess protecting your family."

James continues. "One day my father-in-law asked me if I was protected. He didn't use the specific words, but I knew by this he meant, did I have a gun. I do have guns, but I wasn't sure how to answer his question, and so I just ignored it. He called me to his house later and when I came in on his living room floor was a huge pile of ammo, thousands of rounds. I asked him what it was for and he said that's yours, and I didn't ask any more questions, and that was it, he didn't say anything and I left. But I knew he was trying to tell me that it was my duty, my responsibility, to protect his daughter, and our children, his grandbabies, and that here on the reservation there were real threats, and this was a very serious responsibility."

"I am trying to stress the importance of why it was such a big thing for us to come out here, where my wife's family had some land. We used to live in an apartment complex on the west side of New Town. We were packed in tight and there was mold and my daughter had nosebleeds and was coughing all the time and our neighbors were up to no good. They always had people over and I knew there were drugs there, and so it was really important for us to get out of that apartment. In 2014, we picked the home site out here, out in the country."

"Unfortunately, when we first moved there was a road that ran right next to our house and serviced some wells to the south. Our daughters were maybe 7 and 11 at the time, and there would be all types of oilfield trucks on this road, all hours of the day. We did everything we could to indicate our land was private property. We would be out there making our home and these guys would drive by, and they wouldn't have their eyes on the road. I had guys fucking rubbernecking, go off the road and into our yard, and I got really annoyed. I said you are out here to work, what the fuck are you staring at? Are you eyeing my kids?"

"They would just stop their rig and sit in their truck right there next to my house, and I had to let them know. You do not stop near my house, you do not linger near the premises, you keep it moving. This one driver from Marathon Oil said, you live in the green house right there and you've got the two little girls, and I said that right there is a red flag mister, you a pedophile? You a fucking pedophile!? You observing my family? That don't make me feel comfortable. He said, oh no, I'm former law enforcement. I said, you're former law enforcement, you need to understand this makes someone feel uncomfortable, you need to understand how you approach a dad on that topic. How do I protect my family in these circumstances?"

"I have a buddy down the road, and he'd see a convoy of blacked-out SUVs come same time every morning, and he went up there to get a better look and said they were all kitted out, just loaded down with weaponry. He said he seen a KRISS Vector, which is a type of sub-machine gun that can shoot 1,200 rounds a minute. These guys feel like it is something they would kill for. The oilfield is not just a job for them, it is a lifestyle. You see these stickers, *Fuck, Fight, Trip Pipe*. Certain clothes, olive green jacket. I seen another guy at the grocery store, he ended up being military, and I started chatting with him, didn't take long before he said Three Percenters, which is a militia group. And I started to realize, there were more of these people around than I thought."

"I have heard enough of them talking about us like we are subhuman, like we are not people. It's like the second coming of the cavalry, these guys treat our land like it's the Wild West. They come here to the rez at Fort Berthold thinking they are soldiers of fortune. There is this gunslinger mentality, this mercenary mentality. A lot of these guys work for oilfield security companies with logos that look like kids drew up some military shit, real aggressive, almost cartoony, snakes and guns and eagles, I remember one with a skeleton's face wearing an Army helmet. But you never know who they really are. With one guy who stopped by our house, I go over like I always do to check him out. It's an oilfield security guard with a chambered 5.56 rifle in the front seat of his company vehicle. That means there is a round in the chamber, you are ready to roll. You are ready to shoot something."

"It is like a zombie horror movie. If you show weakness you will get runover, but if you show strength it becomes a game for them. You eventually have to put up boundaries, because there is no accountability, nobody is willing to bring the law down on these guys. Not our tribal council, not the sheriff, not the Feds. And I have to look long-term, for the future of my children, that is the sole basis for everything."

"We had a trespasser at my little girl's birthday party. And I am not going to lie, I wasn't very polite with him. From my perspective, he was trespasser number 999. We argued over whether it was private property or not, I tried to convey to the man he was trespassing. He got in an aggressive pose, stuck his arm out, balled his fists and started rushing toward me. He kept coming, and I kept trying to push him back, but he kept coming, so there we were in each other's faces. I took a defensive posture, which was necessary to show this guy that his behavior was not to be tolerated. And he retreated back toward his work vehicle."

"Everything he telegraphed was that he was going back to his vehicle for a weapon. I have seen guys come at me with shovels, crowbars, with anything they can get their hands on. But this guy, I felt with every ounce of my being he was getting a gun. I didn't want to get in a shootout with him. I am trying to keep my space, I am trying to maintain my discipline. But mind you I am scared, and this is a birthday and I have a bunch of kids in my home, a house full of little girls eating cake, and also, my wife is pregnant. And so I did what I had to do, the only thing I could. I yelled back to my wife to get me my gun, and I had to make him feel like my gun was going to be bigger."

"My wife Victoria is tough. She graduated from the Federal Law Enforcement Training Center, and she has worked as a corrections officer, and in the tribal domestic violence prevention program. In that position she got to be familiar with human trafficking, with all the shit, all the heinous, heinous shit that goes on with our women, our children, here on this reservation. So she has dealt with all the above, she has enough background on some of this stuff that would probably make a guy like me stay up at night. There was a story one time that there were fifty sex slaves living in an RV parked behind the casino, I went around myself looking. Or that women were being held in fucking cages down at a man camp. That turned out to be unfounded, but there were so many stories we had to pick through over the years. You hear these rumors, and then your mind fast forwards to some of the things you know to be a reality."

James steps out the door at the back of the living room and onto the porch. It is frigid, with the temperature now near 12 degrees Fahrenheit. And as black night falls across the reservation a strange bobbing glow emerges on the horizon, like an orange egg of light bouncing up and down, contracting then expanding, at times shooting out a ripple of fire. He points to a second, a third, and a fourth, fifth, sixth and seventh. My brain wants to make something mystical and beautiful out of these colorful nighttime mirages, but they are just flares, from all the natural gas being burned off wells across this part of the Bakken.

"The joke is this place was going to look like Mordor in five years," says James. "Or in H.G. Wells' *Time Machine*, when they fast forward to the deep future and there's just these machines crawling on top of the earth. That is what this industry reminds me of, because they are invasive, and they have taken all the farmland, all of the land, and transformed it into an industrial zone, and to see the lack of oversight that has accompanied this rush to exploit a natural resource has been so painful."

"From any window in my house, I look out and see a flare. Sadly, the windows that get the most light are also facing the direction of the nearest well pad. We have blackout curtains for all of the windows, because the light from the well and the flares is so unnatural. The flares block out the stars. They shake the house. When I see my moonlight out my window it's nostalgic, it's like, where have you been? It is an eerie feeling, and you can't help but wonder, what am I breathing in? There is an orange glow and I know that is from the light of the flares getting trapped under the clouds, and I wonder what else is getting trapped underneath those clouds?"

James continues. "I have to tell you, there was one night when that flare was shaking the fucking house. We had blankets over the windows, we had the TV on, we had fans to block out the noise. And this was at 3 o'clock in the morning. I looked at Victoria and I saw tears in her eyes, and I just ran out the door. I found one of the security guys, and I didn't tell him they had brought the woman I love to tears in the middle of the night, but I laid into him. I said, you are fucking making us crazy! If there is one moment I could implant in the head of someone who knows nothing about any of this, it would be that moment."

In 2016, the road that ran by James's house and was used regularly by oilfield trucks was taken out of use. This was done because Marathon Oil had begun clearing land for a new frack pad, and an access road for this pad would now be taking the truck traffic. James and his family already had a frack pad about 650 yards from their home, the new one would be even closer. Initially, it was to have five wells.

"Before that new pad went in, it was the highest point in the area," says James, "and it was a beautiful field. You could go up on that ridge 200 yards behind my house and see every point in every direction. When the farmer wasn't farming it my kids would get off the school bus and I would pick them up and we'd drive through that field and across these little dips. When you hit them just hard enough you'd get that butterfly feeling, so we called that butterfly hill. It was a place to sit back and be alone and get away. I remember walking through those fields one day and I had my hand in the farmer's wheat and I was thinking I better soak this in, because I probably always won't be able to do this, and of course, now I can't. I lost my butterfly hill, I lost my thinking spot, I lost my peace of mind. I lost a lot."

"One day there was a storm that came in and living where I do you can sometimes appreciate a good storm, because it is clouds rolling in, and seeing the lightning, and hearing the thunder. Those are natural sounds, I don't mind hearing those, they are natural vibrations. Not noise from a set of generators going all night, or trucks hitting their engine brakes. I was on my back porch and looking at these clouds and I saw this huge cloud of dust and I was thinking, what the fuck is that? This greasy heavy dirty smell. Then I realized, I know what this is. A big rush of wind came, and it literally picked up everything from that well pad, and it blew it over here, and I could taste it. I felt like I was actually at the well pad, because I could taste your guys fucking stench."

"For a brief time in 2015," he says, "I worked with the industry. The boom had been going on long enough by that period. I suppose the reason in me mentioning this is because they are here on our land, extracting our resources, and the way they are doing it is very complicated and dangerous, and we have entrusted them with that, with our land, our environment, our lives, and there is no decorum, no honor, no respect, and because it is complicated, you think at least they would be on it, they would be safe, but no, they are completely reckless fucks. I was on a drilling rig, and remember looking off the drilling floor there, looking off into the hills, and I was watching these guys piss around the corner on the floor, watching the driller smoke cigarettes when the floor is covered in diesel, watching it all, and I was thinking, these guys are fucking crude, and they are fucking everywhere, shitting and pissing in my backyard. Even though it is our land, it is their industry."

"I remember eating lunch in the doghouse, which is like the break room on the drilling rig, and hearing guys talk about doing speedballs and heroin. Tribal members are granted a certain number of jobs for any business carried out on reservation land, it's the Tribal Employment Rights Ordinance, or TERO, and what they would do is say things to make me feel little, to put me in my place. You one of those TERO workers? It must be nice getting free shit? What's it like being an Indian? You are sitting here having a social experience with these guys, the minute they find out you are Native, you have to prove yourself. They call us paycheck workers because we come for one paycheck then leave, but why would you stay longer if somebody doesn't have your back in a job when you can get lit on fire, get crushed, lose your limb, why would you want to stick around on a job like that if you can't trust them?"

"At one point, the driller sent me down to power wash the sub, which is the lower part of the derrick and where the pipe that brings up all the oil and gas actually goes into the earth. There is a maze of I-beams and there is gunk and shit everywhere, because sludge and diesel and whatever spills from the rig floor falls here. If you are spraying it and you don't have a visor your face is covered in shit, and it's all over your lips, and when you try to wipe it off your glasses get smudgy, and when I was down there it was literally freezing, and I didn't have slicks on. He had sent me down there without waterproof gear, and the fucker knew that. Within so many minutes I was caked in ice. That is the moment when I realized if I stayed there working on that rig I was going to get abused, and I was going to get hurt, and it wasn't worth getting hurt. I have to think of my family."

"In October 2019, a Marathon worker came and called us to lunch. We go, we just ordered a salad and tea. He said they were going to come and put another six wells up on the pad behind the house. I spit that salad back in the bowl, got up and left. You guys put me through hell with the flaring, the dishes were shaking, my wife in tears in the middle of the night. Now you are going to come back and do it to my unborn son, are you fucking nuts!? Victoria was maybe seven months pregnant. She was sitting there at the café with this little son in her belly. I was pissed, I was irate. And from October to December my campaign was to get away from here, my campaign was to get our tribal council to put more regulations on the flaring and the drilling. Before, my concern was the militias, the human trespassers, and now my main concern was the emissions, the invisible trespassers, and how they might affect our little son in my wife's belly. That is when the panic slowly started to progress."

"I sent emails to every tribal council member we had. I wore my heart on the sleeve. I threw myself on the mercy of these motherfucking bastards for nothing. All I wanted was a commitment, that they would not drill so close to our home while my wife was pregnant and our son was an infant. We visited an OB-GYN in Bismarck, and she was very concerned. She did not think it was good for a baby to be born 500 yards from an active frack pad, and she did not think it was good for us to be living by a pad with so much flaring while Victoria was pregnant. She recommended that we relocate for the remainder of the pregnancy, and she wrote a letter."

"We showed that letter to Marathon, and to the tribal council. I showed that letter to everyone. I used to have a job working PR for the tribal government, and I loved that job, because when the job is done right and you're not trying to cover up bullshit and you are talking about the good things your organization is doing and giving people credit, it is a good job, and the kind of work I like to do. But when I began writing these letters I lost that job. And of course, we couldn't relocate, because we had nowhere else to go. I asked Marathon for their mercy, and they didn't give it to me. It is not like they didn't know the harms, they just acted like we didn't fucking exist, the old Jedi mind trick. They just said fuck you and did it anyway, and they came back and drilled six more wells."

"This is when the gloves come off. These guys have established that there are no real rules to this. And now it is drawing a line in the sand, I am not going away you fuckers, I am a human being, I am still alive. People say get over that, but at what point do you get over that, and at what point do you settle up? I have been removed from my people, I have been stripped of my identity, I feel faceless. I am a Native American without a fucking tribe, that's what it is."

"I want to inspire my people to take back what is theirs. Our tribal leaders run this reservation like a dictatorship, we've already lost so much, so much land, so much money, and I don't feel like there's any end in sight. I once wrote a poem about Crazy Horse. I always thought that was the ideal, sticking up for your people, but then you realize at the end of the story what he went through. That he ended up giving up, because he realized he was fighting an endless battle. He ended up getting killed by his own people. When I read that poem I wrote and fast forward to now, I know I damn sure ain't Crazy Horse, but I can tell you how he felt."

"If I could go back to my high school days, I'd tell myself, don't be like Crazy Horse. You don't want that feeling of being stabbed in the back. You don't want to watch your land get teared apart, land that you were taught to respect. At one point I was emboldened, I was impassioned, I thought I was fighting something I cared about, and when it all came crashing down my worse enemies were my own people. And I am fighting something that can't be stopped. And when you are fighting something that can't be stopped there is so much sadness in your heart. There were times where I felt like it would have been better for me to not be around the people I cared about, because it was not good for them to see me like that. But you still have love, and you are living for that."

"I chug along forward like an out-of-control choo choo train. For better or worse I am on this track and there is no turning back. I don't know if I'm naïve, but I cannot just sit by when what you're doing is not right. In my eyes, if you are going to do this to my little girl, if you are going to do this to my little boy, then you are going to do this to every other little Indian boy, every little Indian girl, every human boy and girl, and I can't sit here and watch that, I have to step up, as a human. I want people to see that what I am doing is really a fight for life. I just want to be the best man that I can."

"On January 29th, 2020, my son was thankfully blessed into this world. He is healthy. When he was born they said he was born fast, with some fluid in his lungs. Nothing major but at the time Victoria and I were stressed out. He was born at 7:01 that night. When Victoria was in there I went across the street to get a juice. It was Bismarck, it was a foggy night, not a scary foggy night, kind of chilly. The kind of night you expect someone to light a fire someplace, and you sit in front of the fire and look out your window. It was serene. I thought it was just a perfect night for my little boy to come out into the world."

The temperature has dropped to 9 degrees, and James steps back inside. The package is small, and he walks past the plants and big sectional couch, to the other end of the living room where there are two sets of doors leading to bedrooms. One belongs to his youngest daughter. "Her window faces the well," says James, "which is where the sun is, and that is the problem. My daughter is carefree and we always keep her window open." He opens the package, a home radon detector.

"I hate to say it, but I've given up with depending on other people to protect my family, we're done with all that shit," says James. "Please don't forget there is still a people with connection to the land, that no matter what they were facing, the desire to protect their culture superseded all that. And some of them stepped up, and some spoke out."

It is near midnight on a cold North Dakota night. The flares have lit the sky with their strange orange halo, and James goes off to bed. Marathon Oil has not replied to my questions, regarding the letter from the OB-GYN, wellhead emissions, radioactivity, the company's firearm policy, or anything else.

8
Radioactive Mountains Across America

If the Creator were to hide her prophets somewhere in Texas, where might it be? One hundred forty miles from the sea, on the edge of a limestone escarpment that funnels springs and streams down from distant highlands, is a terrain of oak woods, tallgrass prairie and thorn-scrub. Out of this spiny embrace rises a city. It is known for its saints and clear clean waters, and it is here, at a sacred ancient headwaters the Indigenous people of this region called Yanaguana, where the Sisters of Charity of the Incarnate Word have established, "a sanctuary for all Creation." Among those who have come to serve is an 87-year-old nun named Sister Elizabeth Riebschlaeger.

The first sisters arrived to Texas in December 1866 at Galveston from Lyons, France, emissaries of a centuries-old Catholic order dedicated to education and healthcare. The concern in America was an epidemic of cholera, the deadly bacterial infection brought on by drinking dirty water, and yellow fever, a tropical virus that leads to yellowing of the skin, organ failure, and bleeding from the mouth, nose, and eyes. The sisters were not spared, on August 18, 1867, Mother Mary Blandine succumbed to the virus. But their spirit prevailed and in 1869 three were chosen by the order to establish a new community in San Antonio.

It is early Friday morning in summer, contemporary times, 2019, and Sister Elizabeth is down the street from Sisters of Charity of the Incarnate Word, at a San Antonio McDonald's. With a day's journey ahead to an oilfield waste landfill the sister is adamant on the point of breakfast, and presently having an Egg McMuffin and coffee. "It's pretty simple," she says, "I answer to one person." And she points up through the ceiling of the McDonald's and toward heaven.

The Sisters of Charity believe in "Earth care." Human beings have a spiritual connection to the planet, a moral obligation to protect it, and in working to heal the land heal something deep within ourselves. Incarnate Word takes its name from the Annunciation, which is the moment, depicted in countless paintings, when the angel Gabriel brought to Mary God's message, asking her to be the Mother of Jesus, Son of God.

When Mary asked how this could be, as she was a virgin, Gabriel answered, "the Holy Spirit will come on you, and God's power will rest on you." To which Mary replied, "I am the Lord's servant." Her acceptance of God's offer was so powerful it took on a lifeforce. Literally, God dwelling among us in the form of a message. Or a holy message come to life—the Incarnate Word.

Sister Elizabeth has devoted herself to this word, and the message it entails. "I was in my senior year of high school, and still looking for what I wanted to do with my one life I had to live and account to god for," she says. In March, 1953, a Passionists priest, part of an order devoted to preaching the passion of Christ, gave a talk at a mission in the San Antonio area and inspired her with the following message: "Each of us can say to ourselves, even if I had been the only individual in the history of the entire human race to have sinned, God would still have sent his one son to die for me out of love and save me from hell, that is how much god loves each individual."

"At that moment," says Sister Elizabeth, "I knew this was the most important message in the world, and I could spend my life sharing it." In 1955, at age 18, she was accepted into the order of the Sisters of Charity of the Incarnate Word. "Much later," she says, "I began to study the encyclicals of the popes and understand the abuse of capitalism and the loss of spiritual values that had affected the economic systems of the West like a cancer." As fracking came to South Texas in the 2000s, she set about to observe it, "to learn about it, and to reflect on the environmental science and the technology of fracking in the light of the gospel."

Sister Elizabeth wears black sneakers, blue slacks, a light blue and white checkered flannel shirt, with dark glasses, and a headset like an air traffic controller, which allows her to handle regular phone calls from her contacts, flung far and wide across the great state of Texas.

"I am like a bulldog," she says, speaking quickly over her breakfast sandwich. "When I start after something it's hard for them to shake me. And that's fine, I hope they're really uncomfortable." She believes it is her work as a messenger of God to comfort the uncomfortable and bring discomfort to those who are too comfortable. "If you look at Jesus's life," says Sister Elizabeth, "that is what Jesus did, and that's what Jesus died for."

But she doesn't have time to get into that right now. Earth's lifegiving star is nudging higher, daylight is a-wasting, and she has a date with a young mother who lives with her children and multiple farm animals across the road from a fracking waste disposal site, in the tiny community of Nordheim. It is an hour and a half drive southeast from San Antonio, and Sister Elizabeth bops out the door and into her Honda Civic, then lunges into morning traffic.

Outside of Floresville, she stops at Tractor Supply Company, a spacious store that sells animal feed, gun safes, backyard barbecue cookers, tricked out lawn mowers, and all manner of items both delicate and gigantic to aid and abet the farm or ranch life. Tractor Supply is one of the first stores to setup in a community being heavily fracked, explains

Sister Elizabeth, "because the ranchers have all this new money." It is not necessarily her scene, but she needs a new pair of 9-volt batteries for a Geiger counter she is carrying in her purse.

Ahead on U.S. Highway 181, traveling down to the coastal plain, are flat prairie lowlands and signs for the Rio Grande Valley. The Eagle Ford Shale is shaped like a slithering snake and extends from the Mexican border northeast, roughly 50 miles wide and 400 long. It hosts a particularly attractive sweet spot of oil. "A fine light crude," says Sister Elizabeth, "I've been told it looks like honey." The southern side of the play is also rich in natural gas, and the formation is notorious for its gigantic flares, where much of this gas is simply burned off into the atmosphere. Although development here didn't begin until 2008, within five years the Eagle Ford had become one of the most heavily fracked new oilfields in America.

Sister Elizabeth grew up in Cuero, a small handsome Texas city on the edge of the current boom in DeWitt County, where her father and mother operated a family pharmacy, and she worked briefly as a soda jerk, fixing fountain cokes, milk shakes, malts and banana splits. The oilfield waste landfill she's steering for is on the other side of the county. We pass Panna Maria, the oldest permanent Polish settlement in the United States, where a brilliant white church touches Texas blue sky. Later, she discusses the Wends of Texas, a group of Slavic Lutherans who emigrated from the historic central European region of Lusatia in 1854 seeking religious and cultural freedom—her grandmother is a descendant. At a memorial for veterans in Falls City, she points to the old names: Moczygemba, Bartkowiak, Korzekwa.

Past Falls City the tones and colors of fracking emerge. The large trucks of frack sand, with humps in the middle like a camel. The dust-coated oil tankers, carrying that fine honey-colored crude. Trucks with long sleek cylindrical tanks, carrying oilfield brine, and different than the squat brine trucks of Appalachia bound for injection wells. Though it's the same dismal technology where the waste ends up, only here, like in North Dakota, they are called saltwater disposal wells, or SWDs.

As the road shoots south flares rise all around and the landscape takes on a real dinosaur feel. "We have entered the heart of the Eagle Ford," says Sister Elizabeth, and dips into her handbag for some eye drops. The landfill is known as the Hohn Road Facility and on the east side of what the sister describes as "honest, hard-working, sleepy little Nordheim," just past the high school, the U.S. Post Office, and also the Broadway Bar, known for their buchhorn bacon cheddar burger. When the wind blows in from the southeast, as it does during monsoon and hurricane season, the stench of fracking waste mingles with cooked beef.

The Hohn Road Facility is a large scratched-out patch of bare earth where a regular bead of trucks arrive to dump and big yellow excavators maneuver the waste about. "You see all that dust!" cries Sister Elizabeth, as she follows a waste truck down Hohn Road. She turns into a dirt driveway at a modest ranch house directly opposite the landfill entrance. Here, Amanda lives with her three young children, Colt, 7, Weston, 4, Jessica, 2, and with her spouse runs a small ranching business offering services like hay baling, soil aerating, and veterinary care for livestock. Amanda, in blue jeans and a ranch shirt, meets Sister Elizabeth in the yard, sniffs the air, and says, "Doesn't smell like cow poop, and that's the only thing I should be smelling out here."

Indeed, the air has the smell of diesel fuel, which is used in the drilling muds that provide lubrication and structural support in drilling a well and remain soaked into the drill cuttings that end up at landfills like this one. Amanda chaperones Sister Elizabeth by a bull, reclining in the dust and sun in the front yard, then inside, where piled on the kitchen table is an impressive stack of board games. Amanda, who is home-schooling the children, has just purchased them at a tag sale in Floresville. She seats the sister on a sofa in the living room. "On some days," Amanda tells her, "my headaches from the smell are so severe I have to lie down."

The couple started with 28 acres of land and now have more than 200, and have doubled their number of cows. "And I didn't have to stab you in the back or throw someone under the bus to get here," says Amanda. Still, she doesn't think continuing to raise her family in this place is wise. She worries about the bull in her yard that's breathing in all the dust blowing off the landfill, and is even wary to eat her own pigs. She also wonders about the cows, foraging outside in fields that surround the landfill, pointing out they will eventually become somebody's hamburger.

"If they offer me a buyout," says Amanda, "and include enough for me and my kids' future medical expenses then yes, unfortunately, I will take it."

"Here's my problem with that," cuts in Sister Elizabeth. "To build a facility and create conditions so bad that you need to move is what I call immoral force."

Amanda and neighbors, aided by the sister, local attorneys, and environmental consultants and scientists, including the Louisiana environmental toxicologist Wilma Subra, fought the landfill's permits, going up against the Texas Commission on Environmental Quality and also the Railroad Commission of Texas, which regulates the state's oil and gas industry. "I'll be candid, I don't like the site," one Railroad Commission official said at a 2016 hearing. Amanda's cousin-in-law, Paul Baumann, who lives around the corner and even closer to the landfill, said it will "ruin my property value, ruin our school, ruin our roads, and there will probably be wrecks on the highway." But in the end, resistance was futile, and the landfill was constructed. It accepts used drilling muds, drill cuttings, contaminated soils, and other oil and gas waste that has been deemed nonhazardous by the Bentsen and Bevill Amendments exemption to the Resource Conservation and Recovery Act.

"I really hoped they wouldn't begin dumping waste while I was pregnant," laments Amanda, "because a lot of stuff blows over onto our property, and it's more damaging for a newborn than a two-year-old." She brings out two Mason jars, filled with what she says is oilfield waste that dropped from the back of dump trucks and onto the road in front of their home. "It had been rainy that day, and globs of mud were falling off literally the size of softballs," she says. "Whatever they drop kicks up and is in my mailbox and all over my yard." Amanda's spouse gathered the samples, she says, "his hand stunk for two days."

"I grew up among these people," says Sister Elizabeth, peeling back out of the driveway and on to our next appointment, Amanda's uncle, Paul Baumann. "They're hard-working, honest, respectful. Most families came to America as immigrants from Europe and are grateful to have a patch of land of their own to steward." But Amanda and Chris were fated to live next to oilfield waste. Nordheim is in a booming part of the Eagle Ford and located along Texas State Highway 72, a major thoroughfare through the formation.

Uncle Paul's driveway runs the southeast side of the landfill. The home is so close he can chuck a baseball from his front door over the chain-link fence and have it land in freshly dumped waste. In fact, as an act of retaliation against the facility's incessant stench, his son, Paul Jr., once did chuck over a dead skunk. Sister Elizabeth gets out of the Civic and is immediately peering through chain-links into the landfill and tracing a dump truck down a graded road and onto a flat splotch of ground. It backs up, making typical truck backup beeping noises, raises its tailgate, and allows a huge pile of black waste to slide to the ground, kicking up a dust cloud. Then Cats begin moving the waste around. The dump truck exits, kicking up more yellow dust, and I notice dust devils rotating across the landfill. Meanwhile, a new dump truck has already arrived.

As trucks enter their waste is evaluated for liquidness using what's known as the Paint Filter Test. "A predetermined amount of material is placed in a paint filter," says EPA, and in the space of five minutes, "if any portion of the material passes through and drops from the filter" it is said to contain liquids. This wet waste goes to a receiving pit, where it is dried by evaporation or mixed with a drying material, and when it's dry enough to pass the Paint Filter Test it is transferred to the disposal cell. The waste that immediately passes the Paint Filter Test can go directly to the disposal cell, which is directly opposite Paul's home. "I call it Neanderthal engineering," says Sister Elizabeth.

She relaxes under an oak tree beside the house. The smell coming off the landfill is so bad it induces tears. In this part of South Texas the weather is often hot and dry, until it's not, like during hurricane season. With the Gulf just 60 miles away remnants of tropical systems regularly plow through the area and can drop feet of rain, says Sister Elizabeth, breaching the landfill's earthen berms and running streams of water onto Hohn Road. She shows me photos. Eventually, Paul Baumann Jr. emerges from the house, in flip flops, jean shorts, a surfing T-shirt, and Houston Astros baseball cap. "You can go all around the United States," he says, "you ever see an oil and gas waste landfill this close to a house?" The answer is no, I have not.

Paul Jr. makes a living selling stuff he buys at garage and estate sales on eBay and lives here with his wife, son, and two teenage daughters. The family has two dogs, One-Eyed Jack and Kagomi, both presently laying under the oak tree. They love to run along the fence-line barking at waste trucks, and sometimes get under the fence to explore the landfill, which, after all, is just like getting into the next-door neighbor's yard. But canines and oilfield waste don't necessarily mix. "I got a pug for my wife in February," says Paul Jr., "last month he came back and it looked like someone threw some diesel on him." The pug died. Another dog incident involved his Chihuahua, Izzy, buried with a homemade cross beneath trees that lined the driveway. In building the landfill workers cut down the trees and, according to Paul Jr., "desecrated" Izzy's grave.

As Paul Jr. and Sister Elizabeth talk in the shade of the oak, the dump trucks continue to unload waste. "They go all night," he says. Which means the noise, lights, and smells do too. He says he typically manages to sleep for about four hours. The application to build the landfill was filed in 2013 by the subsidiary of a company called Petro Waste Environmental, and after the resistance put up by Sister Elizabeth and the community ran its course, construction began in 2018. "My question," says Paul Jr., glancing over at the dump, "is all this dust that's blowing in going to eat the paint off my house? And is it going to eat my lungs up?"

Documents I receive under a records request to the Railroad Commission of Texas show that on repeated occasions materials such as produced sand, pit liners, contaminated soil, "non-injectable fluids" deemed exempt by the Bentsen and Bevill exemption, and tank bottoms were disposed here. Tank bottoms can contain radium and radioactive lead at levels far above radioactivity limits the Railroad Commission has set for Texas landfills that accept oilfield waste, of which there are 25.

It begs the question of just how accurately and honestly incoming loads of waste are being screened? The operating permit at the Hohn Road Facility requires that at the landfill entrance waste be "scanned for the presence of NORM," or naturally occurring radioactive material. But when I ask for proof, the Railroad Commission says landfills do not have to submit documents indicating they are actually performing these tests.

Our little crew in the shade of the oak tries its best to understand the complex web of financing and fracking waste. Sister Elizabeth mentions Petro Waste's founder, George Wommack, a young businessman from Midland Texas. Although to her, he is not a businessman, because even business is part of human society and requires adherence to a moral code. "He's an exploiter of people, of land, of ranchers, of the environment," says the sister. "It doesn't come and go just on Sundays. Like is said in Matthew 25, 'For I was hungry and you gave me something to eat, I was thirsty and you gave me something to drink, I was a stranger and you invited me in, I needed clothes and you clothed me, I was sick and you looked after me, I was in prison and you came to visit me.'"

"This is real worship," she goes on. "We must rid our body of selfishness and go into the world the way Christ did. We become his hands, his feet, his eyes, and we become bread for the whole world. Christ said whatever you do to the least of my brothers and sisters, you do to me. It doesn't matter what you profess with your mouth, it's what you profess with your heart, that's what real faith is. We all as human beings have obligations, and a corporation is still human beings, and bound by these obligations. Words are cheap, and simply to bear witness is not enough, to love is not enough, to be truthful is not enough—we are supposed to stand for justice."

In all the excitement, Sister Elizabeth has neglected to pull out her Geiger counter. And now it is time for lunch, although that is put on hold, as a new call comes in over her headset.

¤ ¤ ¤

Before founding Petro Waste, George Wommack was into commercial real estate and saltwater disposal wells. He has a polished look and has been described as an up-and-coming leader in the oil and gas industry. Wommack told Hart Energy, an industry news site, that as the Eagle Ford boom came on he noticed very few companies "pursuing the solution for the drilling waste disposal needs."

A photo from 2017 shows Wommack at the ribbon-cutting for a Petro Waste landfill in the West Texas town of Orla. The landfill is located just behind the town's post office. At the ribbon-cutting, Wommack wore jeans, a short-sleeved white dress shirt, aviator shades, his hair blew in the warm West Texas wind, and he held a gigantic cartoon-sized pair of scissors. "I think the best advice I'd give to anyone young who's looking to be successful in the industry," he had told Hart Energy, "is don't wait too late to go out on your own and start a company...and don't worry about failure, because if you fall you're probably going to fall forward."

In 2019, Wommack indeed fell forward. He sold Petro Waste to Waste Management, the nation's largest solid waste disposal company, for a figure in the hundreds of millions. "We are very proud of the platform we've built," Wommack said in a Waste Management press release, and "excited to be selling to the best company in the industry."

Waste Management has headquarters in Houston and operates 267 landfills across the United States, Canada and Puerto Rico. The company traces its origins to a Dutch immigrant named Harm Huizenga who in 1893 began collecting garbage in Chicago for a small fee with a horse-drawn wooden wagon. Plastics changed everything for the waste industry. No more reusable glass milk jugs. No more cloth diapers, paper packaging, glass medicine bottles. No more reusing. “In the post-war period,” says Waste Management, “something happened that most waste providers weren’t ready for: a shift toward disposable products that were designed to make lives simpler.”

America’s throwaway culture turned out to be good business for landfills, which at the time were often independently owned, poorly designed, and weakly regulated. In 1968, Harm Huizenga’s grandson, Wayne Huizenga, and two other investors founded Waste Management, with the goal of “properly managing the waste produced by a rapidly growing population consuming more and more products built for convenience.”

This was a good time to be starting a waste company, as the nation was facing a crisis. Waste from homes, small businesses and industry was being dumped in oceans, rivers, swamps, backyards, and thousands of little neighborhood and community landfills across the country. The Solid Waste Disposal Act of 1965 had attempted to address the issue by setting rules for landfill development, and the Resource Conservation and Recovery Act of 1976 laid out even stricter ones. “Disposal... has gone largely uncontrolled,” EPA stated in December 1976, “resulting in numerous instances of serious effects on human health and environmental quality.”

The new rules required things like landfill liners and controls for leachate. These regulations bankrupted small operators that couldn’t afford to follow them, and Waste Management ate up smaller waste disposal companies and expanded their waste empire. Like restaurants, like clothing shops, like drugstores, like so much else in an American community, what was once mom and pop had become corporate, with a spot on the New York Stock Exchange. Waste Management went public in 1971, with an initial offering of 320,000 shares. By 1982 they had become the world's largest waste disposal company, with more than $1 billion in sales.

But the company needed a way to generate the continuous growth investors liked. One opportunity was natural disasters like fires and floods, which in wrecking a community creates lots of waste destined to be landfilled. Humanmade disasters were good for business too, like say, an offshore oil spill, which as it rolls to shore slathers tar onto sandy beaches that must be removed, soaks into absorbent booms that must be trashed, and contaminates the PPE of cleanup workers which must be tossed at the end of each workday. All of these items are heavy and take up space, making good business for a landfill, and oil spill debris is not classified as hazardous waste, meaning it can be buried in the same landfills as household trash.

In 2010, Waste Management's annual report cited "the oil spill along the Gulf Coast and the substantial flooding in Tennessee" as helpful in boosting revenue. Waste Management had an arrangement with BP, the British company primarily responsible for the oil spill, regarded as one of the worst environmental disasters in US history. The cleanup netted Waste Management an additional $99 million worth of waste. But as their 2010 annual report stated, "special projects" like floods and oil spills "have a limited time span." America's fracking boom appears to have presented the company with an even more durable waste platform.

In 2013, Waste Management purchased two oilfield waste service companies in North Dakota's Bakken oilfield. "These acquisitions," said Harry Lamberton, the company's vice president of energy and environmental services, in an August 2013 press release, "give us access to an element we haven't previously served." The company's annual report from 2012 had called oil and gas an "industry with growing, complex waste management needs." As domestic oilfield activity expanded and the techniques of modern fracking enabled drillers to "unlock hydrocarbons from shale rock formations," the report stated, lots of new drilling waste was going to be created. And Waste Management's landfills would be there to accept it.

At an annual industry waste conference called WasteExpo, held in New Orleans in 2013, the amount of solid waste the fracking industry generated was a hot topic. "There's clearly a need to manage an increasingly complex waste stream, in part because of the change in drilling technology going from a vertical approach to a horizontal is yielding a significant increase in the volumes coming at us," stated John Gibson, the chief executive of Tervita, a multibillion-dollar Canadian company running oilfield waste landfills across the US and Canada. An executive at Wunderlich Securities, a wealth management firm, told attendees oilfield waste represented a $20 to 30 billion market.

Indeed, a trend had already been established. In 2012, the waste disposal company Waste Connections bought the oilfield waste treatment and disposal company R360 Environmental Solutions for approximately $1.3 billion. In 2014, Republic, America's second largest waste disposal company purchased most of Tervita's assets in the US. The acquisition, said CEO Donald Slager, allows Republic to establish "a significant platform" in the oilfield waste sector and "positions us well for future growth opportunities." The value of oilfield waste is no secret, J.P. Morgan and Goldman Sachs served as advisors on that deal.

And America's largest landfill companies continue to advertise to the fracking industry. Republic's website has called on the oil and gas industry for their "solid and liquid disposal needs." The company's landfills take in drill cuttings, drilling fluids, tank bottoms, sludges, contaminated soils and flowback, all of it exempt from the Resource Conservation and Recovery Act's hazardous waste protocols thanks to the Bentsen and Bevill Amendments exemption. The act had transformed American landfills into major corporations, and its loopholes would keep them profiting.

Waste Management has put out an Oil & Gas Brochure. "The oil and gas industry is driving our energy future, and Waste Management can help you get the job done right," it says. They specifically offer to dispose of drill cuttings and the industry's radioactive wastes, and say they have, "proven technologies to treat flowback and production water." But how they do this notoriously difficult and expensive treatment is not elaborated. "The bigger the challenge you face in oil and gas, the better our solution," says the brochure. "So partner with Waste Management and let us guide you to a greener future."

In 2020, Waste Management paid $4.6 billion for Advanced Disposal, the fifth largest solid waste landfill company in the US, and one with oilfield waste operations in Pennsylvania. We had "an exceptionally strong start to the year," Waste Management president Jim Fish stated in 2021, results achieved by "generating strong yield, flexing down our cost structure," and buying Advanced Disposal. Of course, in 2019, Waste Management also bought Petro Waste, which was George Wommack's company. Wommack is no longer involved with oilfield waste landfills and presently manages wealthy people's money as CEO for Headwall Investments. He is also partner in a boutique hotel in Zihuatanejo, Mexico called Casa Cielo Zihua that, according to Wommack's LinkedIn page, is "well suited for destination weddings," and family vacations.

Meanwhile, Waste Management continues to grow, and present an image of sustainability. On April 5, 2023, the company hosted what they called, "Virtual Sustainability Investor Day" to spotlight investments in recycling and renewable energy. Even if you don't happen to be an investor, or pay the company your monthly trash bill, you've surely seen their trash. Go to any subdivision, mini mall, or office park in America and one is liable to see a green dumpster with a little green and yellow "WM" symbol, that's them. They are in schools too. At the beginning of 2024, I catch up with Paul Jr. from Nordheim, Texas, and he tells me to walk into the gym where the high school basketball team plays, "look up to the left, and you see a big old Waste Management sign." It is right beneath the scoreboard.

If all the radioactivity in all the landfills accepting oilfield waste across the United States were added up and doled out to the people with the biggest investments in these landfills, the most radioactive man around would likely be—Bill Gates. Gates is the fourth richest person on earth, and also the largest shareholder in Republic. The Bill & Melinda Gates Foundation, the charitable arm of Gate's fortune, has more than 35 million shares invested in Waste Management, putting the foundation, in terms of total shares owned as of September 2023, ahead of BlackRock and State Street and just behind Vanguard Group. These are massive asset management firms that invest for pension funds and universities and together manage $22 trillion. Meaning there are millions of Americans with money invested in oilfield waste and they don't even know it.

Why do wealthy investors like Bill Gates love waste disposal companies like Waste Management, the analyst Steven Cress asks in an article published with *Forbes* in 2018. Cress believes it is because they run big recycling programs and have been working to transform methane produced at landfills into energy, which lends them a shade of green. Waste Management "is also relatively recession-proof since people will always generate garbage," says Cress. "This rare combination of strength and sustainability, along with 14 years of increased dividends," helps draw the rich to the stock.

¤ ¤ ¤

On the oilfield waste trail, I go on to northern West Virginia, where I meet Bill Hughes, a master electrician and former Trappist monk who spent his retirement chasing down dump trucks in an old Chevy Blazer equipped with a walkie talkie, two CB radios, a ham radio, two GPSs, five cameras and a collection of paper maps. His reconnaissance led to several encounters with police, a lawsuit, and on one occasion, waste falling from the back of a truck and onto his windshield. I learn that unlike out West, where oilfield waste gets dumped at landfills that hold only oilfield waste, in the East it's disposed in the same landfills as household trash.

At Meadowfill Landfill, in Bridgeport, West Virginia, a local environmental consulting firm found as the landfill accepted more oilfield waste, radium levels in the leachate showed "clear increasing trends." Meadowfill is owned by Waste Management, and located down the road from an expansive high-tech FBI facility focused on national security. Just across the border in southwestern Pennsylvania is Arden, a towering landfill located beside a county fairgrounds, and just half an hour from Pittsburgh. Locals refer to Arden as Mount Trashmore, it's also owned by Waste Management, and since 2012 has accepted well over one million tons of oilfield waste.

I go to Ohio, where I meet Dr. Julie Weatherington-Rice, an earth scientist who has been studying oilfield waste since the 1970s. Her master's thesis, completed in 1978, addressed oilfield brine contamination in a community in central Ohio. She explains that the two radioactive isotopes at the top of the decay chain, which eventually decay into all of the other radioactive elements of primary concern in oil and gas are uranium-238 and thorium-232, and their story goes back to what is currently regarded as the beginning of time, roughly 13.6 billion years ago, when existence broiled out from a point smaller than a grain of sand. Within about three minutes the first elements, hydrogen and helium, were forged and these eventually became stars, which superheated and exploded, creating many of the universe's heavier elements then ejecting them into space. This included radioactive ones, like uranium and thorium, and these elements lived as dust, and that dust coalesced to become planets, like Earth.

As the mountains of Earth erode, uranium and thorium in the rocks along with other sediments and nutrients washed off the land are carried by rivers to the sea, where they fall like snow to the bottom and are buried, together with the drift of dead marine algae and plankton, in the mud of the seafloor, forming a rich blackish-gray carpet that under heat and pressure, and blanketed by other layers of material over time, and starved of oxygen, will create the geologic formation known as a black shale. Black shales are the motherlode, the source rock, for most of earth's crude oil and natural gas.

Over millions of years oil and gas has naturally seeped out of black shales, flowing up through fissures and cracks in the earth until it hits up against a geologic layer that doesn't have a lot of cracks and pools up, creating what geologists sometimes call a trap, a gigantic bulge of fuel stuck underground. Drill into these deposits and oil can burst from the surface like a fountain, and the gas may rush out in a roar. Although much of the oil and gas in black shale layers has migrated out over time and we have tapped it, much still remains locked in the shale, stuck too tight to access. The techniques of modern fracking changed that. Drillers could drill down vertically to the black shale, then drill horizontally through, gaining access to its oil and gas. "But drilling through a black shale means the drill cuttings can contain elevated levels of thorium-232 and uranium-238," says Weatherington-Rice.

Now, not only did the industry have a radioactivity problem with radium in the brine and sludge, and radon in the natural gas, issues that existed even before fracking, but they had a radioactivity problem in the drill cuttings, which, as Weatherington-Rice puts it, contained these little radioactive gifts from the early days of the universe. The Marcellus and Utica are black shales. And black shales make up parts of the Bakken in North Dakota, the Woodford formation in Oklahoma, and the Eagle Ford and Permian formations in Texas. The uranium-238 and thorium-232 in black shale drill cuttings have half-lives of 4.5, and 14 billion years. This means for billions of years that uranium and thorium will be decaying into radium, and radon, and radioactive lead, and polonium. "These landfills," says Weatherington-Rice, "will be radioactive until the sun burns out."

I return to North Dakota, where I meet with Sarah Vogel, the former Commissioner of Agriculture and now an attorney, who tells me there is "a significant though largely unknown amount of radioactive waste unaccounted for." "If you can stop the waste stream you can actually stop the industry, it's a kill strategy," Scott Skokos, with the Dakota Resource Council, tells me. "Unfortunately, the funding world doesn't want to fight this fight, they want to fight climate." Darrell Dorgan, an award-winning journalist and former director of the North Dakota Cowboy Hall of Fame has researched the matter and is looking to come up with money to test the urine of children who live near one oilfield waste landfill for traces of radioactivity. We are "on the edge of a man-made ecological disaster. Radioactive and toxic waste can and will cause cancer, and tons of it," he wrote in a 2014 op-ed in the *Grand Forks Herald*. "Unless something happens quickly," he continued, then "this could result in some big portion of northwestern North Dakota becoming a 'Superfund site'—simply put, a national sacrifice zone."

And I travel, in May 2019, with a North Dakota environmental attorney named Fintan Dooley on to eastern Montana, not far from the Yellowstone River, where we meet with a rancher named Seth Newton who lives along the remote country road that leads to Oaks Disposal, a landfill that since the facility opened in 2013—and as of June 2022—has received more than 687,000 tons of oilfield waste, much of it from the Bakken and too radioactive for North Dakota's own oilfield waste landfills. Seth tells us that from 2013 to 2016, when the landfill was busiest, a dump truck headed for the landfill would pass his home once every 30 minutes. From the high perch of his tractor he observed, on numerous occasions, waste the color and consistency of "cream of mushroom soup" slop out the side and onto the road. Since 2016 the truck traffic has slowed somewhat, and the trucks have been tarped, but Seth says waste can still spill out the top or kick off the tires.

A 2019 hydrology report indicated the Oaks Disposal landfill may be leaking radioactivity into groundwater, a nightmare scenario for ranchers like Seth, who has 15,000 acres of wheat, pulses and grassland and gives the groundwater to his 350 cows. Seth is mad the landfill was put in without public meetings. Personally, I am worried about the Montana Department of Environmental Protection's plan for dealing with leachate by recirculating it back over the landfill with sprinkler heads "to promote additional evaporation." In essence, letting the atmosphere evaporate away the toxic liquids for free. When I ask, the agency tells me it's not testing to see whether the radioactive element radium may be blowing away in the wind and landing on farmland producing food people are eating. "At the end of the day it's going to be dead cattle that spurs people to action," says Seth. "I hope it never goes there, but that's my fear."

When I reconnect with Seth in early 2024, he says he is working regularly on landfill issues with the Montana Department of Environmental Quality and Northern Plains Resource Council, a grassroots conservation group established in 1972 by Montana farm and ranch families standing up to the coal industry.

The most unlikely place I encounter oilfield waste are the beautiful woods of southwestern Connecticut. This privileged piece of the state is known for its prep schools, golf courses, and being one of the hedge fund capitals of the world. One early spring morning, skies are silvery, trees budding out in neon green, and the creeks and brooks rushing through these gentle hills are flush. Brooks such as Chestnut Hill Brook, which meanders through the Wilton Woods Corporate Campus, and at one spot has been dammed to form a pond, with a little island in the middle, and a little bridge to the little island, and picnic tables on the shore of the pond where business executives can eat their lunch. Headquartered here, alongside a plastics company and one that books luxury Italian tours is Altus Capital Partners, a group of "conservative investors" focused on what they call, "lower middle market niche manufacturing businesses."

In 2017, Altus Capital acquired MAX Environmental, which owns two landfills in Pennsylvania oil and gas country. When they bought MAX, Altus issued a press release touting that one of the company's landfills was "strategically located to serve the large, growing industrial and government hazardous waste opportunities along the East Coast" and the other was "in the heartland of the Marcellus and Utica Shale gas plays." Between 2012 and 2015, MAX's Yukon, Pennsylvania landfill received 67,340 tons of oilfield waste.

On one of my visits to Yukon I am joined by several scientists, organizers from Mountain Watershed Association, a local watershed and environmental justice group fighting for hazardous waste reforms, and medical professionals from Physicians for Social Responsibility, a national health and environmental advocacy group that shared the Nobel Peace Prize in 1985 for their work publicizing the health consequences of using nuclear weapons—they are now focused on oilfield waste. We meet Tina Marie, who at the time lives behind an auto repair shop on Millbell Road, just down the street from the landfill, and our whole group takes a walk toward it. Several people immediately experience a burning sensation in their throats and develop piercing headaches.

"The owner in the house on the left passed away from cancer," says Tina Marie, and the home beyond that has cancer dead, and the next one too. She counts more than a dozen deaths on her little stretch of Millbell Road, largely from cancers like lung and throat, which as she puts it, are caused by "breathing in your environment." This landfill, as well as taking in oilfield waste, which has been deemed nonhazardous under the Bentsen and Bevill Amendments exemption, also accepts hazardous waste, which is processed in a building onsite that sometimes, according to Tina Marie, emits "orange clouds." "People aren't aware that we don't have capacity to move," says Tina Marie, "because this is our home, and these are our lives."

Tina Marie thinks Altus, the Connecticut firm that owns the landfill, may be behind the intrusion of small planes and helicopters she sees regularly fly in and swoop down over it, aircraft she imagines to be packed with hedge fund managers in slick suits, assessing their asset. "They live so corruptly," says Tina Marie, "and think everyone else is just a bunch of dumb hicks."

She writes regular letters to the state complaining about the landfill but doesn't have faith they will be acted on. Carl Spadaro, who used to be a Pennsylvania Department of Environmental Protection official in charge of reviewing waste permit applications is presently a manager at MAX, in charge of the landfill's environmental permitting and compliance. Part of Tina Marie's frustration is the Pennsylvania Department of Environmental Protection knows the landfill has been sloppily managed yet still allows it to operate. She tells me to examine the agency's inspection reports, and one day I do. Violations began soon after the landfill opened and continue to the present:

January 9, 1985: "Mismanagement of hazardous waste"
February 6, 1985: "Mismanagement of hazardous waste"
February 28, 1985: "Mismanagement of hazardous waste"
March 27, 1985: "Mismanagement of hazardous waste"
May 23, 1985: "Mismanagement of hazardous waste"
January 23, 1989: "Mismanagement of hazardous waste"
October 31, 1990: "Mismanagement of hazardous waste"
November 7, 1990: "Mismanagement of hazardous waste"
December 3, 1991: "Appropriate controls or practices not used to prevent spills and overflows from tank(s) or secondary containment"
August 3, 1992: "Mismanagement of hazardous waste"
December 17, 1992: "Mismanagement of hazardous waste"
June 3, 1997: "Unspecified Violation"
August 19, 1997: "Unspecified Violation"
September 5, 1997: "Unspecified Violation"
October 7, 1997: "Unspecified Violation"
January 14, 1998: "Unspecified Violation" and "Treatment process or equipment not compatible with waste and treatment agents" and "Facility not maintained/operated to minimize possibility of fire, explosion, or discharge of hazardous waste or hazardous constituents"
March 18, 1998: "Immediate remedial action not taken where a hazard is imminent or has already occurred."
May 18, 1998: "Waste streams not covered by permit approved by DEP before acceptance" and "Facility not maintained/operated to minimize possibility of fire, explosion, or discharge of hazardous waste or hazardous constituents"
August 11, 1998: "Emissions, discharge, fires, explosions, and groundwater contamination not reported as required" and "Mismanagement of hazardous waste"
September 15, 1998: "Unspecified Violation"

December 30, 1998: "Containers of hazardous waste not labeled to accurately identify contents" and "Chemical and physical analysis not repeated as required"
January 21, 1999: "Chemical and physical analysis not repeated as required" and "Improper containment and collection system(s)"
February 17, 1999: "Mismanagement of hazardous waste" and "Closure requirements are not complied with" and "Waste streams not covered by permit approved by DEP before acceptance"
March 23, 1999: "Effluent limits for Conventional pollutant(s) were violated"
April 8, 1999: "Mismanagement of hazardous waste"
June 22, 1999: "Containers of hazardous waste are not managed to prevent leaks" and "Mismanagement of hazardous waste" and "Improper containment and collection system(s)"
July 20, 1999: "Containers of hazardous waste are not managed to prevent leaks" and "Containers of hazardous waste not labeled to accurately identify contents"
August 26, 1999: "Preparedness, Prevention and Contingency Plan not developed and implemented in accordance with Chapters 264 and 265"
October 6, 1999: "Facility not maintained/operated to minimize possibility of fire, explosion, or discharge of hazardous waste or hazardous constituents"
November 3, 1999: "Mismanagement of hazardous waste" and "Containers of hazardous waste not in good condition."
December 17, 1999: "Mismanagement of hazardous waste"
April 18, 2000: "Mismanagement of hazardous waste"
May 10, 2000: "Improper containment and collection system(s)" and "Containers of hazardous waste are not managed to prevent leaks"
June 28, 2000: "Generators must determine if their solid waste is a hazardous waste" and "Person or municipality dumps solid waste unlawfully" and "Facility not maintained/operated to minimize possibility of fire, explosion, or discharge of hazardous waste or hazardous constituents"
August 23, 2000: "Containers of hazardous waste not in good condition"
September 20, 2000: "Tanks not managed to prevent leaks, ruptures, corrosion or failing"
October 25, 2000: "Handles solid waste contrary to rules and regulations, or orders of the Department, or any permit condition, or in any manner as to create a public nuisance" and "Facility not maintained/operated to minimize possibility of fire, explosion, or discharge of hazardous waste or hazardous constituents"
November 9, 2000: "Handles solid waste contrary to rules and regulations, or orders of the Department, or any permit condition, or in any manner as to create a public nuisance"

December 19, 2000: “Tank or secondary containment system, that has leaked or has a spill, not removed immediately from service”
January 17, 2001: “Residual Waste is mismanaged”
January 31, 2001: “Mismanagement of hazardous waste”
March 27, 2001: “Contingency plan does not contain an up-to-date list of names, addresses and phone numbers of all persons qualified to act as emergency coordinator”
April 10, 2001: “Manifest discrepancies not resolved or reported within time limits” and “Mismanagement of hazardous waste”
May 14, 2001: “Mismanagement of hazardous waste” and “Contingency plan does not contain an up-to-date list of names, addresses and phone numbers of all persons qualified to act as emergency coordinator”
June 22, 2001: “Efficient drainage not provided from base to sump or collection system”
July 20, 2001: “Mismanagement of hazardous waste” and “Treatment process or equipment not compatible with waste and treatment agents” and “Leachate and run-off not collected and properly managed” and “Containers of hazardous waste not labeled to accurately identify contents” and “Containers of hazardous waste are not closed during storage”
August 17, 2001: “Containers of hazardous waste not labeled to accurately identify contents”
September 18, 2001: “Containers of hazardous waste are not closed during storage” and “Contingency plan does not contain an up-to-date list of names, addresses and phone numbers of all persons qualified to act as emergency coordinator” and “Mismanagement of hazardous waste” and “Person or municipality has violated Act 97, Department regulation, order, or term of permit” and “Contingency plan not on-site and implemented”
November 17, 2001: “Handles solid waste contrary to rules and regulations, or orders of the Department, or any permit condition, or in any manner as to create a public nuisance” and “Improper management of hazardous waste” and “Containers of hazardous waste are not closed during storage” and “Containers of hazardous waste not labeled to accurately identify contents”
January 18, 2002: “Handles solid waste contrary to rules and regulations, or orders of the Department, or any permit condition, or in any manner as to create a public nuisance”
March 28, 2002: “Containers of hazardous waste not labeled to accurately identify contents”
April 9, 2002: “Tanks not managed to prevent spills/overflows” and “Secondary containment systems not designed, installed and operated to meet the requirements”

April 29, 2002: "Standards for Contaminants, Fugitive Emissions, Prohibition of certain fugitive emissions. Failure to take reasonable actions to prevent particulate matter from becoming airborne"
May 23, 2002: "Containers of hazardous waste are not closed during storage"
June 24, 2002: "Person or municipality has violated Act 97, Department regulation, order, or term of permit"
July 25, 2002: "Facility not maintained/operated to minimize possibility of fire, explosion, or discharge of hazardous waste or hazardous constituents" and "Tanks not managed to prevent spills/overflows"
August 14, 2002: "Improper Laboratory procedures were used for analysis of effluent"
September 27, 2002: "Improper management of hazardous waste" and "Run-on into containment system not prevented"
October 20, 2002: "Improper management of hazardous waste" and "Mismanagement of hazardous waste"
November 26, 2002: "Handles solid waste contrary to rules and regulations, or orders of the Department, or any permit condition, or in any manner as to create a public nuisance" and "Containment system does not have impervious base free of cracks"
January 23, 2003: "Containers of hazardous waste are not managed to prevent leaks" and "Mismanagement of hazardous waste" and "Containers of hazardous waste are not closed during storage" and "Mismanagement of hazardous waste"
February 19, 2003: "Handles solid waste contrary to rules and regulations, or orders of the Department, or any permit condition, or in any manner as to create a public nuisance" and "Handles solid waste contrary to rules and regulations, or orders of the Department, or any permit condition, or in any manner as to create a public nuisance"
March 27, 2003: "Improper management of hazardous waste"
April 28, 2003: "Containers of hazardous waste are not closed during storage" and "Spilled or leaked waste and accumulated precipitation not removed from sump or collection system with sufficient frequency to prevent overflow"
May 23, 2003: "Containers of hazardous waste not in good condition" and "Mismanagement of hazardous waste"
June 12, 2003: "Spilled or leaked waste and accumulated precipitation not removed from sump or collection system with sufficient frequency to prevent overflow" and "Mismanagement of hazardous waste" and "Containers of hazardous waste not in good condition" and "Improper containment and collection system(s)"
July 17, 2003: "Handles solid waste contrary to rules and regulations, or orders of the Department, or any permit condition, or in any manner as to create a public nuisance" and "Containers of hazardous waste are not managed to prevent leaks"

August 6, 2003: "Containers of hazardous waste not in good condition"
August 20, 2003: "Containers of hazardous waste not in good condition" and "Residual Waste is mismanaged"
September 22, 2003: "Handles solid waste contrary to rules and regulations, or orders of the Department, or any permit condition, or in any manner as to create a public nuisance"
October 10, 2003: "Improper management of hazardous waste" and "Facility accepts hazardous waste accompanied by a manifest not approved by DEP" and "Manifest discrepancies not resolved or reported within time limits"
March 18, 2004: "Improper management of hazardous waste" and "Containers of hazardous waste not labeled to accurately identify contents" and "Mismanagement of hazardous waste"
April 28, 2004: "Handles solid waste contrary to rules and regulations, or orders of the Department, or any permit condition, or in any manner as to create a public nuisance"
May 25, 2004: "Data from monitoring and leak detection equipment not checked" and "Improper management of hazardous waste"
July 28, 2004: "Improper management of hazardous waste"
September 24, 2004: "Facility not maintained/operated to minimize possibility of fire, explosion, or discharge of hazardous waste or hazardous constituents"
November 23, 2004: "Containers of hazardous waste not labeled to accurately identify contents" and "Improper management of hazardous waste"
December 21, 2004: "Improper management of hazardous waste"
February 17, 2005: "Handles solid waste contrary to rules and regulations, or orders of the Department, or any permit condition, or in any manner as to create a public nuisance"
April 5, 2005: "Handles solid waste contrary to rules and regulations, or orders of the Department, or any permit condition, or in any manner as to create a public nuisance"
July 21, 2005: "Facility not maintained/operated to minimize possibility of fire, explosion, or discharge of hazardous waste or hazardous constituents"
December 28, 2005: "Person or municipality dumps solid waste unlawfully"
January 24, 2006: "Handles solid waste contrary to rules and regulations, or orders of the Department, or any permit condition, or in any manner as to create a public nuisance" and "Mismanagement of hazardous waste"
February 23, 2006: "Person or municipality dumps solid waste unlawfully"
March 29, 2006: "Containers of hazardous waste are not closed during storage"

April 25, 2006: "Containers of hazardous waste are not closed during storage"
May 25, 2006: "Containers of hazardous waste not in good condition"
July 26, 2006: "Containers of hazardous waste not in good condition" and "Storage containers are not labeled properly" and "Operation is not in accordance with operating requirements of Act 97, regulations and permit conditions"
October 27, 2006: "Containers of hazardous waste not in good condition"
May 24, 2007: "Containers of hazardous waste are not closed during storage"
July 18, 2007: "Failure to treat, store and dispose hazardous waste in accordance with rules, regulations, permits, permit conditions and orders of the department"
November 20, 2007: "Mismanagement of hazardous waste" and "Adequate aisle space not maintained to allow unobstructed movement of personnel and equipment during emergencies" and "Efficient drainage not provided from base to sump or collection system" and "Residual Waste is mismanaged" and "Failure to treat, store and dispose hazardous waste in accordance with rules, regulations, permits, permit conditions and orders of the department" and "There is a violation of Act 97, Department regulation, order, or term of permit" and "Handles solid waste contrary to rules and regulations, or orders of the Department, or any permit condition, or in any manner as to create a public nuisance" and "Waste is blown or otherwise deposited outside storage area" and "There is unlawful dumping" and "Containers of hazardous waste not in good condition"
June 26, 2008: "Improper containment and collection system(s)"
July 11, 2008: "Person or municipality has violated Act 97, Department regulation, order, or term of permit" and "Access road is not designed, constructed or maintained properly and not negotiable by collection vehicles"
August 27, 2008: "Improper management of hazardous waste"
November 7, 2008: "Failure to maintain required records"
January 28, 2011: "Secondary containment systems not designed, installed and operated to meet the requirements" and "Required inspections not conducted at least once each operating day" and "Closure and post-closure requirements not complied with" and "Facility not maintained/operated to minimize possibility of fire, explosion, or discharge of hazardous waste or hazardous constituents"
March 1, 2011: "Containers of hazardous waste not labeled to accurately identify contents" and "There is a violation of Act 97, Department regulation, order, or term of permit"
April 22, 2011: "Containers of hazardous waste not in good condition"
August 16, 2011: "Effluent limit(s) were violated (non-IMAX)"

September 20, 2011: "No waste analysis plan on-site" and "Written operating record does not contain records and results of all inspections" and "Containers of hazardous waste are not closed during storage"
October 11, 2011: "Containers of hazardous waste not in good condition"
December 27, 2011: "Containers of hazardous waste are not closed during storage"
February 13, 2012: "Containers of hazardous waste not labeled to accurately identify contents" and "There is a violation of Act 97, Department regulation, order, or term of permit"
July 10, 2012: "Operation and Maintenance violations were present" and "Pollution incident was not reported to DEP"
January 28, 2013: "Containers of hazardous waste not labeled to accurately identify contents" and "Containers of hazardous waste are not closed during storage" and "Containers of hazardous waste not labeled to accurately identify contents"
February 28, 2013: "Containers of hazardous waste not labeled to accurately identify contents"
July 30, 2013: "Effluent limit(s) were violated (non-IMAX)"
November 12, 2013: "Contingency plan does not contain an up-to-date list of names, addresses and phone numbers of all persons qualified to act as emergency coordinator"
July 9, 2014: "Treatment, storage, disposal of ignitable or reactive wastes or mixing of incompatible wastes or materials not conducted according to requirements" and "There is a violation of Act 97, Department regulation, order, or term of permit"
August 26, 2014: "Containers of hazardous waste not in good condition" and "Improper management of hazardous waste" and "Containers of hazardous waste are not closed during storage" and "There is a violation of Act 97, Department regulation, order, or term of permit"
September 19, 2014: "Containers of hazardous waste not in good condition" and "Containers of hazardous waste are not closed during storage" and "Container storage area not inspected weekly for leaks, deterioration, etc." and "There is a violation of Act 97, Department regulation, order, or term of permit"
November 18, 2014: "Containers of hazardous waste not in good condition"
May 16, 2015: "Documentation of claims that materials are not solid wastes or are conditionally exempt"
May 30, 2015: "NPDES - Violation of effluent limits in Part A of permit"
December 28, 2015: "Improper management of hazardous waste" and "Person or municipality dumps solid waste unlawfully" and "There is a violation of Act 97, Department regulation, order, or term of permit"
December 29, 2015: "Efficient drainage not provided from base to sump or collection system" and "Containers of hazardous waste not

in good condition" and "Containers of hazardous waste are not closed during storage"
May 23, 2016: "Construction, Modification, Reactivation and Operation of Sources, Plan Approval Requirements, Compliance requirement. Failure to Operate and maintain a source or control device in accordance with the specifications"
August 15, 2017: "NPDES - Violation of effluent limits in Part A of permit"
August 14, 2018: "Leak detection violations" and "Failure to meet performance and design standards"
July 18, 2019: "Failure to comply with a permit condition"
February 21, 2020: "NPDES - Violation of effluent limits in Part A of permit"
June 30, 2020: "NPDES - Failure to properly operate and maintain all facilities which are installed or used by the permittee to achieve compliance" and "NPDES - Failure to monitor pollutants as required by the NPDES permit"
July 19, 2021: "NPDES - Violation of effluent limits in Part A of permit"
May 12, 2022: "NPDES - Violation of effluent limits in Part A of permit"
October 23, 2023: "NPDES - Failure to collect representative samples" and "NPDES - Violation of effluent limits in Part A of permit" and "NPDES - Failure to properly operate and maintain all facilities which are installed or used by the permittee to achieve compliance"

In 2023, EPA visits MAX Yukon and delivers a scathing report on landfill practices. Yukon is one of at least 30 landfills across Pennsylvania that has regularly accepted oilfield waste. One concern is that leachate from these landfills may contain elevated levels of radium and is piped to sewage plants that have little ability to remove it then discharged into the same Pennsylvania rivers where people recreate, fish, and draw their drinking water. *Public Herald*, a Pittsburgh-based nonprofit investigative journalism outfit co-founded in 2011 by Pennsylvania journalists Joshua Pribanic and Melissa Troutman investigated the topic and published a series of exposés, complete with maps that showed which sewage plants were taking leachate from landfills that had accepted oilfield waste, and what rivers they were discharging into.

In April 2019 I visit the sewage treatment plant in Belle Vernon, Pennsylvania, and meet with then superintendent Guy Kruppa and a gruff coworker. We sit at a gray table inside the plant's laboratory, with flasks and microscopes lining the counters. Kruppa wears work boots and a blue Belle Vernon sewage plant shirt. Both men are chewing tobacco and spitting into little paper cups.

The Belle Vernon sewage plant, aside from taking about 600,000 gallons of household sewage a day, had an agreement to accept leachate from the Westmoreland Sanitary Landfill, which also now resembles a waste mountain and is located just outside the town center. The landfill, from 2011 through 2017, accepted 197,922 tons of oilfield waste. The sewage plant received the landfill's leachate, on the order of 100,000 gallons a day, through a sewer pipe. As sewage enters a sewage plant it flows through a screen, which removes large floating objects like rags and sticks, then passes through a grit chamber, where cinders, sand, and small stones settle to the bottom, then through a sedimentation tank, where fine solids settle to form a sludge. One of the key processes in a modern sewage treatment plant involves a set of tanks thriving with bacteria that consume the remaining organic waste. At Belle Vernon, the treated wastewater is tested for a variety of contaminants then discharged into the Monongahela River, which serves as drinking water for a significant portion of southwestern Pennsylvania, including parts of Pittsburgh.

"What was happening," says Kruppa, "is we were getting such a toxic shock-load from this leachate it was killing the bugs." Which was a problem that potentially constituted a federal crime. Because through the EPA, and overseen by the Pennsylvania Department of Environmental Protection, the sewage plant has permits that control exactly how much of a variety of different pollutants they can discharge into the Monongahela. With the sewage-eating bacteria dead, the sewage plant was going to be breaking their permit, and spewing contaminants like ammonia, phosphorus, and fecal coliform into the river.

"We thought it was our fault," says Kruppa, and nods at his colleague, the gruff coworker, who raised the question, "what are we getting from the landfill?"

The sewage guys reviewed lab results showing what was in the fluids they were discharging into the Monongahela. "The things that stood out," says Kruppa, "were chloride, Total Dissolved Solids, high conductivity, and all your metal counts were high, including barium and cadmium." He showed the data to a colleague who worked in wastewater treatment at a large multinational corporation, and says they replied back: "There is no doubt about it, this is indicative of frack waste." Radium is not required testing in the sewage plant's discharge permits. Neither are the other radioactive elements common in oilfield waste.

The Pennsylvania Department of Environmental Protection tells me: "DEP has no evidence...that would indicate levels of heavy metals or radioactive elements in leachate" and they are not worried about the leachate entering Pennsylvania rivers or harms to human health, "given the enormous volume of water in the receiving river." Although Dr. John Stolz, Director of the Center for Environmental Research and Education at Duquesne University, in Pittsburgh, tests the leachate and reports elevated radium and later co-publishes a scientific paper in the journal *Ecological Indicators* that found "elevated sediment radionuclide concentrations downstream of facilities treating leachate from landfills accepting oil and gas waste." A radionuclide refers to any specific form or isotope of a radioactive element.

The Pennsylvania Department of Environmental Protection also tell me, "generators are required by Pennsylvania law to perform sampling and analyses to demonstrate that their waste is suitable and authorized for disposal" and all Pennsylvania landfills have radiation monitors set to alarm if readings of about twice background are detected. Westmoreland Sanitary Landfill doesn't answer my questions on this topic, but I learn, via a letter sent to one Belle Vernon area local from a whistle-blowing truck driver that has delivered to the landfill, waste is being snuck in.

The letter describes "Numerous overlooked DEP violations," operating the landfill "through the night" and "Dumping of Frackwater Material & Sludge in excess of legal limits." The company "is getting away with everything that they can," says the whistleblower. "I am writing to you because I know your quality of life is being affected, and I don't want you to get a raw deal."

"What this place basically is," Kruppa says, "is a permit to pollute. We are taking their waste and putting it in the Monongahela."

The river, the coworker points out, is where people fish, boat, and swim, and it serves as drinking water too.

"It's a loophole, almost an under the table sort of thing," says Kruppa. "They found a way to take waste to the landfill and get rid of it in the form of a liquid through the leachate."

"Essentially," Kruppa says, "we are the asshole of the fracking industry."

¤ ¤ ¤

In May 2019, a county judge ordered the Westmoreland Sanitary Landfill to stop sending the Bell Vernon Sewage Plant its leachate.

I file questions to George Wommack, via a correspondence form at Headwall Investments where he currently serves as CEO, on management practices at Petro Waste's Hohn Road Facility and associated health and environmental concerns and liabilities and have not received replies.

Buckhorn Waste Services, which runs Oaks Disposal in Montana has not replied to my questions on oilfield waste, radioactivity, and associated health and environmental concerns and liabilities.

Altus Capital Partners has not replied to any of my questions on oilfield waste, radioactivity, and associated health and environmental concerns and liabilities. This includes questions which, citing the numerous violations at their Yukon landfill, demand to know whether the firm believes this manner of operating to be appropriate and whether or not they believe their operating practices are putting landfill workers and the people that live near the landfill at risk. Altus has also not replied to my question concerning whether the firm has a moral, ethical or spiritual code regarding what they choose to invest in. MAX Environmental has not replied to questions.

Republic tells me that, "industry produces hazardous and non-hazardous waste streams that require disposal at facilities equipped to properly handle the material" and the company operates a number of disposal facilities designed to safely and responsibly manage these waste streams in compliance with all local, state and federal regulations. I press them to answer my specific questions on oilfield waste, radioactivity, and associated health and environmental concerns and liabilities, but they tell me: "We are declining to provide any additional information.

Waste Management has not replied to any of my questions on oilfield waste, radioactivity, and associated health and environmental concerns and liabilities.

The Bill & Melinda Gates Foundation has not replied to any of my questions regarding their significant investments in Waste Management, a landfill company that accepts copious amounts of 'nonhazardous' and 'exempt' oilfield waste. The Foundation has also not answered questions on how these investments meet their mission of "fighting poverty, disease, and inequity around the world."

9
Welcome to Oklahoma, Where They Spread Drilling Waste on Pastureland

While out West I am introduced to an Oklahoma engineer regarded as one of the nation's top experts on oilfield contamination and one day during the summer of 2020 I receive their call. They have worked in the oil and gas industry for 30 years and tell me that in Oklahoma it is common practice to spread oilfield waste on grazing and pastureland for cattle, a practice called land-spreading.

"The primary thing they are trying to land-spread," says the engineer, "is drilling waste."

There are regulations, the engineer explains. The state says you must measure the salinity, or salt content, of the waste and based on that determinations are made for how much can be spread.

"But that is what it says on paper," continues the engineer. "Here is what happens in reality, people wanting to dispose of drilling waste will find a landowner who needs some money. They will offer the landowner money to spread waste. They will lie to the Oklahoma Corporation Commission to get a permit. They will even lie to the landowner to say it is good for grass and good for the land and actually makes crops grow better. There are certain rules and limitations and calculations, they will totally and completely ignore that. They will just go out there and dump and spread the waste on the ground and drive away and say *fuck you*. It is one of the biggest scams ever, and it is going on everywhere in Oklahoma."

"But this waste must do some good for the rangeland, have some benefit?" I ask. "How else could the practice develop?"

"No, it is not beneficial," says the engineer. "That is just a total and complete lie."

Drilling waste refers to drill cuttings and also drilling mud. Drilling muds are not just mud, they often contain chemical additives that give the mud additional properties important to their task of keeping the drill bit lubricated, stabilizing the well and preventing cave-ins, and helping to flush the drill cuttings back to the surface. These chemicals include corrosion inhibitors, lubricants, viscosifiers, dispersants, fluid loss reducers, flocculants, surfactants, biocides, and sometimes also diesel fuel. Drilling muds in some areas can also contain heavy metals and radioactivity.

I discuss with the engineer what I know about black shales, and that with the advent of modern fracking, for the past 20 years oil and gas development in Oklahoma has involved drilling horizontally through the Woodford, a black shale known, at least since a 1944 publication in the Bulletin of the Geological Society of America entitled, "Distribution of Radioactivity in Ancient Sediments," to have especially elevated levels of radioactivity. And broken up bits of the Woodford are exactly what are being spread all over these rancher's pastures and rangelands. Surely, the state of Oklahoma must be checking for radioactivity before enabling the waste to be spread?

"No," says the engineer, "to my knowledge, no one is testing for radioactivity."

But beef from Oklahoma cows is served in restaurants across America?

"No, to my knowledge no one is testing for radioactivity," repeats the engineer.

There is a pause on the phone line. The engineer has been at this for too long. They have dealt with attorneys, dealt with oil and gas companies, dealt with government regulators. What they are revealing is a damning scientific confession, gleaned over a life's work.

"In Oklahoma, it is out of sight, out of mind," says the engineer. "If you don't want to deal with it, you don't study it, you don't examine it—it doesn't exist."

I hang up the phone, and a few weeks later go to Oklahoma.

¤ ¤ ¤

Entering the state from the northeast via Interstate 44 on a bright green summer day is like leafing through a calendar on cows. There are cows grazing on open plains. Cows rippling across rolling savanna land. Cows resting near muddy ponds. Cows beneath shelterbelt trees. Cows almost up to the edge of the highway.

The engineer is seated at an outdoor café table on the outskirts of Tulsa, in blue jeans with a pen in the breast pocket of a plaid shirt, having just finished a cup of coffee. Their tone is one of irritation. They boil with it.

"If you are in the environmental arena in Oklahoma a lot of your opportunities to do work is oil and gas," says the engineer. "That is a testament to how many problems the industry causes."

"Ironically," they continue, "the oil and gas industry has some of the best environmental scientists in the world. You watch the commercials on TV and think they are wonderful environmental stewards but unless you're making them, through regulations, solve the problems they created they will get out of it as cheaply as possible."

"The oil and gas industry's mode of operation is to push as much of the real cost of exploration and production onto individual landowners, states, and society in general," the engineer says. "They put the true cost for disposal of drilling waste onto the landowner, whose land they are going to ruin."

There are many places to lay blame, but the engineer puts it squarely on Bentsen and Bevill, the exemption which declared the oil and gas industry's waste to be nonhazardous. "It was the biggest piece of shit that ever came down the pike," they say, "and the biggest victory oil and gas ever had." And yet another example of the industry privatizing profits and socializing problems.

"Workers, especially at smaller oil and gas production companies, are typically not protected," says the engineer. "There is no more macho culture in this country than oilfield workers. You got this cowboy attitude, this anti-government attitude. Many times, someone who stands up for safety is basically looked at as a pussy. You are not going to tell me what to do, I am a man."

One problem is the big oil companies contract out to smaller oilfield service companies to do their dirtiest work.

"Contractors are disposable," says the engineer. "Being safe slows things down. Slowing things down costs money. The more money a field supervisor spends the less of a bonus they get at the end of the year. They are incentivized to ignore safety and environmental damage. It is totally ass-backwards. You should be incentivized to *prevent* injury and exposure. You should be incentivized to *prevent* environmental damage."

It is near the height of the morning rush and Tulsans bustle in and out of the café. They seem like fine people, and I imagine some must care about the environment, and their own health. "Someone," I question the engineer, "must be fighting the oil and gas industry in Oklahoma—where are the environmentalists?"

"Many of them have just been sitting across the kitchen table bitching about it but not doing anything," they say. "It takes a lot of money to go up against the oil industry. They will spend you to death and drive you crazy. Money is always one of the industry's considerations in working on someone's land, do they have the resources to come after us? The only landowners who can effectively resist are the ones who are politically connected or have deep enough pockets and the stamina to fight."

And thus, in Oklahoma oil and gas has been produced for so long, and across such a wide swath of territory, and with such little regard for the environment, that contamination is widespread across the state.

The morning rolls on. The café scene lulls, that gap between late breakfast and early lunch. At some point, I ask the engineer, there must be a reckoning for the state?

They shake their head.

"State budgets are stretched thinner and thinner and thinner," they say. "The amount of budget going to the regulatory agencies is resulting in a lot of good people being laid off or leaving to get a better job. For the people still around, there are not enough resources for them to do their job effectively, so there are fewer and fewer people to oversee the industry."

"Basically," they say, "the oil and gas industry has bought the state of Oklahoma lock, stock, and barrel."

¤ ¤ ¤

One Oklahoma environmental regulator who worked to study and understand oilfield contamination across the state is Patricia Billingsley, who for many years oversaw cleanup operations on properties contaminated from oil and gas production as manager of the Oklahoma Corporation Commission's Brownsfield Program. She cannot meet in person but will happily answer questions on a set of presentations and reports conducted while she was manager of the Brownfield Program. They show a troubling pattern of contamination.

For much of the 20th century in Oklahoma the industry's toxic brine was spewed into unlined pits or spilled directly into the environment.

A 1940 photo in one of Billingsley's presentations shows oilfield brine flowing along a roadside ditch, right beside a farmer's field. Another one of her images shows a smoking and seemingly endless plain of oil derricks and tanks. A plume of oil sprays high, and dark debris can be seen falling out in a mist. "Oklahoma City," the caption reads. The American Indian Cultural Center and Museum, now known as the First Americans Museum, was later built on the site.

Most alarming is Billingsley's data regarding groundwater. Nearly two-thirds of Oklahoma communities are located within an active or once-active oilfield, and groundwater supplies 73 percent of all irrigation water for agriculture in the state, 295,000 domestic wells, and more than 300 cities and towns. When members of the public called the Oklahoma Corporation Commission to complain about possible contamination, Billingsley's team was sent out to sample. They found that levels of lead and arsenic, common heavy metals in oilfield brine, were above EPA limits at 23 percent of the groundwater sites they tested, including numerous drinking water wells. More than one-third of the groundwater tested was contaminated with barium, a drilling mud additive. Benzene, a carcinogen that affects the bones and blood, exceeded limits in 30 percent of the shallow groundwater tested. Toluene, which can lead to kidney and liver problems and xylene, which can cause nervous system damage was also present in some shallow wells. These chemicals are called volatile organic compounds and indicators of drilling waste.

To learn Oklahomans were consuming carcinogens from drilling waste in their drinking water seems like an extraordinary find, and I ask Billingsley why the state didn't assess human health impacts or use this data to conduct a more detailed investigation?

"We had no toxicologists on staff," she says.

Billingsley's team also found much of the groundwater and many of the wells they tested across Oklahoma were contaminated with salts they believed came from oilfield brine. This was concerning. If salts from oilfield brine have been spilled all over the state, it would be expected that the radium in oilfield brine would have been spilled across the state too.

The first known data on radium in oilfield brine comes from the 1927 work of Tcherepennikov, who found high levels in a sample from the Ukhta oilfield, in Russia's Komi Republic. Radium levels in brine vary across oilfields, and within wells of the same field, and I ask the Oklahoma Corporation Commission what data they have on radium in oilfield brine across their state. I am shocked to learn, the agency "does not have any."

In a presentation entitled "Old Oilfield vs. New Homes," Billingsley lays out the real-life scenario of Clifford Farms, a subdivision of large angular homes with stone and brick façades on the northwest side of Oklahoma City. One "recent homebuyer Mrs. Z complained that her water well tasted salty. Soon after, her neighbors were also complaining." Billingsley's office was contacted and in 2011 one of their field inspectors went out to investigate. They found evidence of salts seeping up through patios and salted dead zones in front lawns. Every well but one tested over EPA limits for salt in drinking water.

A modern map superimposed over a 1941 aerial photo shows fancy houses straddle old wellhead sites, and old brine pits fester directly beneath living rooms and backyards. "The homes are sitting on an old oilfield," Billingsley's presentation conveys. One home's water well was actually drilled "through a former pit." She concluded old oilfield activity was probably responsible for the pollution. But when Mrs. Z and her neighbors tasted "salty" water, were they drinking the oil and gas industry's radium too?

"We did not look at radioactive isotopes at all," Billingsley tells me. "No budget for that."

I head over to the northwest side of Oklahoma City to see the site for myself and find black cows grazing just off the highway and open prairie being overtaken by housing developments. Clifford Farms is behind a gate, $500,000 homes with tiled roofs surrounded by fine green lawns.

Sale pages for the subdivision's homes show lavish patios with outdoor fireplaces, spacious interiors with shiny home offices, vast entertaining spaces, and enormous walk-in bedroom closets. I spot a trampoline in one yard, with a mesh safety net around the side to keep children from falling out.

During the mid-1930s, Continental Oil and Transportation Company, now part of ConocoPhillips, drilled eight wells here. The wells generated oilfield brine, often referred to as produced water in Oklahoma, and per standards of the time was stored in unlined pits. As Billingsley's presentation indicates, the waste leaked into the surrounding soils, contaminated the groundwater, and the grounds on which these homes now stand.

"Produced water resulting from oil and gas exploration and production in this particular area is enriched in uranium and radium," wrote Dr. Daniel Tormey, a California geochemist who served as an expert witness in a 2016 lawsuit brought by Clifford Farms residents against ConocoPhillips. Tormey concluded metals and radioactive compounds leftover from ConocoPhillips' oil and gas production operations "are well above local background concentrations, and continue to threaten groundwater quality, human health, and the environment."

The conditions found in this neighborhood, he added, "are exactly the same resulting conditions present and reported at other locations in Oklahoma."

¤ ¤ ¤

One day, pacing about an Oklahoma City hotel room thinking of my next step, I connect by phone with Dr. Bert Fisher, a former Amoco Production Company research scientist. He presently lives in Tulsa and runs an environmental consulting firm. Our talk doesn't touch on land-spreading, but he has an important story about radon.

Fisher received a degree in geology and geophysics from Yale, in 1973, and a PhD in earth sciences from Case Western Reserve University, in 1979. He began working as a research scientist for Amoco in 1981. "It was the best job ever," he says. "Nearly limitless resources and a lot of interesting problems to work on." In 1993 he traveled to the Hugoton embayment of the Anadarko basin, a famous natural gas producing area in Kansas and learned of a major problem.

Across America are an untold number of natural gas wells located in backyards and farmer's fields. While most gas is piped off to market by the gas company, a small pipeline can be set up that runs some gas directly from the wellhead into a farm or residence, where it can be used to run machinery, fire a furnace, or cook food on a stove. People can be eager to have this gas, because it's free. Part of Fisher's work in 1993 in Kansas was to collect samples of it in a steel cylinder called a Lucas cell that measures the radioactive gas radon. "I didn't really know there was radon in natural gas," he says. But he soon learned.

"The first sample sounded like an alarm going off," says Fisher. "Holy Jesus." Typically, the Lucas cell would ping every so often, but here it was "a whir: ping, ping, ping, ping, ping." He realized the gas these residents were using to cook food was loaded with radioactivity.

"Of immediate concern is potential radon exposure to individuals taking gas from residential gas taps," Fisher wrote in a six-page memo sent on July 1, 1993, to Amoco senior officials. "Domestic use of this gas may involve burning inside living spaces for cooking. Cooking generates abundant aerosols which can serve as inhalation and ingestion vectors for radon decay daughters."

Fisher's recommended solution, laid out in the memo to Amoco was rather simple. Measure the amount of radon at the wellhead, and residents with high levels should be prevented from using the gas. Fisher even provided an analysis of how much this testing would cost the company—$3,500 and several weeks of work. But Amoco took no action. In fact, the oil and gas giant made sure Fisher's alarm bell on radon in natural gas was never rung.

"It got buried pretty quickly, and I got drawn into legal," he says. "It was obvious that they weren't interested in me carrying the ball any further, and they didn't want any mention of radioactivity, that was for damn sure."

Ever the meticulous scientist, Fisher kept the six-page memo, complete with handwritten notes that show who at Amoco he contacted about the problem. According to one note, Terry Adamson, at the time a senior member of environmental management in Amoco's Denver Office, told Fisher to, "have all drafts of this destroyed." Adamson would go on to become Director of Regulatory Compliance and Environment for BP North America.

This book is the first time it has been revealed that Amoco had knowledge provided by a company scientist that the natural gas they produced contained dangerous levels of radioactivity. That this radioactivity was putting human beings at risk. And that the information was ignored. And not just ignored, orders were given to have it destroyed. In 1998 Amoco was acquired by BP. I ask spokespeople there when Amoco learned of the radioactivity risks posed to residents taking natural gas directly from the wellhead and how the company has acted on this information, but I have not received replies.

After our call, Fisher sends me a copy of the original letter he sent Amoco. His handwritten notes remain legible. He laments that many of the people being affected live in rural areas, and their voices aren't heard. Fisher believes that radon in natural gas is much more of a concern in places like central Kansas, where residents often draw gas straight from the wellhead, than it is in places like New York City, where gas travels for dozens, or hundreds, of miles in a pipeline and has more time to decay. "It would be interesting to do a study," he tells me, "and see how many lung cancers you find."

I ask several government agencies how many people across the United States continue to take gas straight from the wellhead, potentially loaded with radioactivity? "EPA does not track this information," an EPA spokesperson tells me. The U.S. Department of Agriculture "does not have that information," a spokesperson there tells me. A spokesperson with the Department of Energy is more forthcoming: "We believe it is a fairly common practice in rural communities."

¤ ¤ ¤

I finally learn about the practice of land-spreading in Oklahoma from a small group of former Texas oil and gas industry workers that have setup a drilling waste data company called Waste Analytics LLC, which provides information to investors. Waste Analytics has impressive industry access, and detailed records on where drilling waste is being produced and ending up. One of the firm's experts, at that time, was Jeff Tyson, who had been closely monitoring trends in Oklahoma. Although he is no longer at Waste Analytics, in 2020 when we were introduced Jeff was living in Colorado, and he agreed to come out and help me observe the process of land-spreading in action.

We meet in the back parking lot of a Dairy Queen in Chickasha, southwest of Oklahoma City. Jeff is sporting an orange beard and driving a tricked out Jeep Rubicon, already splattered with orange Oklahoma mud. On the way into town he scouted out a few sites of intrigue. The first is a facility operated by Heartland Environmental Resources. Peeling out of the Dairy Queen parking lot he dials in GPS coordinates.

"In Oklahoma," Jeff explains on the drive, "oil and gas companies have an array of permitted options on where to dispose of drilling waste."

One, oil and gas companies can hire a land-spreading company to spread waste on farm fields, a process the state refers to as land application.

Two, oil and gas companies can send the waste to a commercial facility called a soil farm where it is spread out over the ground, like a horizontal landfill.

Three, oil and gas companies can connect with county officials to spread waste on public county roads, this is called road-spreading or road-application.

Four, oil and gas companies can also contract with a traditional landfill, like the one operated by Waste Management on the east side of Oklahoma City, or pile waste up at a special oilfield waste landfill, typically some dusty pile in the middle of farm country.

And five, oil and gas companies can take the waste to a reuse-recycle facility, which is, apparently, what is happening at Heartland Environmental Resources. There is a pit of black drilling waste, stacks of hay bales, and a worker with a cigarette on a tractor. "I have read the permits for this facility multiple times and I still have no idea what they are doing here," says Jeff, as he surveys the site from the window of his Rubicon.

Jeff has plucked the company's engineering report from an Oklahoma Corporation Commission database. It states: "The process of properly mixing various inert materials with oil and gas exploration and production generated deleterious substances and wastes has been shown to result in a beneficial final solid product that is no longer classified as a waste or deleterious substance."

In Oklahoma, Jeff says, the oil and gas industry has gotten very good at rebranding their toxic waste as something beneficial and kicking the stuff out to farmers, small town public works departments, or as was the case at an Oklahoma recycle-reuse facility run by a company called Polk Operating, golfers.

At least, that was the plan. What tends to happen, Jeff explains, is these companies get overwhelmed with waste, it piles up at their facility, and then they simply need to get rid of it. Polk's product found a home in paving the paths of a public golf course in the southern Oklahoma city of Waurika.

"Their process," says Jeff, "was to bring in drill cuttings, spread them over a drying pad and let the water evaporate, then add fly ash and lime or cement and potentially also certain geotechnical elements for structure to create some type of road material."

"We wish to thank you for your cooperation and generous donations," states an October 2013 letter from Waurika's city manager to Polk. "It is a company like you that benefits a small town and enables us to offer a higher standard of living to citizens that enjoy the game of golf."

Polk's product was also requested by Brad Scott, a fifth-generation Waurika rancher who told the Oklahoma Corporation Commission's Pollution Abatement Department that his family has "been long-time stewards of our land" and he believed putting "recycled drill cuttings and fluids on private ranch roads" represented "progress." Meanwhile, in the nearby town of Ryan, Oklahoma, the high school athletic director, the school superintendent and the five school board members wrote a letter to the Oklahoma Corporation Commission expressing their desire "to utilize Recycled Oil Based Drill Cuttings in the base material for the roads, common area and parking lots at Ryan's athletic complex."

"I know this seems simplistic but think of the process of treating oilfield waste as a black box," says Jeff. "What goes on inside this black box doesn't really matter, and the regulators don't seem really concerned with what goes on inside that black box, as long as something goes on inside that black box."

"People in Oklahoma have a lot of trust in the Oklahoma Corporation Commission," he adds, "and if they say something is approved, then the people are going to say, okay the Corporation Commission has already looked into it, therefore it's safe."

Essentially, Oklahomans have been duped by their own state officials, and the state officials have been duped too. "The regulatory agencies believe everything industry tells them," says Jeff. "I don't think they understand the science of what is going on."

He dials another location into the GPS and meanders the Rubicon around a grid of washboarded county roads of baked red clay and crushed white lime rock, searching for a certain section. The farmland seems endless, and the Rubicon kicks up whirls of dust. Large crickets pop up from the fields and smack against the vehicle. He finds the site, gets out to examine the road surface, and kicks away the top bit of crushed rock to reveal a thick dark goopy layer, which is running off the side of the road as a black ooze. This is drilling waste, and it is regularly laid down on roads by counties in Oklahoma oil and gas country.

The process of road-spreading oilfield waste involves first applying dirt to shape and frame the base of the road. Then a dump truck will arrive fresh from the oilfield and unload drill cuttings right down the middle of the road. The county will come and roll that with a roller, then put over a layer of crushed rock. The result is a sandwich, with standard road base material on bottom and top, and in the middle a layer four to eight inches thick of oilfield drilling waste. “The benefit to the county,” says Jeff, “is there is little to no cost involved.”

I ask him how many miles of road he thinks have received drilling waste in Oklahoma? “I would venture to say in the hundreds to low thousands,” says Jeff. “We haven’t done a firm analysis yet. What I can say is that it is a practice that has gone on for many, many years.”

Jeff knows a thing or two on roads, having worked as an engineer with the Florida Department of Transportation. “If I was going to build a road,” he says, “I would use a material such as lime rock, because lime rock has good bearing capacity. But if I replace lime rock with oilfield sludge, that has poor bearing capacity. So this is not about road building, because the material provides no value and has no utility. This is about another convenient way for the industry to dump their waste.”

The late afternoon light illuminates tiny animal footprints in the oil waste oozing off the side of the road. Not far away is a marsh, and beyond that farmland. Jeff is not aware of any testing the state has done to determine how the application of oilfield waste to roads is affecting nearby wildlife, or crops. “All of this is just leaching into creeks, farms and ranches,” says Jeff. “We have a video of a school bus coming down a road laid with oilfield waste, and dust billowing up behind the bus.”

The practice is entirely legal. Form 1014W with the Oklahoma Corporation Commission defines "Application For Oil or Drill Cuttings Use By County Commissioners." The form asks for the source of the material, the operator name, and whether the material is "waste oil or waste oil residue," "crude oil contaminated soil," "oil-based drill cuttings" or "freshwater drill cuttings." The state instructs for the waste to "be applied in such a manner that pollution of surface or subsurface waters will not likely occur," but there appears to be no means of enforcement. It is, in total, a two-page application.

In Jeff's eyes, it again all goes back to Bentsen and Bevill. "One of the things we've run into for years," he says, "is just because this material is exempt from hazardous waste rules doesn't mean it's not harmful or problematic—it just means it's exempt."

¤ ¤ ¤

Back near Chickasha, Jeff locates land-spreading. Just off the main road and directly adjacent to a field of honey-colored cows is a large drilling rig in action. It is operated by Continental Resources, one of the pioneering companies of America's fracking boom. As the drilling mud and drill cuttings come back up the well to the surface they enter a device called a shale shaker, a vibrating screen that separates out the cuttings from the muds. The industry tries to reuse drilling muds, given the high cost of making them new. The drill cuttings, which have a thick soupy consistency, are spewed into a large metal dumpster called a half-round then transferred with a backhoe to an adjacent red spreader truck. Once filled the red spreader truck takes off and Jeff follows it.

The red truck bends across fields of corn on a set of country roads. Farmers tractor by, sunflowers sway in the breeze, cows laze beneath shade trees. The red truck enters a field and begins driving back and forth in a line, making runs in the soil as would a tractor sowing seeds. Jeff points to a set of white posts with ribbons, "those are his lanes," markers that direct the driver where to deposit waste. No alarm bells going off, no complicated testing procedures, no special hazmat suits and no fancy frills. Just a red truck on a sunny summer day in Oklahoma spreading drilling waste with an unknown chemical and radioactive signature in a farmer's field. "This goes back to the naïve idea," says Jeff, "that dilution is the solution to pollution."

In states like Ohio and North Dakota this type of waste is either brought directly to landfills, or to oil and gas waste treatment centers where workers scoop it around in piles and mix it with other material to lower the radioactivity signature enough for it to be hauled to local landfills. But in Oklahoma none of that is necessary. The waste can be taken directly from the wellhead and spread on pastureland.

Continental has not replied to my lengthy list of questions on the company's land-spreading policies, but Jeff has dug up the files for this particular application of drilling waste. They show waste is to be spread across a few hundred acres, on land belonging to a number of different local farmers. "The going rate last time I checked was roughly a dollar a barrel," Jeff says, "so if you spread 10,000 barrels of waste, you cut the farmer a check for $10,000."

Companies that apply drilling waste in this manner are called soil farmers. Jeff says the soil farming companies often tell owners that the waste is good for the land but this is mostly a lie. There is a type of clay in some drilling muds called bentonite that can help increase water retention of soil. And there is a lime product drilling waste can be mixed with that may add some benefit. But the harms far outweigh any good.

"If that waste was so great for the land, then there would be a market for it and they would be selling it to farmers, not paying farmers to take it," says Jeff. "The fact that much of the waste is soaked in diesel fuel, which is used as a lubricant in many types of drilling muds, should be an immediate red flag. If diesel was beneficial to my land, I would just go buy diesel and pour it out."

There are rules to land-spreading. Title 165, Chapter 10, Section 165:10-7-19 of the Oklahoma Administrative code addresses the practice.

Waste cannot be applied more than once every three years, on steep slopes, and closer than 100 feet to a perennial stream, freshwater pond, lake, or wetland. When the ground is so frozen, or so saturated that "the soil cannot readily take the addition of drilling fluids," land-spreading cannot be done. The Corporation Commission requires tests of drilling waste for salinity and hydrocarbons—such as oil and gas residues—from each well that plans to employ land-spreading be submitted by drilling companies. And the commission has limits on how much waste can be spread per acre. But there is nothing in the regulations that require testing be done for heavy metals, cancer-causing agents like benzene or radioactive elements.

And no one, says Jeff, mentioning one of his personal pet peeves with the practice, "is keeping track of the amount of contaminants that leach over time into the groundwater."

Before we part, Jeff suggests I speak by phone with the president of Waste Analytics, J. Blake Scott, who used to run an oilfield service company and has been in the industry for almost 30 years.

"Please don't misunderstand what I am about to say," Blake tells me. "Waste is an astronomical cost they don't want to pay for if they don't have to, so they spend whatever money it takes lobbying legislators to ensure this material is never regulated, and that costs a lot less than actually paying to deal with the waste in an appropriate manner. This has been the playbook of the oil and gas industry since the beginning."

"There is zero incentive for companies to handle this right," he adds. "I have known for some time that this train would hit a wall."

As for the issue of pits of oilfield waste lurking beneath homes and communities, like Clifford Farms, the problem is far greater than anyone could imagine.

"Because pits don't show up on a home's title, many people are living on top of oilfield waste and don't even know it," says Blake. "I'm talking about a national problem, states where people don't know there was oil and gas, like Florida and Washington, and places like Los Angeles—Los Angeles is like a bomb."

¤ ¤ ¤

One of the companies approved to apply drilling waste from the Continental drill site outside Chickasha is family-owned H.L. Morris Farms. The company's literature says they strive to be a cost-effective solution and believe in safety "while disposing of the waste stream produced by drilling operations in an environmental friendly way." They claim to be "one of the best and most efficient Soil Faming companies in Oklahoma." I call into company president Danny Morris and find a man knowledgeable on the history of land-spreading in Oklahoma and, perhaps not unsurprisingly, in favor of the practice's legitimacy.

"This is what I can tell you," says Danny. "I have been around the oil business a long time and of all the different ways to mitigate the waste stream from a drilling operation, I think that probably land-application is the best."

"The reason we keep doing soil farming is because the farmers like it," Danny continues. "When I talk to a farmer about putting drill cuttings on his land what I tell him is it's a business deal. It's ugly and it's smelly but in the long-term the money that we pay you, it's a fair trade."

He recalls an anecdote from one rancher whose land he has done a lot of work on. When asked what he thought about the practice, Danny says the rancher replied: "This is what I tell people I go to church with, wherever they put that black mud, that is where my cattle graze the hardest, and the grass that doesn't get the mud they don't want it, and I get a check for ten or twenty thousand dollars, and I'm happy."

Danny says that drilling mud used to contain nasty chemicals like formaldehyde, and chromate, a compound that keeps pipes from corroding and is a carcinogen. "Roughnecks used to go out and just dump it in the ground," he says. But you can't do that type of thing anymore. Now, he says, the only "bad" ingredient is caustic soda. "I don't know what it is like in other oilfields, but in Oklahoma safety and environmental steers the ship," says Danny. "For the most part, there is very little they put in drilling mud that has a skull and crossbones, those days are gone."

As Danny tells it, the practice of land-spreading was invented in Louisiana, where drilling waste from offshore rigs was brought to shore and plowed into fields. He says a man named Kenton Burgess popularized the practice in Oklahoma. Kenton ran grain elevators for W.B. Johnston Grain, in the far northwestern part of the state. Drilling for oil here involves very deep holes drilled through layers rich in salt. The salt contaminates the drilling mud, making it difficult to reuse. This created a large amount of waste that needed to be disposed, and operators put it in gigantic pits, but this wasn't always sufficient to contain everything, says Danny.

"They knew the farmers," he continues, "and they knew the famers were starting to go broke." And so oil and gas companies began paying farmers to plow their waste into fields, and Oklahoma land-spreading was born.

Much of the drilling waste initially went on fields of wheat, of which Oklahoma typically produces more than 50 million bushels a year. Danny got into soil farming in 1995, nine years after state rules on the practice were written. He says lobbyists working for the energy company Kerr-McGee ensured these rules were crafted to favor the oil industry. "Every rule was written to protect the oil companies from liability," says Danny. "It had nothing to do with protecting the farmers."

Still, Danny thinks the practice of land-spreading is just fine for farmers. "In Oklahoma, the only environmental impact I have seen," he says, "is the smell from the hydrocarbons evaporating and too much salt." When I remind him that many of the drill cuttings presently being spread on fields in Oklahoma come from the Woodford, and the Woodford is a black shale, and black shales are known to be elevated in heavy metals and radioactivity, and these contaminants are in fact *not* being tested for,

Danny is dismissive. He is also confident this is something he does not have to worry about it.

"We have a RCRA exemption," he says, alluding to Bentsen and Bevill, "and are not required to test for heavy metals and radioactivity."

¤ ¤ ¤

Despite the state's inattention, there is a trail to follow, and there are hints that a public health catastrophe may be unfolding in Oklahoma.

In 1966, British researchers published an article on "the metabolism of radium in dairy cows" that determined "radium might as a result of accidental circumstances enter food chains and constitute a radiological hazard by its transfer to milk."

A 1978 research article published by Charles Garten Jr., a biogeochemist at Oak Ridge National Laboratory in Tennessee, stated one of the most important factors involved in the transport of radioactive elements like plutonium, uranium, and thorium into "terrestrial food chains" was the ability of crops to catch radioactive elements being blown about in the wind. Garten referred to this process as the "fractional interception of particulates by vegetation," but it later came to be known as foliar deposition.

The oilfield waste being spread regularly on fields in Oklahoma is potentially elevated in radium from the brine-soaked drilling muds, uranium and thorium from the drill cuttings, and also the daughters of these elements, including radioactive lead and polonium. These are some of the same radioactive elements present in the waste left behind at uranium mills, where fuel for reactors and nuclear weapons is concentrated from naturally occurring uranium deposits. The U.S. Geological Survey, in a 2011 report, says "it is not known" whether research has been conducted on the uptake of the oilfield's radium into crops and livestock, but the ways in which uranium mill waste can enter the human food chain has been assessed.

Argonne National Laboratory, a Department of Energy facility and one of the US's premier radiological research centers has done significant research into human radioactivity exposure and in 1983 published a paper that assessed ways in which radioactive waste leftover from uranium mills could contaminate humans. "One of the major pathways of radiological exposure," states the report, "is through the beef/milk food chain."

It's simple. Radioactive metals in soil are taken up by plants just like the metals iron and zinc are taken up by plants. Radioactive elements may also be blown by wind off piles of uranium mill waste and deposited on plant leaves—foliar deposition. These contaminated plants are eaten by cows. While eating their meat can be a concern, drinking their milk may be more of a concern.

In one 2012 paper, Slovenian researchers examined a dairy farm located about one-third of a mile from piles of waste leftover from closure of the Žirovski Vrh uranium mine. The concern, said the researchers, was that radioactivity in the waste could be blown by the wind or carried by surface or groundwater to the farmer's fields, where it "can be transported via fodder into cow's milk, which is an important foodstuff for Slovenian people."

The researchers tested the farm's soil, grasses the cows were eating, and their milk, and found the yearly amount of radiation infants would receive from drinking the milk would be about 40 millirem, the equivalent of four chest X-rays. "This study," state the researchers, "provides new data quantifying the transfer of natural radionuclides to milk." In 2017, another set of Slovenian researchers found detectable levels of radionuclides from the uranium-238 decay chain in infant formula made from cow's milk.

Unlike the leftover piles of uranium mill waste in Slovenia, the Oklahoma practice of land-spreading involves intentionally unloading waste directly to a field that beef or dairy cows will graze on. Land-spreading also occurs in Arkansas, Texas, and Colorado. The practice has not been thoroughly examined by US academic researchers. In fact, they have enabled it.

"Drilling fluids, including muds and liquids, can be applied to surrounding land," states the press release for a 2013 article on the practice of land-spreading by researchers at Texas A&M University. "If done properly on soils that can accept these types of materials, no detrimental effects should occur."

When I speak to one of the co-authors by phone, the soil chemist Dr. Tony Provin, I ask him a number of questions on exactly what types of crops receive waste. He tells me that drilling waste is not regularly applied to row crops, like corn and beans, "simply because the timing issues don't seem to work out." Typically, it is Bermuda grass and other range food eaten by cattle that receive the waste, and there "is no requirement for testing of the Bermuda grass or the cattle to see if things are bioaccumulating," says Provin. He says neither he nor his colleagues have ever actually tested the waste being applied to farm fields for heavy metals or radioactivity. When I ask how he can make a determination that a practice is safe when he has not examined all of the likely contaminants, Provin replies: "Fair enough."

I ask if oilfield tank bottom sludge, well-known to be dangerously radioactive, could be put on farm fields too, he replies: "Oh yeah, if there is some nutrients in there we can put it out there." He indicated radioactivity was the jurisdiction of Texas regulators, and says his lab openly suggests to landowners that full assessments of the liquids and solids be made before any discussion of land application. "Our testing aspects with Texas A&M AgriLife Extension Soil, Water and Forage Testing Laboratory," says Provin, "is solely with the potential of salts and nutrients associated with these materials."

I ask the Oklahoma Department of Agriculture, Food and Forestry just how much drilling waste is spread each year on fields, exactly what crops receive the waste, whether it is permissible to spread waste on fields where organic crops are grown, if the agency is monitoring for heavy metals and radioactivity in the waste and crops themselves, and whether or not some of the more highly radioactive oilfield waste streams like sludge and scale are also being spread, but my questions have gone unanswered.

One 2017 paper of Oklahoma State University's agricultural extension does offer a certain clarity, stating, "little to no data is available" on the metals and radioactivity content of drilling mud. So, with no data, and no one gathering data, and no one interpreting data, the amount of radioactivity the spreading of drilling waste onto range and pastureland in Oklahoma has introduced into the American food system and our human bodies remains a mystery.

There has been at least one attempt to look into the matter. Argonne National Laboratory, the Department of Energy radiological lab, published a paper in 1996 that assessed radiation doses across the oil and gas industry. "Landspreading," the paper determined. "Presents the highest potential dose to the general public." But this paper remains hidden from the American public. As far as I can tell, Argonne National Laboratory never issued a press release, and they have not answered any of my questions on oilfield radioactivity.

According to Oklahoma Ag in the Classroom, a program of the Oklahoma Department of Agriculture, Food and Forestry, the Oklahoma State Department of Education, and Oklahoma State University, the state has 440 dairy farms, 82,000 dairy cows, and annually produces 1.3 billion pounds of milk. Milk, in November 2002, was named Oklahoma's official state beverage. And the state's milk travels far beyond its borders. Hundreds of Oklahoma dairy farms "provide milk, cheese, yogurt and other dairy products to residents of Oklahoma, the U.S., and dairy consumers around the world."

If Oklahoma is milk, and Oklahoma is cows, Oklahoma may also be cancer. Statistics of the Centers for Disease Control and Prevention show that Oklahoma has the fourth highest cancer death rate in the nation, behind only Mississippi, West Virginia and Kentucky. My questions of whether the Oklahoma Corporation Commission has enabled a culture to develop that downplays health harms associated with oilfield waste and puts the health and safety of Oklahomans at risk have gone unanswered. But answers indeed may be waiting, in the bodies and bones of Oklahomans themselves. And eventually researchers, shall they choose to investigate, may eventually put together the pieces.

In 2021, a paper published in the journal *Energy Economics* examined two decades of data from 76 Oklahoma counties and found that an increase in the number of fracked wells—those completed with the techniques of modern fracking—led to a statistically significant reduction in life expectancy, an increase in the mortality rate, an increase in cancer, an increase in cardiac diseases, and an increase in respiratory diseases. No state or local newspaper published the findings, lead author Dr. Nicholas Apergis tells me. No state health or environmental official asked him to elaborate.

If you focus your gaze as you drive across Oklahoma, out among the cows, fields of corn and wheat, and oilfields, you will see the cancer centers too, emblems as normalized as the crops and derricks.

There is Cancer Care Associates, Cancer Centers of Southwest Oklahoma, Northeast Oklahoma Cancer Center, Northeastern Oklahoma Cancer Institute, INTEGRIS Health Cancer Institute North, St. John LaFortune Cancer Center, Saint Francis Cancer Center, and Oklahoma Cancer Specialists and Research Institute.

One night, I exit the state to the southwest via Interstate 44. Out there in the dark, I know the cows are still there.

10

Radioactive Liquid Waste on Roads and in Lowe's

Drivers headed south out of Cleveland on Interstate 77 used to encounter an interesting billboard—it advised people to use a product called AquaSalina and said the stuff could be purchased at Lowe's. What exactly is it?

AquaSalina is manufactured with brine from conventional gas wells by a company called Nature's Own Source based in the Cleveland suburb of Brecksville. The product has been used along the Pennsylvania Turnpike, which runs from near Philadelphia past Pittsburgh, and in Ohio, from 2019 to 2021, 1.56 million gallons was applied by the Ohio Department of Transportation to state and US roads and interstates. Dave Mansbery, president of Nature's Own Source, and also the company that helps generate the product, Duck Creek Energy, tells me it's "400 million year old ancient seawater from the Silurian Age" that "contains a perfect natural balance of chlorides uniquely suited for snow and ice management." He told regional news station WKRC that he soaked his sore feet in AquaSalina.

Indeed, AquaSalina has been easily available for personal use. It comes in a plastic jug and has the fun blue-green color of a gas station slushy. The product's front label says it is "Safe for Environment &

Pets" and recommends applying with a garden sprayer on driveways, walkways, and patios to melt ice and also before snowstorms. In 2004, the Ohio Department of Natural Resources issued Duck Creek Energy a Chief's Order to "produce AquaSalina as an alternate disposal method for conventional oil and gas production brine." Thirteen years later, on June 2, 2017, an official with the Ohio Department of Natural Resources entered a Lowe's in Akron, Ohio and purchased a jug of AquaSalina with the aim of testing it for radioactivity. They also purchased a jug from Hartville Hardware in Hartville, Ohio.

Samples were drawn from the jugs, preserved with nitric acid, a chain of custody was established, which is a legal record of the sample's movements, and they were delivered to Pace Analytical Laboratories in Dublin, Ohio. A set of radioactivity testing methods known as EPA Method 903.1 and EPA Method 904.0 were used. Samples are heated on a hot plate to evaporate away water, dried in a drying oven, then cooled in a desiccator. Radioactivity is tabulated by counting the energy different radionuclides release as they decay.

The results Pace delivered back to the Ohio Department of Natural Resources, when listed beside different government radioactivity limits, are striking:

Radium-226 levels in picocuries per liter
Nuclear Regulatory Commission discharge limit: **60**
Level at which EPA defines a liquid as "radioactive": **60**
AquaSalina sample from Lowe's: **1,059**
AquaSalina sample from Hartville Hardware: **1,158**

Radium-228 levels in picocuries per liter
Nuclear Regulatory Commission discharge limit: **60**
Level at which EPA defines a liquid waste as "radioactive": **60**
AquaSalina sample from Lowe's: **604**
AquaSalina sample from Hartville Hardware: **1,333**

Radium-226 and radium-228 combined levels in picocuries per liter
EPA Safe Drinking Water Act limit: **5**

Level at which EPA defines a liquid waste as "radioactive": **60**
AquaSalina sample from Lowe's: **1,663**
AquaSalina sample from Hartville Hardware: **2,491**

A number of researchers I'm in touch with are aware of AquaSalina. "If I had a beaker of that on my desk and accidentally dropped it on the floor, they would shut the place down," says Dr. Yuri Gorby, the former Department of Energy scientist. "If I dumped it down the sink, I could go to jail."

"Every time you put this solution onto your front steps you are basically causing a small radioactive spill," says Dr. Avner Vengosh, the Duke University geochemist, who has examined AquaSalina.

The Youngstown Battalion Fire Chief Silverio Caggiano points out deer, horses and house pets love to lick salt. "What do you think Spunky the dog is doing to the AquaSalina after this stuff dries?" he says. "It is licking it up, then it licks you, it licks the furniture, it licks everything, and people will wonder why 10 years from now Spunky dies of doggy bone cancer."

But the Ohio Department of Natural Resources made no public announcement in 2017 after learning Lowe's and Hartville Hardware were selling a product in their stores containing worrisome amounts of radium.

In 2018, and again in 2019 and 2023, I ask Lowe's how many of their stores carried AquaSalina? If Lowe's outside of Ohio sold the product? If Lowe's was still selling it? Approximately how much AquaSalina they have sold? And if Lowe's has ever tested this product for radioactivity? The company hasn't replied to any of these questions.

Meanwhile, Nature's Own Source has continued producing their perfect blend of salts from "the Silurian Age." And it has kept on snowing.

¤ ¤ ¤

Pacific Northwest Snowfighters may be the nation's most highly respected organization for evaluating deicers and runs products through a variety of tests to earn them a spot on its Qualified Products List. But the group "does not currently test products for radioactive elements," Jay Wells, a Pacific Northwest Snowfighers representative tells me in 2018. Nor does the group track product sources, making it impossible to determine just how many deicing products made from radioactive oilfield waste the organization has already approved. Their Qualified Products List, as of September 2023, had 158 products, and AquaSalina became one of them in 2013. When I ask Pacific Northwest Snowfighters in 2023 if AquaSalina is still on their Qualified Products List, they tell me that list is now managed by a group called Clear Roads. AquaSalina remains on it, and deicing products still are not being tested for radioactivity.

Part of the confusion may be there are so many forms of brine. There are the brines associated with food, like turkey brine, and pickle brine. Some people use the term natural brine, to refer to any brine that comes up out of the ground. Much of the nation's salt supply for road salts comes from massive solid salt deposits located beneath parts of Michigan, New York and Ohio, which when mixed with water forms a liquid deicing solution referred to as brine. This brine is essentially a liquid version of the classic road salt formula and historically has not been expected to contain significant radioactivity.

An interesting relationship has developed between public works departments and the oil and gas industry. Maintaining roads is expensive. Keeping them clear of snow and ice in winter, and dust in summer, represents one of the largest budget items for many rural townships. The lack of regulation around oilfield brine has left the door open for hucksters. And the oil and gas industry has taken advantage by offering local officials and roads departments the free gift of brine.

In 2016, Dave Budd, a former Michigan Department of Transportation official, posted on his blog, Deiceman Dave, about the "Oil Field sales person that shows up at your door" with claims of a superior deicing product. Dave points out that oilfield brine is inconsistent. Even though it may have some compounds that are effective in melting ice or keeping down dust, like calcium chloride, it can be rich with other compounds, like sodium chloride, that "actually adds to the dust problem." Dirt roads ill-applied with this brine can become dustier, and even icy roads can become dusty. Just think of a highway after a big snowstorm and salt trucks have been through, "remember the dust?" Dave asks. "What impact does this have on residents with breathing problems? What impact will this create in the future for our lakes, streams and drinking water?"

When I ask about brine in 2018, the U.S. Department of Transportation says, "we don't track brine hauling" and don't consider oilfield brine "a hazardous material," a designation the industry again has the Bentsen and Bevill exemption to thank for. At the end of 2020 came the prospect of a more rational policy, as President-elect Joe Biden nominated the infrastructure-focused former South Bend, Indiana mayor Pete Buttigieg to lead the Department of Transportation. "Pete Buttigieg," one financial news site stated in 2021, as President Biden signed a historic trillion-dollar infrastructure bill, "is about to become the most powerful transportation secretary ever." But his agency is yet to respond to my questions about spreading oilfield brine on public roads and does not appear to be tracking the issue. Neither is the Nuclear Regulatory Commission or EPA.

This lack of attention by government regulators means deicing and dust suppression products with an unknown radioactive signature will continue to be used on US roads. And it's not just a US problem. From 2001 to 2013, Canadian energy company Junex drew brine from gas wells in Quebec for use as a liquid deicing product they called "natural brine." According to their website they sold the product "to municipalities throughout Québec, Ontario and northeastern United-States."

"New York was interested in using oil field brine," I learn from Dr. Yusuf Mehta, an engineer who in 2012 co-authored a 212-page New York

State Department of Transportation study of liquid deicers. "In the end, our report recommended to New York state that Junex brine was a good product." But spokesperson Joseph Morrissey tells me, "the New York State Department of Transportation does not use Junex brine and never has."

Quebec government spokesperson Daniel Messier says Junex brine was tested in 2013. Radium-226 and radium-228 combined levels were recorded at 3,892 picocuries per liter. These levels would make it illegal for a US nuclear power plant to discharge the stuff into the environment, but it's okay to spread it on a US public road, and apparently a Canadian one too. In 2018, Junex merged with the Canadian energy company Cuda. Matthew Lavoie, a vice president at the new venture, tells me, in a phone conversation that takes place in September 2018, that Junex brine was mainly used in rural Quebec, and that the company, "did not send too much to the US." Where exactly in Quebec, a land of dairy farms, fruit orchards, and eight-month winters the product was spread, neither Quebecois or Canadian environmental agencies have been able to inform me.

Dr. John Stolz, at Duquesne University, and other researchers assessed the practice of applying oilfield brine for snow and ice removal in an urban setting and noted risks may be greater for low-income communities spliced with numerous roads, cancer patients and "pregnant humans." The authors also raised the scenario of someone regularly using a deicer made from oilfield brine without their neighbors even knowing.

Another deicing product, Seneca Mineral LS25, is produced by a company based in Erie, Pennsylvania called Seneca Mineral. Their website says they are a leader in ice and dust control products and specialize in liquid deicers for airport runways, although the site doesn't specify whether or not Seneca Mineral LS25 is applied on runways. According to Dr. Bill Burgos, a Penn State environmental engineer that has tested Seneca Mineral LS25, the product contains elevated levels of radium.

When in 2018 I press owner Sherm Shollenberger on the radioactive signature of his company's deicer he hangs up the phone. A follow-up email solicited a reply from an attorney with the firm MacDonald, Illig, Jones & Britton: "We have no comment at this time and do not wish to participate in your story."

In 2018, a bombshell paper co-authored by Burgos was published in the journal *Environmental Science & Technology*. The researchers found that brine from conventional wells contained not just radium, but cadmium, chromium, benzene, lead, strontium, and arsenic, all potential human carcinogens. Brine-spreading, the researchers determined, released more radium to the environment in Pennsylvania than brine spills—something of a contradiction, as brine-spreading is essentially a drawn-out brine spill.

Burgos and his colleagues revealed spreading oilfield brine on roads, at least as of 2017, when the paper was researched, was legal in 13 US states, including New York, Pennsylvania, Ohio, the Dakotas, Kansas, Indiana, Illinois, Wyoming and Michigan. Brine-spreading, the authors write, could be a significant contributor to local environmental pollution "and has been largely ignored."

Late one September afternoon I find Burgos in his office at Penn State leaning back in a swivel chair, wearing brown slacks, black shoes, and a green plaid shirt. He describes to me just how he learned of the oil and gas industry's sacred art of applying its radioactive waste to roads. While examining documents that showed different ways Pennsylvania disposed of oilfield brine he found a category called road-spreading. "I was like, what is road-spreading?" says Burgos. "Surely no one is *actually* spreading this stuff on the road. But it turns out, that is exactly what they were doing."

Pennsylvania was mainly using brine to keep down dust on gravel and dirt roads. Burgos found this application even more worrisome than winter applications of brine for snow and ice. His research team simulated a dirt road in the laboratory to figure out where all the heavy and radioactive metals go after application of brine and learned that some flowed off and accumulated in ditches. This raised the concern contaminants could be transported to surface water, groundwater or buildup in the soil. "Radium is known to have a strong affinity for clay particles," says Burgos, and dirt roads typically contain at least some clay, raising the specter of radioactive dust.

Dust, says Burgos, is insidious. Dust easily lifts off a dirt road and into the air, coating everything—tires, trees, crops, and also the shoes, clothes, skin and lungs of passersby. Mail delivery people could be particularly at risk. Also joggers, dog walkers and their dogs, and people pushing lawn mowers. All these activities stir up road dust. Which could be enriched in radium from the brine, representing, "an inhalation pathway not even yet considered," Burgos tells me. An evaluation of brine-spreading conducted by his team in 2022 concluded: "When applied as a dust suppressant, oil and gas produced waters were little to no more effective than rainwater."

Indeed, research has emerged to suggest using brine as a dust suppressant is a sham. "There appears to be a complete lack of data indicating the practice is effective," reads a 2018 paper published by Dr. Bryce Payne, of the University of Texas at Arlington. Brine-spreading, the paper notes, helps to break apart the road surface and create more dust.

When the Pennsylvania Department of Environmental Protection attached radiation detectors to the back of a sport utility vehicle and traveled over unpaved roads in parts of the state where brine-spreading has been common they detected above-background levels of radioactivity on most of them, but to my knowledge have conducted no follow-up studies. Burgos found that of the 11 million gallons of brine spread in 2016 on roads in Pennsylvania, more than 95 percent was spread in rural townships in the state's northwest corner.

¤ ¤ ¤

The northwestern corner of Pennsylvania is exactly where Siri Lawson lives with her husband Wayne. During summer, and also much of the spring and fall, contractors pick up oilfield brine directly at the wellhead, says Siri, then head to her area in Farmington Township to douse roads, under the belief it will keep down dust. On a single day in August 2017, 15,300 gallons were reportedly spread. "After Lindell Road got brined, I had a violent response," reads comments in a 2017 lawsuit she brought against the state. "My tongue swelled to the point my teeth left indentations. My sinus reacted with a profound overgrowth of polyps, actually preventing nose breathing." And for nearly 10 days she experienced "excruciating eye, nose, and lung burning." With the help of a community-minded nonprofit law firm called Fair Shake Environmental Legal Services, she won that lawsuit, and in 2018 the practice of brine-spreading was put on hold in Pennsylvania.

Siri, who is in her sixties, holds the excessive brine responsible for worsening previous exposures connected to the oil and gas industry, redefining her life around an endless series of doctor visits, and also keeping her from her profession and passion, working as a horse trainer. She keeps her files on brine the old-fashioned way, heaps of scribbled over folders and photographs, stapled and paper-clipped together and stored in boxes and bins she drags out of a closet. Brine, she says, is spread regularly on roads that abut cornfields, cow pastures, and trees tapped for maple syrup sold at a local farmer's market. "Our township roads became brine dumpsites," she posted on the PA Environment Digest Blog. "There were also reports that tow trucks had to dislodge vehicles that became mired in the brine mud" and "chisels were needed to remove the toxic caked muck."

Siri's cousin-in-law, Blair Miller, happens to be northwest Pennsylvania's most famous brine-spreader. On a hot July day in 2019 I find him seated at his farm outside Columbus, Pennsylvania, with sweeping views of the rolling countryside. At his side is Bandit, a big black dog, and Sabrena, his business partner, originally from Santa Barbara,

California. They met while deer hunting in 2003 and were married on the fifth episode of season two of the Country Music Television show, *My Big Redneck Wedding*. Sabrena has just brought out a collection of wild mushrooms gathered from the wooded hillsides above. There are chanterelle and coral, "you eat that with butter and garlic," she tells me, "tastes like shrimp," and also American Caesar, a bright red mushroom and close relative of the death cap, which shuts down internal organs and was used by plotting family members to murder emperors in ancient Rome.

"Pretty much everything we eat comes right off the farm," says Blair, who wears a camouflaged tank top and has a massive scar across his neck, arm and chest, leftover from third degree burns he received when thrown onto the muffler of a bulldozer while repairing a motocross ramp. He is not necessarily what I would have expected of someone who spreads oilfield waste on public roads for a living. "We raise our own chickens, raise our own beef, hunt our own deer and fish the crick for trout," says Blair. "I'm probably more of an environmentalist than most environmentalists."

It has already been a busy morning for Blair. He has just returned from a septic run at a church, and earlier used his truck to load up waste of the human variety at a nearby summer camp. His tool for the task is a $350,000 black septic tank pump-out truck built by a Pennsylvania truck body-building company called Pik Rite. In yellow lettering on the side it reads, "Cornfield 500," an annual monster truck, auto racing, and food and music festival Blair and Sabrena host on a racetrack at their farm. Naturally, Blair douses the course with oilfield brine, as crashing around monster trucks and drag racing beater minivans on a dirt track tends to be a pretty dusty affair.

Blair and Sabrena see no problem with the practice of brine-spreading. "I been pumping septic tanks since I was four years old," says Blair, a job done with his grandfather, and "driving a septic truck since I was 16." In 2010, he told Pumper Magazine, an industry publication dedicated to trucks that pump things, "I'll never get out of the vac truck business. It's in my blood." But in response to Siri Lawson's lawsuit, in February 2018, the Pennsylvania Environmental Hearing Board ruled that brine-spreading involved disposing of waste without an appropriate Pennsylvania Solid Waste Management Act permit and was thereby illegal, effectively halting the practice not just in Farmington Township, where Siri lives, but across the state. "We're in bankruptcy right now," says Sabrena. And that year's Cornfield 500 has been canceled.

At a conventional gas well, Blair says, explaining to me the process, he would load in brine from the brine tanks, drive to the township where he was permitted to spread it, unload the brine through a spreader bar on the truck's rear at the rate of approximately a truckload every mile, and follow up with a report to the Pennsylvania Department of Environmental Protection. While some bad apple spreaders may douse a road two or three times a week, Blair says he wouldn't spread the same road more than once or twice a year. "The producers of these gas wells can't afford to send their brine to a waste treatment plant," he says. "If they are unable to spread brine on roads, they'd have to shut the wells."

"People don't realize," says Sabrena, "a lot of this brine is more safe than your asphalt."

It's an interesting point. Asphalt is made from a mix of tiny rocks and sand held together with thick black sticky asphalt cement, which is extracted as a part of oil refining, and known to cause severe burns and lesions upon contact, and when heated emits pungent chemical fumes that can cause nausea and vomiting. "Everyone seems to be concerned with the radiation in brine," says Blair. "They are worried about the metals, like arsenic, but most people don't understand there's arsenic in a blade of grass. The earth's not as clean as people think." And in fact, there is arsenic in a blade of grass.

Besides, Blair says, it is illegal to spread brine or flowback from fracking operations, so none of the highly radioactive Marcellus materials are making it onto roads. "We deal with the Bass Island, the Medina, the Oriskany," he says, listing geologic layers that contain conventional oil and gas deposits. But therein lies a problem. State regulators seem convinced that only the brine from fracked layers contain harmful contaminants and radioactivity, and conventional brine is okay to spread. However, this is not necessarily the case.

The U.S. Geological Survey National Produced Waters Geochemical Database is an online map listing the chemical makeup of brine for 114,943 wells across the nation, including oil and gas and also geothermal wells, which produce brine too. It's the most important publicly accessible collection of data on the chemical makeup of oilfield brine, and radium levels in the formations Blair mentions are concerning.

A well in the Medina formation, not far west of Blair and Sabrena's farm in Columbus, recorded combined radium-226 and radium-228 levels of nearly 8,300 picocuries per liter, and nearby conventional wells in the Bass Island formation, just over the state line in New York, show levels in the range of 1,800 picocuries per liter. I point out brine from conventional wells can be dangerous too, but Blair doesn't buy it.

As Blair and Sabrena are speaking a crew of local farmers arrive. They are friends with Blair, and fans of brine. "We couldn't farm without the brine," says the most talkative of three farmers, dressed in red and with big dirty boots. "It's like drinking, if you're gonna drink two bottles of whiskey you're gonna die, and you're eating more radiation out of your banana and steaks," he says. His point seems to be, everything in moderation. "The bottom line," the farmer in red continues, "is how clean is clean? The good lord put the oil, the gas, the coal there, it's all natural."

"If you shut the oil and gas off, how the hell we going to get anything to the stores?" questions Blair. "If you shut them trucks off, how the hell you going to get food to the cities? You're going to be hungry the next day, and you're going to have some hungry people coming out of them cities, and they're going to come to me, because I have a cow."

He picks up a blue and gold macaw named Sky and begins walking around with it. To him and Sabrena, many of the people who make a lot of fuss about environmental issues like brine-spreading don't know a damn thing about the environment and aren't being realistic about their own lifestyle's impact upon it.

Him and Sabrena, on the other hand, know quite a lot. He has spread brine for 30 years, spread it on his own racetrack, and "no one in the area has had an issue."

"We don't have tumors," says Sabrena.

"I take great pride in what I do for a living, and I've never had a complaint from anyone," says Blair. "Trust me, I'm not going to do something that's harmful to my body."

I ask Blair what he would do if he learned that the brine he was spreading really was radioactive. "I would never do it again," he replies immediately. "I need to be able to sleep at night too."

Meanwhile, talking about Blair makes Siri Lawson furious. "It is a complete fucking myth this works, after brine the roads are dustier," she says. "The oil and gas industry has found a legal way to dispose of waste!" And that, in her eyes, is that.

She believes herself, and her husband Wayne too, may die from complications brought on by brine. "It's a helluva way to go," Siri tells me when we speak in July 2023. But there are others she worries about. This part of Pennsylvania has a sizable Amish population. They farm their own crops, run their own stores, and regularly walk the area's dirt roads or travel them in open carriages pulled by horses. One summer day, Siri noticed a group of Amish girls in aprons and blue bonnets who had taken off their shoes and were walking barefoot along a country road. It had been freshly laced with brine.

¤ ¤ ¤

Late one summer evening I drop by the home of LuAnne Kozma and attorney Ellis Boal, in the woods of northwestern Michigan. The activist couple has collected an extraordinary packet of information on brine-spreading, which in Michigan has occurred for nearly 90 years. "One of the biggest problems of the oil industry just now is how to get rid of this brine," reads a 1936 article in the *St. Louis Leader*, a local Michigan paper. Putting it on roads was an easy way to make the waste disappear, and the article notes that "state highway workers" said when it came to keeping down dust, the brine was "working wonders." That same year, the first reports of contamination surfaced. Oilfield brine appeared to be damaging leaves on roadside trees.

A 1953 paper of the Michigan Geological Survey Division, "Salts of the Earth, Brine Disposal Is Oilmen's Headache," provides an important warning. "Surface vegetation including shrubs and trees was destroyed," property damage near brine ponds resulted in numerous lawsuits, streams and lakes were polluted with brine and "damage to fish life followed," groundwater was contaminated, and cities and towns "became alarmed at possible permanent damage to their water supplies because of the escape of sizable amounts of oil field brines."

But the most important thing I learn in Michigan is how hard it is to change a practice that has been written into the culture by a powerful industry. The Michigan Department of Natural Resources had conducted a study in August 1984 which showed that the oilfield brine used on roads contained alarming levels of benzene. Dr. William Cooper, Chairman of the Michigan Environmental Review Board, examined the data and said if they found another industry dumping toxic material like this, "we would have had them in court the next day."

In Plainwell, a city in Allegan County, in southwestern Michigan, the state examined roads under an approved county brine management plan and still found groundwater contaminated with benzene. "This is an extremely high quantity of a known human carcinogen," the state warned. A toxicologist in the Department of Public Health pointed out that as a cancer-causing agent, there should be no benzene in drinking water, and any increase would be expected to increase the amount of cancer in the population, specifically, leukemia.

In 1985, the Michigan Department of Natural Resources issued Special Order 1-85, which halted the use of brine for ice control purposes and laid out a timeline to restrict brine-spreading for dust control based on levels of benzene, toluene, and xylene, and perhaps, eventually, end the practice altogether. “Supervisor’s Order 1-85 is not a hasty, reactionary, total ban on the use of oil field brines,” the state said. “Rather, it is a realistic, reasonable approach to ensure that all necessary parties confront this problem.”

But a group of 24 county road commissions did not see it that way and filed a lawsuit against the Department of Natural Resources. “We desperately need brine restored to control ice on the roads immediately,” testified Henry Wayer, the sheriff of Mecosta County, in central Michigan. He said he was “very fearful that a busload of children or a car full of people will be injured or killed unless the Order banning brine for ice control is lifted immediately.” Dr Thomas Chulski, a professor of chemistry at Ferris State College, in Big Rapids, Michigan, said he was familiar with benzene and other oil and gas byproducts and based on his analysis and opinion, which in the court case’s transcript is just five sentences, he concluded “oil and gas brine may be safely and economically used on Michigan Roads as it has been for 30 years.”

In the end, the Circuit Court for Ingham County handed down an incredible victory for the brine spreaders. The practice could continue, says the 1986 ruling, as long as benzene, toluene and xylene were kept below certain rather generous limits. And the practice of brine-spreading continues in Michigan, for dust and also snow and ice control. Heavy metals and radium are not mentioned in the court ruling, nor are they mentioned in the current rules. Not only is Michigan not testing the oilfield brine applied to public roads for radium, brine in Michigan’s oil and gas formations have been shown by Argonne National Laboratory to have among the highest levels of radium. And Michigan, the state’s geologist specialist Ray Vugrinovich tells me, is not checking to see where brine is being spread and how much is spread over time. "No agency at the State level compiles statistics," he says.

But thanks to Michigan residents like LuAnne Kozma and Ellis Boal information is compiled, like the case of Karla and Bryan Black. On June 4, 2014, Bryan observed an oilfield service company spread several tankerloads of liquid waste on a county road in Benzie County, in northwestern Michigan. "I'm quite concerned about a situation my husband witnessed yesterday," Karla wrote in a letter the following day to the Benzie County Road Commission. "While working on our property that borders the Platte River Watershed, he noticed an oil tanker proceeding north on Lake Ann Road." According to the letter, it geared down, turned east onto Douglas Drive, and commenced spraying. "Besides the strong, noxious petrochemical odor which hung in the air, I noticed that the puddles of rainwater that had collected alongside the road were covered with a bubbly, opaque scum," wrote Karla. She said her nostrils burned for an hour and in the morning she and her husband "were hacking." The county took samples which showed the waste applied to the road was absolutely loaded with benzene—and xylene and toluene.

In May and June of 2012, a potentially even more concerning event occurred, when 54 barrels of fracking waste was spread on camp roads at Mackinaw Mill Creek Campground, a popular spot on the Lake Huron shoreline. Even more waste was spread on roads and trails in a state forest. "Isn't the radioactivity level a concern that should have been communicated to nearby landowners, users, and campers?" Ellis wrote in 2013 to Hal Fitch, Director of the Oil, Gas & Minerals Division of the Michigan Department of Environmental Quality. Surely, Ellis pointed out, "some campground users were children."

Hal Fitch didn't reply, Ellis tells me, and has since retired and started a consulting firm that markets to the energy sector. Lab analysis turned up in records requests filed by LuAnne and Ellis show radium in this waste to be about 40 times Nuclear Regulatory Commission discharge limits. Of course, they don't apply here.

¤ ¤ ¤

In October 2018, at EPA headquarters in Washington D.C., there is a public meeting on oilfield waste and what to do with it all. "The issue of how to deal with the production wastes from oil and gas and turn it into a usable resource is critical," says Deputy Assistant Administrator for Water, Lee Forsgren, opening the meeting.

Many in the lofty EPA room, decorated with a magnificent blue and gold map of America, are entrepreneurs, and have traveled to Washington D.C. in an effort to rewrite federal rules and make it easier for oilfield brine to be used in irrigation or made into commercial products, potentially not so different than AquaSalina. The EPA is yet to issue a final decision on the matter.

Whether or not the federal government gives the entrepreneurs and the oil and gas industry what they want, states are moving forward on their own. Oklahoma, Texas, and New Mexico either have already passed or attempted bills that would make it easier to transform oilfield waste into consumer products. Pennsylvania legislators have pursued a bill that would reverse the decision in Siri Lawson's case and relegalize brine-spreading, and in Ohio, State Representative Bob Young has pushed a bill that would allow products with roughly ten times more radium than AquaSalina to be sold in stores. "We are simply trying to take this environmentally friendly product," stated Young, in a statement he made about the bill, "and make it regulated and accessible for everyday consumers."

But Ohio has also seen something of a reckoning. In August 2021, the Ohio Department of Transportation decided to stop purchasing AquaSalina. In 2022, the Ohio Department of Health analyzed the radiation risks posed by the continual application of a radium rich brine each winter in a residential setting and determined the dose received by an adult or child would be considerable. "Due to the increased levels of human exposure to radiation," the department concluded, "use of products derived from oil and gas production brine is not recommended."

Then there is this. Silverio Caggiano, the retired Youngstown Ohio battalion fire chief, the geologist Dr. Julie Weatherington-Rice, and the late Ohio activist, the tenacious Teresa Mills, formed a Brine Task Force. They have purchased radiation detectors, set up trainings, and are working with a network of local activists and residents to sample the state's most brined roads for radium contamination.

11
Death by Injection

Travelling west across Oklahoma green becomes shades of orange then brown until not far from the Texas border the landscape has formally shifted from prairie to a semi-arid environment. This is Major County, a land of dusty mesas and spiny grasses, and it is here that the Oklahoma attorney Randy Miller, working with a team of geochemists and hydrologists has mapped an underground plume headed toward the Cimarron River. He says the data indicates it is leaking from a pair of injection wells, represents at least twenty years of fracking wastewater, and may extend across an area three times larger than New York City's Central Park. Frack chemicals, toxic levels of salt, and radioactivity may all be infiltrating this arid environment's only reliable water source, a shallow aquifer that historically has been used for drinking water and to irrigate wheat fields. "And they use that wheat," says Miller, "to fatten their cattle."

The waste, Miller believes, is also seeping up into people's water wells, and at least one home basement. In the lower level of one ranch home was found, according to a lawsuit he filed in 2021 in the District Court of Major County, a "white residue" with "chemistry indicative of oilfield produced saltwater."

Miller has worked 40 years in the oilfield sector and represented some of the biggest oil and gas companies on earth, ARCO, Occidental Petroleum, Amoco, Chevron. As fracking, with all of its machinery and chemicals was revolutionizing Oklahoma's oilfields in the 2010s he gave a talk at the University of Tulsa to industry representatives and lawyers on how to profit from the boom and avoid lawsuits: use local labor, befriend community members, keep tabs on anti-drilling county officials and strategically donate to schools and volunteer fire departments.

But Miller has also represented landowners across Oklahoma and Texas whose land has been ruined by the industry, and recently come to acknowledge a new set of truths. The fracking boom has generated way too much liquid waste for the oil and gas industry to safely shove down holes in the earth, and across the country billions of gallons may be leaking out. In few places is the problem more serious than Oklahoma. Like in Texas and North Dakota, out here injection wells for oilfield wastewater are often referred to as saltwater disposal wells. The state has more than 10,000 and injects approximately 200 million gallons of oilfield waste down them each day. "The logical question," says Miller, "is once underground where does that movement of waste go, and where does it end?"

He believes his case in Major County may begin to provide an answer. "The magnitude of what we have discovered," Miller says, "is staggering."

It is all the more staggering because the chief defendant in Miller's lawsuit is Harold Hamm, the legendary Oklahoma oilman and 77th richest person on earth. Hamm was born in Oklahoma in 1945, the youngest of thirteen children to sharecropper farmers. He got his start cleaning oilfield tanks and hauling water in the mid and late 1960s and went on to found Continental Resources, one of the oil and gas production companies credited with helping to kick-start the fracking boom. He has major assets in Oklahoma and also North Dakota, where he helped establish the Harold Hamm School of Geology and Geological Engineering. In 2015, the Western Energy Alliance named

Hamm "Wildcatter of the Year," and in 2016 he received the Horatio Alger award, which "honors outstanding individuals who personify the American Dream." Hamm has been inducted into the Oklahoma Hall of Fame.

"If Harold Hamm did not exist," one fellow inductee, a renown Oklahoma City physician stated, "Oklahoma would have to invent him. Because I can think of no one who better personifies the virtues of our state—hard work, vision, perseverance and public service."

But in the petition filed with the District Court of Major County in January 2021, a handful of landowners and ranchers represented by Miller allege that Hamm, and the defendant companies, misled the Oklahoma Corporation Commission in obtaining one of the injection wells in question, operated it illegally for more than two decades, didn't appropriately inform regulators that the well had been leaking for 16 years and his workers had pumped down thousands of sacks worth of cement to try and fix it, illegally installed a second injection well on the site, misstated to the Oklahoma Corporation Commission about its distance from the property line, misstated the depth of the casing, misstated on forms saying there were no usable water wells less than a mile away when there were several, submitted a "false map" to state officials, sent "false information" to the local newspapers, "reaped illegal profits and unjustly enriched themselves" and perpetrated a "30+ year scheme and artifice to fraudulently cover-up and hide the fact that thousands of acres of once usable shallow groundwater and near surface soils...have been irreparably polluted by oil and gas well produced saltwater and frack flowback fluids."

"This is the cycle of many oilfields," Miller tells me. "There is a boom, quick money made, and what is left behind is the waste."

¤ ¤ ¤

I do not have to go far from Major County to find allegations of another leaking injection well. About 70 miles southeast and back toward

Oklahoma City, in Kingfisher County, is a curious site that has been referred to as the purge. This area is part of a bustling Oklahoma oilfield called the Sooner Trend Anadarko Canadian Kingfisher, or STACK. And it is here that saltwater has been mysteriously flowing out of the earth and into a set of fields owned by two older farmers, Ronald and Donald Schweitzer. They are twins, and I find them at the end of a dusty farm road with matching plaid shirts, seated against the hood of their pickup truck.

"When it first happened all the water went out there," says Donald, pointing toward the edge of his wheat fields. That would have been around April 2019. The waste pooled at the edge of one field, filled a roadside ditch, and poured across the dusty farm road we're presently standing on then entered a creek on the other side lined with hackberry trees. "I noticed those trees didn't leaf out," Donald says. "They were all dead."

That was an important clue something was wrong. But the waste kept moving. It topped the bank on the other side of the creek and flowed through another wheat field, where it meandered its way down to a pond not far from Kingfisher Creek. "Ron was mowing weeds out here and hit a soft spot," continues Donald. "We tasted it, and it was pure salt."

A local news video describes a devilish scene, "highly toxic saltwater bubbling up from below," with images of the purge waste encrusting crops. "It's the worst thing that ever happened," Donald tells the camera. "The earth is cracked," Ronald adds, "and it's following the cracks and came up here."

At one point the flow of waste was about 15 gallons a minute. The Oklahoma Corporation Commission believed that nearby injection wells were the source and had them shut down. The flow dropped but the purge continued, and in August 2020, when I visited, it was continuing. The solution is Sisyphean. The commission installed a pump that directs the flow into a tank which every so often is relieved by a truck that transports the waste to another injection well outside the purge area—later it would be transported there via pipe. "It never stops," says Donald.

As the farmers are talking a man pulls up in an SUV and steps out wearing smart brown shoes, an undone tie, blue jeans, and a red blazer. It is the farmer's attorney, Justin Hiersche, who has just raced out to meet us from Oklahoma City and received a speeding ticket en route. Ronald and Donald are laughing, of course they know the cop.

Attention quickly returns to the purge, which Ronald says is, "one of a kind."

"Corporation Commission really don't know what to do," says Donald.

"This is clandestine under the cover of darkness stuff," adds the attorney Hiersche.

Then Donald says he must go tend cattle and takes his truck on down the dusty farm road to a pleasant spot beneath a stand of trees.

Eventually a formal lawsuit will be filed, and Hiersche will tell the local news: "It's generational land. This is their legacy and they don't want it polluted."

Files he obtained from the Oklahoma Corporation Commission show that from when the agency began collecting data, in July 2019, through the middle of January 2021 the purge coughed up well over a million gallons of saltwater that had a similar chemical profile to oilfield wastewater injected in the area. When I call Donald in early 2024 he tells me the purge has finally stopped, "it's all dried up, they covered the hole back over, and everything is fine now."

¤ ¤ ¤

If Oklahoma is an epicenter for injection wells in the West, in the East it is Ohio. In 2022, Ohio injected just over 22 million barrels of its own oilfield wastewater down injection wells. Plus, the state accepted an additional 12 million barrels of waste from other states. For each barrel of out-of-state waste injected, Ohio receives twenty cents.

"I am writing concerning injection wells and brine disposal issues... now starting to hit closer to home," wrote Donald Poole, General Manager for Tupper Plains-Chester Water District, in Meigs County, in southern Ohio, in a June 2015 letter to the Ohio Department of Natural Resources. "The brine trucks on our roads are running nearly 24 hours a day" and "this waste has hundreds of chemicals, many toxic or hazardous to health and radioactive materials...Our Board feels that we should be told, along with the public, what is in the injected material."

This area was contaminated by the chemical company DuPont and it took many years, lawsuits, and hundreds of millions of dollars to make their water right again. With injection wells, the water district saw a new threat. "There is a great many voices stating this material will never come back to the surface," the letter states. "We have found that this type of argument is somewhat flawed."

The state replied to Tupper Plains-Chester with a letter of their own, defending injection wells. "I can assure you that the disposal of production fluid and brine by injection wells is a proven, effective and safe method," wrote Richard Simmers, Chief of the Ohio Department of Natural Resources' Oil and Gas Division. He said injection was "best appreciated" when viewed in context of the industry's previous disposal methods—discharge to streams and unlined pits. "Through diligent enforcement," Simmers wrote, "Ohio eliminated those unsafe practices and established underground injection as the preferred method of brine disposal."

In 2018 I meet an Ohio brine hauler who goes by the pseudonym Peter. He knows quite a lot about injection wells, as ever since 2014 when he began the job he has deposited waste there. Injection wells don't just receive oilfield brine, and flowback, Peter points out, but vats of chemicals, the refuse water that runs off a frack pad, impoundment and pit waste, various acids, a thick pungent liquid called sludge, and used frack sand that comes back up a well with the flowback and can be any color from "urine orange to jet black." Peter tells me about a set of hauls he made from a gas well in West Virginia that had started upchucking a vile glowing blue goo. That too, whatever it was, went down an injection well. “Any shit they have at the well pad they don’t want any more and will fit in my brine truck,” he says, “is taken to an injection well.”

“Brine haulers,” says Peter, “are considered the lowest of the low in the oilfield. We are replaceable. You can teach a monkey anything you want, and that is how they look at us.”

“There is something in the frack mixture that is fucking with us,” he continues. “I am not saying it is radioactivity, it could be any of the undisclosed chemicals. But I can tell you this, other drivers are getting scared. Guys are wanting to get tested.”

Peter’s health has declined since he took the job. “My fingertips and lower face is numb, like I been to the dentist,” he says. “The joint pain is like fire, and my fillings are coming out.” He knows some symptoms are hard to attribute, like the nausea, constant pressure on his temple, swelling of his lymph nodes, and blood that doesn’t seem to clot as quickly. But what about the heart attack he had not so long ago at a well pad? He was transported to the Emergency Room. Maybe it’s just stress, knowing the job’s dangers and being incapable of preventing them, knowing the risks he’s dumping upon the public and communities, knowing he too breathes air, drinks water and eats food like anyone else on earth yet also knowing he’s pumping her insides full of toxic waste.

There are stranger things too, ones he is reluctant to mention.

“I am going to tell you a secret,” says Peter. “My dick is numb. When I am with the wife I can’t feel shit anymore. And I am not the only driver complaining of this.”

He believes it’s from his hands getting constantly splashed and soaked with fracking waste, then stopping on the road at a gas station or rest area a short time later and taking a pee. “Problem with gloves,” he says. “They are not waterproof, and ones that are can’t do the job right, so you got to take them off.”

I ask Peter if he is worried about injection wells leaking and fracking wastewater getting in drinking water. "Of course it is going to get in drinking water, it's fucking everywhere," he snaps. "This is the cheapest known way to get rid of a cheap product, which if it's handled right is not a cheap product. Everything is contaminated, and it's never going to end until it hits the right person."

"I don't want to be any part of the story," Peter later tells me, "I just want to know, as I have wanted from the beginning, what have I been in? What have I gotten dripped on, splatted on, splashed on, splattered on, sprayed in, what have I been breathing in? What have I been involved with for the last 10 fucking years? What the fuck is inside of me?" But Peter, after years of trying to figure this out, has become jaded. "This country, until it gets a rude fucking enema from throat to ass, is not going to change," he says. "By the time the government gets off their asses, if they ever get off their asses, how much damage has been done that can't be undone? There is no reversing this, ever." So, he has taken things into his own hands.

He began filling up old antifreeze jugs and soda bottles with samples of the oilfield brine and flowback he was hauling and eventually packed a shed in his backyard with more than 40. "I cover my ass," he says. "Ten or 15 years down the road, if I get sick, I want to be able to prove this." In 2019, through a network of Ohio activists, Peter was able to transfer 11 samples to Dr. John Stolz at the Center for Environmental Research and Education at Duquesne University in Pittsburgh, who passed them on to Dr. Daniel Bain, a University of Pittsburgh geochemist. Testing revealed that radium-226 in four samples was above 3,000 picocuries per liter, and one was as high as 7,370. Any liquid waste bound for an injection well containing above 60 picocuries per liter of either radium-226 or radium-228 is considered "radioactive" by EPA. "So why the hell," wonders Peter, "are we driving non-placarded trucks and given no training?"

¤ ¤ ¤

One local woman who has helped Peter is Felicia Mettler. She teaches archery to kids and lives in the rural southern Ohio community of Coolville, home to an injection well that can receive 100 brine trucks a day, or about one every 13 minutes. In 2015 she co-founded a grassroots group called Torch CAN DO to protest the facility and monitor for spills and crashes.

Felicia has trained her two daughters, Autumn and Alexus, into nationally recognized youth archers. The sport involves a keen awareness of one's tools and the local conditions, and she has inspired the girls to command a similar attention to fracking waste. They have picketed in front of the injection well with handmade signs—"STOP INJECTING TOXIC WASTE," "Brine HAS CANCER CAUSING CHEMICALS," "IF TERRORISTS POISONED THE WATER YOU'D BE OUTRAGED." They dressed as monsters for a Halloween "Frackenstine Rally"—it featured a plywood cutout of the governor, painted with a radioactivity symbol over his chest. Inspired by Alice in Wonderland, they dressed as fairies and hosted a toxic tea party, as the brine trucks barreled by. And one afternoon in their backyard the girls conducted interviews with a team of investigative journalists with a TV station from Norway. Alexus even gave a presentation on oilfield brine in school, she was booed by her classmates.

The first indication of a major injection well problem in Ohio emerges in 2019 from two men who operate conventional gas wells in the southeastern part of the state and happen to have the same name. Call them Bob 1 and Bob 2. Their wells supply natural gas to nearby farms and homes, a local school, and some is piped away for use beyond the region. Not so long ago, the Bobs noticed some of their gas wells were over-pressured, and one was spewing an extremely salty liquid more than 50 feet in the air. They suspected leaking fracking waste from nearby injection wells had found its way into their gas wells. And being tax-paying citizens of this land, they expected the government would be concerned and help them with their problem. The Bobs went to the Ohio Department of Natural Resources, the Ohio Environmental Protection Agency, the EPA. And they say no one took them seriously—until they called Felicia.

On a long-lasting June evening in 2021 the Bobs decide to meet her, along with another Torch CAN DO member, at a rest stop along U.S. Highway 50, and Felicia invites me to come along. The highway begins in Sacramento, California, traverses the Rocky Mountains, the heartland, the Appalachians, and ends in Ocean City, Maryland. If travelers in southern Ohio take a break at the rest stop outside Coolville and Torch and glance across the parking lot, they will see the field where Felicia's children have artfully protested, and beyond that the injection well. Brine haulers loaded with waste once parked at the rest stop, though Torch CAN DO, working with other area groups helped stop this practice.

The meeting takes place at concrete picnic tables on a lawn behind the rest stop vending machines. Bob 1 wears a mechanics cap, jeans, well-worn cowboy boots, and a T-shirt with a drawing of an AK-47 on it, the business slogan of a local weapons training complex. "I try not to let any situation get under my skin to the point where it disturbs my sleep," he says, but this situation appears to have disturbed his sleep.

"We met with the chief of the division of oil and gas and the chief kept telling me, we deal in facts," says Bob 1. "He told me four different times, we deal in facts, as if I don't know what I'm talking about. We soon came to the conclusion the state was not our friend in this thing, they wanted to cover it up. I always thought government was corrupt, but I never knew that corrupt."

"That's the problem," says Bob 2, who has a white mustache and camouflaged hunting cap. "They think they're above the law."

Because the Bobs' gas wells have become overrun, they are no longer usable, and the men have lost an important source of income.

"Initially we thought we could talk to the state, tell them what was happening, and they would be reasonable and compensate us," explains Bob 2, "but they didn't want to hear it."

"I paid a million dollars or more in taxes over the years, and that festers me," adds Bob 1, "because I pay taxes to be protected. What they done is criminal."

The enemy to them is not necessarily the people who drilled the wells producing all of the waste, but the injection well operators.

"Our biggest problem," says Bob 2, "is I don't think the state of Ohio has permission to give them rights to pump brine under my property."

"Since I been involved in this, I got a copy of the Constitution, and I been thinking about the 14th Amendment," says Bob 1. He recites: "No state shall make or enforce any law which shall abridge the privileges or immunities of citizens of the United States; nor shall any state deprive any person of life, liberty, or property, without due process of law; nor deny to any person within its jurisdiction the equal protection of the laws."

"Right in that Constitution it says if you impinge upon a man's property you owe him due compensation," Bob 1 continues, "and we here are the one's suffering and it has ruined our property. So, if we can't rely on that Constitution, then I don't know what we can rely on."

He asks for a piece of paper. Felicia provides one, and Bob 1 sketches the location of the Redbird injection well, which is in the community of Belpre, Ohio, and what he believes is responsible for the waste leaking into his gas wells.

Redbird injects into the Ohio Shale, a geologic layer located at a depth of about 3,900 feet. The Bob's gas wells are at a depth of around 1,800 feet, located in a layer called the Berea Sandstone. "That right there told me the Berea sandstone and the shale are communicating," says Bob 1, drawing a little line on his map to connect the two layers. It would mean waste leaking from the injection well is traveling about one-third of a mile vertically through the earth, and at least four miles laterally.

The Bobs have long been skeptical the fracking industry could continuously inject their tremendous amounts of waste underground without it spouting back up some place. "Everyone in their right mind knows they are basically pumping waste into the earth which is porous, how much can you put until it is going to be in our drinking water?" Bob 1 questions. "I can't understand why the state of Ohio doesn't have someone up there with a brain in their head who can figure this out."

"I am just worried about our drinking water," he continues, "if it gets in our drinking water we are done. There is no way known to man and no amount of money on earth that will remove it."

All the while, Felicia is taking notes and nodding. "This is big," she keeps saying. If the Redbird injection well is leaking, the one right behind us here at the rest stop, in her community, could be leaking too—could fracking waste be getting into her family's drinking water?

Down in the meadow below the picnic area are two deer, small does, making their way across the back of the rest stop and toward the injection well. Both Bobs are hunters, but Bob 1 stares at them with love.

"What's that poor little feller down there gonna drink," he says, pointing to one. "We got things that we done wrong, that we need to straighten up," he says. "I hope I'm man enough to realize that we've come to a point in this business where we got to do something right for a change. It seems like an uphill battle, but I have all the cause in the world we will win if justice prevails, if there still is any justice left in this country."

The little meeting is drawing to a close. The sky turns bright orange, deep blue, then purple cracked by shafts of yellow light, and finally a fiery red. For a moment the hustle of trucks and vehicles on Highway 50 recedes, and all is sky and light. It happens to be the summer solstice. Felicia says she will take the information the Bobs have presented and try to ensure the state actually does something about the situation.

"None of us were ever activists," she tells me. "But my job is to protect my children. What is their future going to look like, are they going to be sidestepping puddles of toxic waste near their playgrounds? They have the right to clean drinking water. They have the right to breathe clean air. And it is my job to make sure they have those things. It is my job to make sure they are going to have a future they can live in. I am their mom. We are the protectors."

In June 2020 the Ohio Department of Natural Resources released a report on the Redbird injection well. It turns out the interior of the earth is not filled with tidy storage lockers waiting to accept endless truckloads of toxic waste. The agency found signatures of fracking waste, such as elevated levels of salts, in 8 different conventional gas wells in the area and identified the source as Redbird.

The state's report also mapped out the pathway of contamination. The Bobs were right. Fracking waste had traveled one-third of a mile vertically, and more than five miles laterally through the earth. "Naturally occurring fissures exist between the Ohio Shale formation and the Berea Sandstone formation," the report states, "allowing wastewater to migrate."

¤ ¤ ¤

On June 22, 1969, sparks from a diesel locomotive passing over a Norfolk & Western railroad trestle on the south side of Cleveland ignited a slick of oil and debris on the surface of the Cuyahoga River. The fire, according to a report filed by Cleveland firefighters, "flared up and mushroomed instantaneously."

It was one of at least thirteen significant fires on the Cuyahoga since 1868, but this time a story was published in Time magazine, along with a photo. The image would come to symbolize the transformation of the nation's rivers by American industry into free-flowing sewers of hazardous waste. In December 1970 the EPA was formed and in 1972 Congress signed the Clean Water Act, which aimed to eliminate "the discharge of pollutants into the navigable waters." But where would it all go? The answer came eight years later, with the Underground Injection

Control program, formally established by EPA in 1980. America's new home for liquid industrial waste would be underground.

In 1950, there were four industrial waste injection wells in the US. Today, just counting injection wells that explicitly deal with the oil and gas industry's wastewater, EPA figures indicate there are 181,431, or roughly eleven injection wells for every Starbucks. If you drove from New York City to Los Angeles at 65 miles per hour and lined the highway with them an injection well would emerge about every nine-tenths of a second. "Injection," states an EPA website, "proved to be a safe and inexpensive option for the disposal of unwanted and often hazardous industrial byproducts."

A report published in the early 1990s by the Ohio Department of Natural Resources presents injecting industrial waste underground as a necessary part of modernity: "A quick look at a list of waste generators illustrates how hard it would be for our society to do without the products from these industries. How different our lives would be without steel and metal alloys or the multitude of plastic products! And without modern fertilizers and fungicides, which dramatically increase the yield of our farmlands, the balance of American society...would be altered."

At an injection well, liquid waste is typically first held in tanks, though sometimes pits, then a powerful pump blasts the waste down an eight to twelve-inch-wide hole drilled through earth's geologic layers and into a specific layer, referred to as the injection zone. Indeed, gigantic storage lockers do not exist below the earth, although some rock layers, such as sandstones, made of compacted sand, or limestone, made of compacted shell fragments and corals have quite a lot of empty space between the rock grains, called pore space. These layers are regarded as good for injection, but they are also the layers most likely to already be filled with other things. Such as groundwater, which seeps down from above to fill the pore space, or oil and gas, which seeps up from below.

Injection wells are defined by a set of ideas. One is that the injection zone will be surrounded on top and bottom by impermeable layers that act as seals to prevent waste from leaking out. To create space in the injection zone the waste must displace the other liquid or gas already lodged in the pore space, which means all of that gets pushed somewhere else. Pressures are greater deep in the earth, so waste will naturally compress more at the bottom of the well and therefore take up less space, allowing for even more waste to be crammed in. Injection well operators can further take advantage of this trick of compression by injecting waste at even higher pressures.

But this all comes with extraordinary risks. If waste pushes out of the injection zone, or breaks the protective layer of cement that surrounds the injection well, escaping fluids would seep upwards—because there is typically less pressure up than down—and eventually reach groundwater and the ground itself. Any deep hole, such as a water well, or an oil and gas well, could act as a conduit for the waste, like a soda straw, pulling it even more quickly to the surface.

EPA's Underground Injection Control program characterizes injection wells by the type of waste being injected. Hazardous industrial waste goes down Class I wells. This includes waste pickle liquor from iron and steel production, incinerator scrubber water, lead and corrosive chemical waste-acids, hydrochloric acids, nitric acid, hot acids, agricultural chemicals, slaughterhouse waste, battery solid waste, metal plating waste, laundromat waste, herbicide waste, pharmaceutical waste, pesticides, PCBs, trichloroethylene sludge, hazardous solvents, Agent Orange, dioxins, benzene, xylene and cyanide. Oilfield waste goes down Class II wells. Fluids used in mining to dissolve and extract minerals go down Class III wells. Class IV wells were used to dispose of radioactive wastes, until EPA banned their use in 1984. Class V wells are used for, among other things, septic system waste.

While it may sound well-organized, what Underground Injection Control really did was legitimize the highly questionable practice of stashing waste deep underground by wrapping a system of regulations around it.

"With the ever-increasing mass of waste produced as a result of society's demand for consumer goods, deep-well injection is a mainstay method of hazardous waste disposal for which no true replacement technology currently exists," states a 1996 paper on injection well regulations published by the Texas environmental attorney Earle Herbert. The paper estimated injection disposes of up to 59 percent "of the 290 million tons of hazardous wastes generated in the United States each year."

We have the oil and gas industry to thank for the concept of injection wells. In the early days of the industry, brine brought to the surface with oil and gas was discharged into streams, swamps, fields, pits, culverts, essentially whatever was just beside the well that could easily swallow it up or make it flow away and disappear. These practices led to significant contamination, then during the 1950s an injection process that had been around for decades became increasingly popular. Often there would be a well on each corner of a square and a well in the center, and operators would reinject oilfield brine down the four corner wells in order to push oil lingering in the formation out the well in the middle. This technique was called waterflooding and generated much of the oil produced in the US from the 1950s through the 1990s. Waterflooding got rid of the waste, and helped generate more oil, but over the decades led to significant groundwater contamination.

In the 2000s fracking spread across the nation. So drastically did it alter the way oil and gas was produced the rules had to be rewritten. The techniques of modern fracking involve shooting incredible amounts of chemicals, sand and water down wells. Because not all of it was going to come back up again, this technically makes each fracked well an injection well. The Underground Injection Control program does have rules for drinking water safety, and the nation's unconventional oil and gas boom would have had to follow them. But the Energy Policy Act of 2005 contained a slick incision, famously nicknamed the "Halliburton Loophole," after the oilfield service company run by former Vice President

Dick Cheney. The loophole ensured fracked wells would not legally be considered injection wells, and without it modern fracking would have been impossible.

Still, as the fracking boom came on, there was the issue of what to do with all the fracking wastewater. Tens of thousands of new wells meant tens of billions of gallons more oilfield brine, including billions of gallons of chemically slickened fracking flowback. This deluge led to new injection wells popping up in oil patches across the nation, and older ones being pushed into greater service. The Oklahoma-based Ground Water Protection Council's 2021 report on produced water volumes and management practices shows that America generates just over a trillion gallons of oilfield wastewater a year, and 96 percent of that will be disposed of down an injection well.

These days, because the EPA formerly regulates injection wells under the Underground Injection Control program and has done so for more than 40 years, the takeaway for the American public is that our nation's environmental protection agency is perfectly fine with the process and believes it to be an appropriate way to get rid of industrial waste. But knowledge that injecting waste underground posed tremendous risks has been there from the beginning.

"There is always the danger of subsequent contamination," reads a 1929 report on the *Disposal of Oil-Field Brines*. "If this method is used," states the report, authored by Ludwig Schmidt, a petroleum engineer, and John Devine, an organic chemist, both with the US Bureau of Mines Petroleum Experiment Station in Bartlesville, Oklahoma, "care must be taken that the brines are delivered to a reservoir formation from which migration can not take place with detrimental effect to sources of fresh-water supply."

In the 1980s, EPA's Environmental Research Lab in Ada, Oklahoma extensively researched injection wells. "Unfortunately, hazardous wastes are complex mixtures of materials," states one of the lab's reports on *Injection of Hazardous Wastes into Deep Wells*. "Making it difficult to predict exactly the action or fate of wastes after their injection." A problem, note researchers, is when one hazardous waste stream is "combined with other mixed waste streams, the potential number of interactions increase factorially." Because "subsurface environments often take many years to reach chemical and biological equilibrium, predicting exactly what will happen a priori may be nearly impossible."

A report prepared by a collaboration between researchers at EPA and the Department of Energy and published in 1987 by the National Institute for Petroleum and Energy Research in Bartlesville, Oklahoma presented four main ways in which hazardous waste injected down injection wells might contaminate groundwater. One, an accidental spill at the surface. Two, old oil and gas wells that were never plugged or plugged incompetently provide "an escape route whereby the waste can enter an overlying potable ground water aquifer." Three, waste is injected at such great pressure that it fractures the rocks deep in the earth, "whereby a communication channel allows the injected waste to migrate to a fresh water aquifer." Four, the piping and cement that forms the injection well itself corrodes apart, enabling "the waste to escape and migrate" back up to an aquifer.

These early papers appear to fracture the notion that injection wells are a safe storage locker for industrial waste. But there is more. In October 1970, David Dominick, Commissioner of the Federal Water Quality Administration, which in two months would become part of the brand-new EPA, warned that injection was a short-term fix to be used with caution and "only until better methods of disposal are developed." When EPA laid out its proposed policy on injection wells in 1974 the agency echoed Dominick's concern, stating in an internal statement on the subject that EPA's "policy considers waste disposal by [deep] well injection to be a temporary means of disposal." The statement continues: "Should a more environmentally acceptable means of disposal become available, change to such technology would be required."

But nothing of the sort has happened. Rather, injection wells have become so much a part of the American fabric they have been allowed to operate on the edge of a shopping plaza in Cambridge, Ohio, within eyeshot of a kitchen window in Vienna, Ohio, down the street from a daycare center for handicapped adults in Coitsville, Ohio. And one morning out in West Texas, I observe a food stand selling tacos in the dusty parking lot of an injection well.

In 2020, I ask Dr. Bill Alley, Director of Science and Technology at the National Groundwater Association and former Chief of the Office of Groundwater with the U.S. Geological Survey what eventually happens to all the injected waste. “I have never looked at it in detail,” he tells me. “It’s not a problem that I have any direct experience with beyond textbook type diagrams.”

Eventually I am led to a 1971 talk by Stanley Greenfield, Assistant Administrator for Research and Monitoring at the newly formed EPA, entitled, *EPA—The Environmental Watchman.* Deep-well injection, says Greenfield, is “a technology of avoiding problems, not solving them in any real sense...We really do not know what happens to the wastes down there. We just hope.”

Greenfield provides an analogy: “There may be another parallel with our current concern over dumping wastes at sea. Men have long assumed that, if you take the stuff out far enough and sink it deep enough, no harm will result—that the oceans are so voluminous they can dilute anything to innocuous levels. We know now that this assumption is wrong; the sea is soilable. The earth’s crust is soilable, too, and vulnerable to damage by man’s activities—not only in ways that we may predict and make allowance for, but also in unexpected ways.”

I find an old bound blue book with gold writing that contains Stanley Greenfield’s 1971 talk. It turns out, 53 years ago, the U.S. Geological Survey, together with the American Association of Petroleum Geologists organized a conference on the issue of injection wells and invited the nation’s leading experts. At the symposium on “Underground Waste

Management and Environmental Implications," held December 1971 in Houston, Texas, there are those who express optimism about the practice, such as Vincent McKelvey, Director of the U.S. Geological Survey and the symposium's keynote speaker, who believes "natural pore space" in rock layers beneath the earth should be assigned value. "On the whole," says McKelvey, "we are looking at an underutilized resource with a great potential for contribution to national needs." But largely, the symposium's speakers express concern, and lay out an eerily accurate prediction of the issues to come.

"It is clear," says Theodore Cook, who is with the American Association of Petroleum Geologists and authored the forward to the book containing the symposium's presentations, "that this method is not the final answer to society's waste problems."

Utah geologist Henri Swolfs explains that injecting chemical-filled waste deep into the earth could affect the strength of rocks and alter their frictional characteristics. "The result could be earthquakes," he says, creating fractures that channel waste out of the injection zone.

Tsuneo Tamura, with the Department of Energy says the disposal of radioactive liquid wastes posed "a particularly vexing problem," even in low concentrations.

"My message to you is not a cheerful one," Frank Trelease, a Wyoming law professor, tells symposium attendees. "It is simply this: if you goop up someone's water supply with your gunk; if you render unusable a valuable resource a neighboring landowner might have recovered; or if you 'grease' the rocks, cause an earthquake, and shake down his house—the law will make you pay."

Robert Stallman, a Colorado research hydrologist with the U.S. Geological Survey presents potential consequences from injecting large amounts of liquid waste underground: Groundwater may become polluted, surface water may become polluted, the permeability of rocks may change, the earth may cave in, earthquakes could be triggered, and mineral resources—such as oil and gas—may become contaminated. The available theories on what happens to waste once injected, Stallman says, "are either so simplified that they do not represent the real system adequately, or they are so complex that they have not been tested." Fast forwarding to the present, scientists at Stallman's agency have indeed linked the practice of injection to earthquakes all across America.

But no one appears to have understood the lack of science behind the practice of injection as well as John Ferris, another U.S. Geological Survey research hydrologist.

For one, says Ferris, "the term 'impermeable' is never an absolute... all rocks are permeable to some degree." So the idea that any rock layer could act as a cork to seal off waste is simply wrong. Waste will always and inevitably escape the injection zone, says Ferris, and "engulf everything in its inexorable migration toward the discharge boundaries of the flow system." Meaning, a water well, a spring, an old oil or gas well, a basement drain, even the roots of plants or a seep on the side of the road.

Interestingly, Ferris explains, wells, springs and basement drains might first surge with freshwater, which is being pushed out of the way by the advancing front of waste. But eventually "the sinister laggard— the waste cylinder" arrives, says Ferris. "In time," he continues, this contamination "would become apparent at ever-increasing distances from the injection site."

"Where will the waste reside 100 years from now?" asks Orlo Childs, the Texas petroleum geologist who closed the 1971 Underground Waste Management symposium. It is a rhetorical question, as Childs does not know. "We may just be opening up a Pandora's box," he says, and peers into the future. "Like ripples in a pond, the great question" is "how does man stop the process he has begun?'"

Since the 1971 symposium so much industrial waste has been shot down injection wells in the United States that if you had instead poured it into standard 42-gallon barrels and stacked them atop one another they would have reached Jupiter. And yet, shoved beneath America's farm fields, forests, desert landscapes, and communities, where has all the waste gone?

¤ ¤ ¤

On a snowy winter morning in February 2021, I receive a phone call from Bob 1. He is upset and speaking quick. Between Dexter City and the village of Crooked Tree it appears that fracking waste from another Ohio injection well has found its way into an old gas well and is pouring out at the surface. "Brine is flowing down the hill, going a mile down into the creek, and killing fish," says Bob 1. "I've got more people calling telling me their gas wells are filling up with brine, so this is happening all over Ohio now."

In response to the event near Crooked Tree, in January 2023, the Ohio Department of Natural Resources issues a letter to a company called DeepRock Disposal Solutions, suspending operations at two of their injection wells in southern Ohio. "If the Wells continue to operate, additional impacts may occur in the future and are likely to contaminate the land, surface waters, or subsurface waters," the state concludes. "Thus, the continued operation of the Wells presents an imminent danger to the health and safety of the public and is likely to result in immediate substantial damage to the natural resources of the state."

In June 2023, the Ohio Department of Natural Resources issues another letter, this one suspending operations at the injection well near Felicia—her worst fears have been realized. Here too waste is leaking out from the injection zone and entering into nearby oil and gas wells then flowing back out at the surface, transforming them, essentially, into conduits of fracking waste. In August 2023, I learn of yet another problematic Ohio injection well. Meanwhile, back in the semi-arid ranch country of Major County, Oklahoma, the attorney Randy Miller takes a long, deep breath. "Companies that run disposal wells get paid by the barrel, and if they can put 100 barrels as opposed to one then they get paid 100 times more," says Miller. "So, they put in as much as they can and run 24 hours a day." Continental has not replied to my questions regarding their oilfield waste disposal practices, and my efforts to run questions by Harold Hamm have been unsuccessful. Miller is once again walking the boundaries of the property beneath which he believes is pooling a massive plume of leaking fracking waste.

He is especially worried about all of the fracking flowback being injected, as it contains a cocktail of chemicals, including surfactants, designed to slicken rocks and break them apart, and acids, whose purpose is to dissolve rock and enlarge cracks. No one knows how these chemicals will mix with the salts, heavy metals and radioactive elements in the oilfield brine being injected, and how all of that will mix with things like the vile glowing blue goo brine haulers like Peter have injected.

We have created a thing out of whole cloth, that nature never intended, that did not exist, slapped a name on it, hacked a process out of it, wrapped rules and permits around it, ignored the science, ignored the past, and ignored even our own gut. It is not that hard to predict what is going to happen next, and indeed, is already happening. In Ohio, Oklahoma, and certainly, many other places too—America's injection wells are leaking.

While for Miller, it might mean a lot of work, he is thinking too about the world of his grandchildren. He has been making regular trips out from Tulsa to Major County. In winter temperatures can occasionally drop to -20 Fahrenheit and there are blizzards, but mostly it is hot, and it is dry. Water, Miller believes, is the key to everything.

"Look at the Colorado River, it is running dry," he says. "LA does not exist without water. States all over are fighting for water. It is a finite resource. And our country is headed into an epic drought. Out here in western Oklahoma, the lakes and ponds can't refill fast enough before the sun takes their water. What is going to happen is more and more, we will have to rely on groundwater."

He looks out over the red mesas and fields dotted with cattle, "and we have ruined our groundwater."

SECTION III

12
Did Texas Save America, or Destroy It?

Depending on how one views the current state of the world, Lee Fuller is either America's greatest unsung hero, or the entire planet's number one enemy. Either way, his pen strokes have surely changed the course of history. Until about four years ago, one could find him perennially hard at work, inside a Washington, D.C. office building on the corner of 15th and Massachusetts, where he served as executive vice president of the Independent Petroleum Association of America. Although the story he initiated is still being written, like any good storyteller Lee believes in the importance of context, and prefers to start at the beginning.

In early October 1973, Egypt and Syria attacked Israel on the Jewish holy day of Yom Kippur and the US backed an effort to resupply the Israeli military. In response, Arab members of the Organization of Petroleum Exporting Countries issued an embargo that banned petroleum exports to the United States. This led to gas lines and fuel shortages across the US, and calls for conservation measures, like refraining from putting up Christmas lights. "The embargo," says Fuller, "put out a fairly clear sign that we were now dependent on other countries to supply our critical energy needs."

American oil production was in decline in the early 1970s, somehow the country had to get off foreign petroleum and revitalize its own drilling program. On November 7, 1973, President Richard Nixon announced Project Independence to achieve these goals. Among other measures, the US would need to conserve energy, explore and develop new oil reserves, and relax environmental regulations. "We must recognize," Nixon said, in a special message to Congress, "that a substantial part of our success in building a strong and vigorous economy in this century is attributable to the fact that we have always had access to almost unlimited amounts of cheap energy."

One obstacle to all of this was the environmental movement, in full bloom in the 1970s. American rivers were catching fire from industrial waste, the oceans had been transformed into dumping grounds too, air in urban and rural areas was increasingly choked with smog and pollution, and "midnight dumpers" were making a mockery of the nation's landfill system. These problems helped inspire some of the nation's most important environmental laws, including the Clean Air Act of 1970, the Clean Water Act of 1972, and the Safe Drinking Water Act of 1974.

During the 1970s, Lee Fuller was a chemical engineer at an oil refinery in Houston and in charge of environmental compliance. The job entailed working with EPA on permitting and pollution and introduced him into powerful political circles. Texas was the petroleum heart of America, producing more oil than any other state and housing numerous oil refineries, and there was no greater champion of Texas oil than Texas Senator Lloyd Bentsen.

Bentsen's grandfather had arrived from Denmark to homestead in South Dakota. Plagued by fire, cold, crop failure and poor medical care, the family eventually found a new home amid the lush farmland in South Texas along the Rio Grande, not far from the Mexican border. The region was regarded as a citrus utopia and the family drove the 1,675 miles from South Dakota by car, a 17-day trip, and arrived penniless. Bentsen's grandfather got a job with a wealthy citrus entrepreneur and land speculator and his father eventually became a millionaire himself buying and selling land. He also had interests in oil.

By the time Lloyd Bentsen was born, on February 11, 1921, in Mission, Texas, the family was prosperous, and he was able to carve a prominent path for himself. Bentsen became a pilot in the U.S. Army Air Forces during World War II and eventually came to command a B-24 bomber squadron. He flew nearly three dozen missions, against heavily defended targets, including the Ploiești oilfields in Romania, critical to Nazi war production, and he was shot down twice. In 1948, at the age of 27, Bentsen was elected as a Democrat to the U.S. House of Representatives, making him the youngest member of Congress. In 1970 he narrowly defeated future president George H.W. Bush to become a senator.

He was "heavily supported by oilmen in his Senate campaign" and "definitely came to the Senate as a friend of the oil industry," notes a profile of Bentsen that ran as a 1974 cover story for *Texas Monthly*. He protected oil profits, made sure the industry wasn't taxed too much, "and generally carried their water in myriad small but meaningful ways," including "protecting oil interests in water pollution control hearings."

Bentsen was tall, thin, and handsome, with a deep, soothing voice, and he wore elegant clothes and played poker. His wife was a fashion model, and he would playfully toss her over his shoulder like a sack of potatoes and carry her out of DC parties. "Throughout his career," the *New York Times* wrote, "Mr. Bentsen was helped by the fact that he looked and comported himself like Hollywood's version of a successful politician." After just two years in the Senate, he was given a seat on the powerful Finance Committee. According to newspaper reports, he got the post in large part because the chairman, Louisiana Democrat Russell Long, wanted to ensure continued favorable treatment to the oil and gas industry.

Bentsen also joined the Senate's Environment and Public Works Committee, a less glamorous post but one that would prove potentially even more important for oil and gas. The committee was working to revamp the nation's antiquated solid waste rules under a new law to be called the Resource Conservation and Recovery Act, or RCRA. The issues were complex, and Senator Bentsen was looking to hire an experienced new staff member with a background in environmental regulatory work to handle them. People in Houston suggested Lee Fuller, who in his oil refinery job had dealt regularly with state regulators and EPA.

The Environmental Protection Agency was born in 1970 into a nation overflowing with toxic industrial waste. Injection wells had taken care of the liquid side, by shoving it underground. Now, the Resource Conservation and Recovery Act would take care of the solids, which had become a national crisis. "Most solid wastes are disposed of on the land, a practice that is as yet largely unregulated," stated one EPA report to Congress. The agency estimated that as much as 90 percent of the nation's hazardous waste was being improperly disposed. Poor practices had led to human exposures, water contamination, cropland contamination, damage to wetlands and landfill explosions.

The Resource Conservation and Recovery Act was passed by Congress on September 30, 1976, and three weeks later signed into law by President Gerald Ford. The order had been given from the top to address America's solid waste dilemma, and now EPA had to write the actual rules that would fix the problem. It quickly became clear the agency was overwhelmed. There was "inadequate technical background, insufficient staff...poor management" and a general pattern of "haste, even frenzy," noted Harvard educators who examined the process. "Furthermore, the underlying knowledge of the problem was appallingly limited. No one, inside or outside EPA, even knew what wastes were being generated or by whom, let alone how they were being disposed of or what hazards they posed."

On December 18, 1978, EPA finally published their proposed rules for the Resource Conservation and Recovery Act in an official government journal called the Federal Register. "Congress directed this action" recognizing "disposal of hazardous waste is a crucial environmental and health problem," it states. "Virtually every day, the media carries a story." The most famous one was Love Canal, a neighborhood in Niagara Falls, New York intended to be a dream community. But it was built over a canal that for years the Hooker Chemical Company filled with drums of toxic waste. By 1978, a foul carcinogenic brew had leached into the backyards and basements of 100 homes and a public school. "Everywhere the air had a faint, choking smell," one government official reported, and children returned from play with burns on their hands and faces. There was also a spree of birth defects, including one girl born deaf and with an extra row of teeth.

EPA's new rules were intended to prevent such tragedies. The core of the program would involve tracking waste from "cradle to grave" and separating it into two different categories, hazardous and nonhazardous. Hazardous waste would have to be specially handled at the place where it was created, tracked and transported differently, and workers handling this waste would have to receive more training, protection, and presumably, pay. Trucks loading hazardous waste would have to be appropriately marked, and the ultimate disposal site for the waste as well as any facilities that treated or stored it would have to be carefully regulated and monitored.

It was an attempt to separate industrial waste filled with dangerous toxic contaminants from what was essentially just household garbage and standard office and business trash. Still, an important question remained—what waste would actually be defined as hazardous? EPA provided two definitions. Hazardous waste could cause or significantly contribute to "an increase in mortality or an increase in serious irreversible, or incapacitating reversible, illness." Or the waste could "pose a substantial present or potential hazard to human health or the environment" when improperly treated, stored, transported, disposed of, or otherwise managed.

To scientifically determine if a random pile of oozing sludge was harmful, specific attributes of the waste were to be measured, and a system of thresholds and limits determined. In the proposed rules presented in 1978 EPA listed eight "candidate characteristics" for determining hazardousness: 1. Ignitability, 2. Corrosivity, 3. Reactivity, 4. Toxicity, 5. Radioactivity, 6. Infectiousness, 7. Phytotoxicity, meaning toxic to plants, and 8. Teratogenicity and Mutagenicity, implying birth defects and permanent damage to genetic material.

While all eight characteristics are described in the proposed rules filed on December 18, 1978, in the Federal Register, EPA stated they would only rely on the first four characteristics to determine hazardousness, because these were the ones with good testing protocols available. EPA proposed the rules be expanded to include radioactivity and other characteristics, but that never happened. I have asked EPA for more details on why radioactivity was never adopted as a characteristic for defining hazardousness and am yet to receive a reply. Had that happened, it would have likely changed the course of history, because of the billions of tons of waste produced by the oil and gas industry every single year, much of it is sufficiently radioactive as to have been considered hazardous.

The radioactivity threshold above which EPA considered a waste to be "hazardous" was 50 picocuries per liter for radium-226 and radium-228 combined for liquid waste. Numbers known today show oilfield waste can be vastly more radioactive. Radium in brine of the Marcellus formation was found by the Pennsylvania Department of Environmental Protection to average 9,330 picocuries per liter and be as high as 28,500 picocuries per liter, 570 times EPA's proposed limits for hazardousness. Radium levels in the Antrim formation in Michigan can be almost as high, and radium levels in the Bakken, the Permian and conventional oil and gas fields across the country can still be dozens of times EPA's proposed radioactivity limit for hazardousness.

As for solid waste, EPA had defined hazardous as an average radium-226 concentration of 5 picocuries per gram, but even EPA's website shows radium levels in oilfield sludge can average 75 picocuries per gram and in oilfield pipe-scale be as high as 400,000 picocuries per gram. And I have files from a waste disposal site in West Texas showing radium-226 in pipe-scale from Louisiana as high as 610,420 picocuries per gram, more than 122,000 times EPA's proposed radioactivity limit for hazardousness.

Radioactivity aside, oilfield waste could still at times be corrosive, reactive, toxic or ignitable, the four characteristics for hazardousness that EPA selected. For industry, there was an enormous question of profit and liability riding on the issue of hazardousness. Lee Fuller believed certain industries were at a disadvantage. Mining the earth for fuels like gas and oil produced a significant amount of material. There was all the material dug up to get the fuels out, and also the material removed as these fuels were treated and cleaned for use. While this was technically waste, in Fuller's eyes it was not all necessarily hazardous, although it might be speckled throughout with hazards.

"Our perception," Fuller says, was that labelling oilfield waste hazardous "would have been a disaster," and represent "a substantial threat to the industry's ability to produce oil and gas." To him, overly strict environmental regulations could grind American industry to a halt, wreck the nation's economy, lead to a depression in wages and widespread poverty, and bolster the countries which controlled our energy supply, making the entire nation vulnerable and impacting national security. Clean air and water were certainly in the country's best interest, but someone had to make sure the environmentalists didn't go too far, and the Resource Conservation and Recovery Act provided an opportunity for going too far. Something would have to be done.

On March 22 and 23, 1979, members of the Senate Committee on Environment and Public Works met to discuss EPA's proposed rules for the Resource Conservation and Recovery Act. There was West Virginia Democrat Jennings Randolph, who hailed from a region rich in coal, gas and oil, Edmund Muskie, a well-liked Democratic Senator of Maine regarded as a champion of civil rights and the environment, Republican

Robert Stafford of Vermont, who served in Navy intelligence and was a staunch environmentalist, and Texas Senator Lloyd Bentsen.

Throughout the two-day hearing issues of hazardous waste, garbage, and landfills were discussed and a statement was made by the prominent environmental group, Environmental Defense Fund, but oilfield waste did not prominently come up. Still, EPA's proposed rules for the Resource Conservation and Recovery Act had put the oil and gas industry on alert, and they defended their waste. Texas Senator Lloyd Bentsen did not present at the March 1979 hearing, but he submitted a set of testimonies from Texas industry and state officials.

"There is no proof" of drilling muds and oilfield brine being hazardous, A. W. Dillard, President of the Permian Basin Petroleum Association, told the senators in his submitted testimony. "Probably most materials used in the oil field are toxic to some extent if ingested," Dillard said. "However, if anyone is dumb enough to eat such stuff he is too dumb to work in the oil patch." Dillard insisted the senators, "go to the various state oil and gas regulatory groups, especially the Texas Railroad Commission for information on the proper handling of these materials" and you "will get it."

Comments from the Railroad Commission were included in the material submitted by Senator Bentsen at the March 1979 hearing. The handling and disposal of oilfield waste was "being effectively regulated" in Texas, they stated. "Massive volumes...are handled in Texas each day. Current disposal requirements for these materials prevents contamination of the environment" and there was no data available "to show that additional regulation is needed." In conclusion, the Railroad Commission said, "Texas recommends that produced brines and drilling muds be excluded from EPA's proposed Hazardous Waste Guidelines and Regulations." There was also no need to scientifically examine oilfield waste, as that would "be expensive and, in many cases, of little value."

Lee Fuller says he worked closely with the Railroad Commission on these comments, and four decades later still believes he did right. "The

EPA regulations would have had profound adverse implications for Texas, and Texas regulators were managing the wastes effectively," he tells me. "There was no indication of systematic environmental problems from oilfield wastes managed under the Railroad Commission."

But in the late 1970s, EPA was still a young agency, bold and motivated, and the country as a whole "was looking at environmental issues more aggressively," says Fuller. To him, EPA's proposed rules for the Resource Conservation and Recovery Act were murky, leaving the possibility that some oilfield waste could still end up being labeled as hazardous. Industry does not like regulatory uncertainty, and "EPA could provide no time frame for action or specificity about what it might do," says Fuller. If Congress did not address the issue of oilfield waste, the EPA could not be trusted to do exactly what the oil and gas industry wanted.

If the worst-case scenario happened, and the waste or some parts of it were labeled hazardous, the issue would surely end up in court. But even the prospect of such regulatory overhaul could tilt markets and sour investment, perhaps leading companies to search for oil and gas in countries with less regulation, or maybe even inspire more investment into alternative forms of energy. In comments submitted for the March 1979 hearing, the Railroad Commission said they had met with members of the American Petroleum Institute to evaluate costs of the proposed hazardous waste regulations and determined it may involve, "a one time cost of over $34 billion to bring existing operations into compliance" and "run as high as $10.8 billion per year."

Senator Bentsen decided the most reasonable solution was to offer "an amendment," says Fuller. And as the senator's Environment and Public Works Committee point person on environmental policy, with an expertise on oilfield pollution and regulatory issues, he was tasked to write it. In the end, two major exemptions were written, known together as the Bentsen and Bevill Amendments. The Bevill Amendment was put forward by Democratic Alabama Congressman Tom Bevill, who was born in a coal town and remained a champion of the industry. It exempted combustion wastes from coal and other fossil fuel-fired power plants, cement kiln dust, and mining waste, including that of the phosphate and uranium mining industries. The Bentsen Amendment was the loophole Lee Fuller crafted. It exempted "drilling fluids, produced waters, and other wastes associated with the exploration, development, and production of crude oil or natural gas."

Later, EPA clarified which particular oil and gas wastes were exempt under the Resource Conservation and Recovery Act, defining the list to include most of the wastes the oil and gas industry produced. Filter socks, exempt. Drill cuttings, exempt. Tank bottom sludge, exempt. Sludge from the bottom of oilfield waste pits, exempt. Crud washed off drilling rigs, exempt. Other gunk-filled filters and filth removed from wellhead equipment, exempt. Materials ejected during blowdown operations, exempt. Pipe-scale, loaded with the bone-seeking radioactive element radium, exempt. Pigging waste, cleaned out of gas pipelines across America and often highly radioactive and containing shocking amounts of polonium—exempt. And on it went, no matter how toxic, hazardous, or radioactive, these wastes were exempt, and under US law declared to be nonhazardous.

The oil and gas industry had gotten exactly what it wanted. The Bentsen and Bevill Amendments were adopted by the Senate's Committee on Environment and Public Works on May 15, 1979, passed by the Senate the following month, and signed into law on October 21, 1980, by President Jimmy Carter. "I am pleased today," said President Carter, "to sign the Solid Waste Disposal Act Amendments of 1980, which will significantly strengthen our power to stop illegal hazardous waste practices...and prevent the creation of new Love Canals."

Bentsen served as a US senator for 22 years. In 1988, he was the Democratic nominee for vice president, on a ticket with Michael Dukakis. They lost in a landslide to Bentsen's old rival, George H.W. Bush, and Dan Quayle of Indiana. But his influence in the Democratic Party remained.

President Bill Clinton asked Bentsen to serve as Secretary of the Treasury, and in 1999 he received the Presidential Medal of Freedom, the country's highest civilian award.

There is an interesting addendum. Written into the Solid Waste Disposal Act Amendments of 1980 were instructions mandating EPA to "conduct a detailed and comprehensive study" on the adverse effects, if any, of oilfield waste "on humans, water, air, health, welfare, and natural resources." EPA was to assess how well states were regulating oilfield waste, and the impact alternative means of disposal would have on American oil and gas production. The head of the EPA would then decide whether to pull oilfield waste into the hazardous waste regulations, or enable Bentsen's extraordinary exemption to continue.

¤ ¤ ¤

Carla Greathouse was born in the San Luis Valley in Colorado, headwaters of the Rio Grande River and at 17 left home and worked her way through college. "I had 3 or 4 jobs," she says, "I painted houses, I waited tables, I tended bar, I worked in a liquor store, and after graduating I moved to Wyoming and worked for Amoco Oil, where I learned how a pumpjack works, and my way around a drill rig floor." She attended graduate school at the University of Colorado, earned a master's degree in public administration, then moved to Washington, D.C. in order to find a job where, as she put it to me, "I could make a difference."

"I had a friend from childhood there, so I had some leads," continues Carla. "One was an executive vice president at Versar," an environmental services firm based in northern Virginia that contracted regularly with EPA. And it was Versar that had been hired for the oilfield waste study EPA was mandated by law to conduct. EPA initially had two years to complete the study but was repeatedly late. When Carla interviewed at Versar, around September 1986, EPA was under a federal court order to finish the report within a year. "When they figured out I had oil and gas experience," she says, "I got the job immediately."

The industry had taken their own initiative to develop parts of the report, and while EPA staff were frustrated by this, says Carla, they didn't have any way to go out in the field and figure out just what was happening. "My intention was to take advantage of every second I had to gather accurate information, leave no stone unturned," she says. "I immediately started booking trips to oilfields across the country."

Her first step was to make contact with state regulators, the actual people in the field whose job was to drive around all day and inspect wellheads and drill sites. No one was paying any attention to them yet they dealt with the waste on a daily basis. "My aha moment occurred the second or third trip out, in West Virginia," says Carla. "These two state guys took me all throughout the hills and hollers. They had been diligently documenting violations regarding oilfield waste, mostly affecting people who live in dire poverty. They had this filing room that was more like a closet, chock full of detailed documentation of violations, but for political reasons, very few enforcement actions had ever been brought. So, I spent two days sitting on the floor of this closet going through everything."

Carla found that in West Virginia, the disposal of oilfield waste had led to fish kills, vegetation kills, and the death of livestock from drinking polluted water. In Arkansas, in an area that represented one of the last remaining large tracts of bottomland hardwood forests along the Red River, there were illegal oilfield waste disposal pits and a leaking injection well on land owned by the Arkansas Game and Fish Commission. In Pennsylvania, there were chronic discharges of oilfield waste to streams and in the northwest part of the state, Carla found that in some communities the domestic water supply had been contaminated, like the village of Belmar, where residents complained the water would "burn your eyes in the shower." In Ohio, one case involved Mr. Bean, whose farm and drinking water well was contaminated with drilling waste, and contaminants showed up in milk produced at the farm.

In Louisiana, oilfield waste was reported to have been discharged into a cypress swamp, a sugarcane field, and a roadside ditch in Cajun country that flowed into rice fields and crawfish ponds. In the state's coastal zone, roughly 1.8 to 2 million barrels of oilfield brine were discharged daily, much of it into waterways, and drilling muds from onshore operations containing high levels of toxic metals were discharged into the same Gulf of Mexico estuaries used for commercial fishing. In one instance in the mid-1980s the Glendale Drilling Company, drilling at the intersection of two bayous, was caught discharging drill cuttings and drilling mud adjacent to an active oystering area. This raised concerns with the Louisiana Oyster Growers Association about heavy metals accumulating in oysters and leading to human health problems.

In Wyoming, there was the case of illegal dumping at Pole Creek Ranch northeast of Cheyenne, which involved a stakeout by law officers, who witnessed drilling waste being drained into a pond. In California, Carla learned about the practice of percolation, in which waste is discharged to seasonal streams then diverted to low areas where it was supposed to evaporate away. But in the San Joaquin Valley officers of the California Department of Fish & Game found animals trapped in oily deposits. In Crocker Canyon, California, a spill of oilfield brine mixed with oil killed an estimated 55 endangered giant kangaroo rats, and 10 doves. In New Mexico, an oilfield waste landfill owned by the Bureau of Land Management leaked an underground plume of contamination into the water wells of the nearby Lee Acres subdivision. And saltwater plumes from leaking injection wells contaminated the Ogallala, one of the nation's most important freshwater aquifers. Yet, Carla says, nothing prepared her for America's most northerly oilfield state.

"In February 1987 I landed in Fairbanks, Alaska," she says. "It was the middle of winter, and enforcement officers rarely make field visits that time of year, so all I could do is go through files. The oil and gas industry knew I was in town and the Alaska environmental regulators provided me with a quiet, private space to work in peace, which turned out to be a closet."

"Alaska's oil operations are divided into two separate areas, the Kenai Peninsula in the south, and the North Slope," says Carla. "Both are remote, and the climate is harsh. The North Slope is a wet coastal plain with interconnected tundra ponds and streams underlain by permafrost up to 2,500 feet thick. Production has been underway since the trans-Alaska pipeline, which was built in the mid-1970s and transports oil from the North Slope across the rugged interior to the southern coast. Drilling is expensive and energy-intensive. The only way for civilians to get there is drive the Dalton Highway, which begins north of Fairbanks and is a 400-mile gravel road. The industry flies in 737s and lands on a massive gravel runway. They lease land from the state and federal government and have built islands out into the Arctic Ocean where they also produce oil and gas. It is vast continuous development, the most industrialized place in North America I have ever seen."

"Transportation costs are such that all materials hauled in are permanently deposited there once no longer useful. This includes timber for drill pad construction, empty metal drums of chemicals and general trash. On the North Slope, drilling waste ends up at the Oxbow Landfill, which is located in a vulnerable location. Drilling can only happen when the ground is frozen solid. But enforcement of Alaska oil and gas state regulations is made virtually impossible in the winter because of the near 24-hour darkness. When I was there, in 1987, the North Slope was producing nearly 20 percent of our domestic oil production. If you used oil up and down the West Coast of the US, chances are it was coming from Alaska."

"The window of when you can see what is really going on is during what they call breakup, when everything melts at once. It is literally an overnight event and occurs in June, which was the time of my second visit. All of the ice from the winter breaks up, and the water on the tundra moves for approximately two weeks. The water doesn't go very far, which is a problem because oilfield contaminants accumulate, and the kill zones around these oil and gas sites are permanent. They will never heal. Produced waters are disposed of by injection below the permafrost, and at the time I was there drilling muds and other drilling wastes were directed into unlined gravel pits. During breakup the pits erode and regularly breach their waste out onto the tundra."

Carla found a 1983 study by the U.S. Fish and Wildlife Service which noted tundra ponds near drill sites were frequently contaminated by oilfield waste heavy metals. A 1985 study found bioaccumulation of metals in fish after prolonged exposure to drilling fluids. At a site in the National Petroleum Reserve, in the northern foothills of the Brooks Range, part of a pit wall washed out during spring breakup and oil, grease and the toxic heavy metal chromium leached into a caribou calving ground.

"Companies like Schlumberger and Halliburton, as well as numerous mom and pop oilfield services operate out of an industrial camp called Deadhorse," says Carla, "which, at the time of my visit, was a hodgepodge of Quonset huts. If you are looking for something like a junkyard or an oilfield pipe-cleaning yard in Alaska, go to Deadhorse." In one instance, the Alaska Department of Environmental Conservation discovered that a company operating in the early 1980s, North Slope Salvage, had accepted the delivery of thousands of drums, many still full or laced with oil and chemicals. The drums had been improperly stored, and an unknown amount of toxic, carcinogenic and mutagenic waste was discharged into the tundra.

"In Kenai, Alaska's other main producing region, much of the development has occurred in the Kenai National Wildlife Refuge," says Carla. "Primarily gas is produced, and the produced water is spread on roads in the refuge. The primary solid waste of concern is the drilling muds, which are filled with naturally occurring heavy metals and oilfield carcinogens."

"Kenai is very densely vegetated," she continues, "there are lots of wetlands, abundant wildlife, and groundwater is only a few feet from the surface. We got there and realized we couldn't see a thing and no one was going to show us anything that we didn't already know existed. The enforcement guy in Kenai was a good ole boy who let the industry do whatever they wanted. So we hired a helicopter and spent a day taking pictures of production pads and we spotted this big dump. It was the Sterling Special Waste Site, which is where the oil and gas waste was ending up."

"Working on the oilfield waste report that year, all I did was travel then come back and document what I learned," says Carla. "I was bringing this information together and collaborating with a number of highly trained scientists, including geophysicists, geologists, and toxicologists, then made monthly presentations to stakeholders who had to agree on the content of my report. These included regulators from every oil and gas producing state, representatives from industry trade groups like the American Petroleum Institute, environmental groups, and industry representatives and their attorneys, lots of attorneys. Talk about doing work under a microscope. I was scrupulous."

"Still, strange things started to happen. I was followed. I had my phones tapped. And someone threw a bag of bricks through one of my of colleague's windows. I lived in a sweet little residential area in Alexandria, Virginia and drove an old 1968 Volvo. One morning, I woke up to go to work and all four tires were slashed, and my car was the only one on the block that had been touched. I could never prove who was behind these things, but I had my suspicions. The oil and gas industry had never been challenged on their waste, and I was challenging them."

"Any geochemist knows if you're poking holes in the earth's crust and pulling stuff out, be it oil and gas or mining material, you're going to pull out a lot of other things, including heavy metals and radioactivity. But my clients at EPA reminded me that the Resource Conservation and Recovery Act only covers four waste characteristics, and radioactivity wasn't one of them. I was formally admonished not to go further into the radioactivity question."

Even without considering radioactivity, Carla had gathered enough information to show that oilfield waste could often be hazardous, had caused health harms to humans, animals, crops, and the environment, and continued to pose risks, even when handled according to existing state laws. She didn't advocate for all wastes to be labeled hazardous, for example she believed with oilfield brine, in part because there was so much of it, that would be impractical. But certain facilities, like commercial oilfield waste landfills, and anywhere dealing with the sludge and scale that formed in tanks and pipes should have hazardous regulation.

One morning in late 1987, Dan Derkics, the EPA official supervising her work called Carla into EPA headquarters in Washington, D.C. "Dan was a great guy," says Carla. "He was irreverent, brilliant, funny, and we had worked nose to nose for the better part of a year. I didn't appreciate it until later, but he really stuck his neck out for me. The industry was very uncomfortable that their waste practices were being exposed and didn't want me to continue, Dan is the one who stood in the fire and protected my work." Yet Dan Derkics only had so much power.

"At that meeting he sat me down in his office," says Carla, "and told me we have direct orders from the White House signed by the EPA Administrator which stated what the conclusion would be." None of the oil and gas industry's waste was to be labeled hazardous, all of it would remain exempt.

The conclusions to her nearly 900-page report were, as Carla puts it, "politically altered." These mandated conclusions said defining oilfield waste as hazardous would be "unnecessary and impractical." The industry simply produced way too much waste, there weren't enough appropriate disposal facilities to put it all, or regulators to regulate it. Labelling oilfield waste hazardous would "cause a severe economic impact on the industry and on oil and gas production in the U.S." and "have a substantial impact on the U.S. economy." It would also disrupt the search for new oil and gas deposits in America.

Carla presently lives in a western state with her two daughters nearby, long ago retired from environmental consulting, though hard at work on other important things. After her time writing reports for EPA on some of the nation's most difficult environmental problems, she says she got burnt out, went back to school for teaching, and has spent the last 17 years working with at-risk youths. Carla says teaching is the most gratifying work she has ever done, and occasionally weeps when she describes it. "It is so difficult," she says, "but there is also so much love that comes back to you."

Even though her conclusions were changed, she doesn't denounce her work for EPA in the late 1980s on oilfield waste. She and Dan Derkics spent weeks going through the report to make sure every single line was entirely accurate. And good came from it, including state rules to address oilfield waste contamination along the Gulf of Mexico, and a reaction to the conditions she had uncovered in Alaska. US Senate staffers called on her for decades, as fighting oil and gas development in the Arctic National Wildlife Refuge became one of the nation's most important environmental battles. And to this day, the refuge has not been opened for drilling. Perhaps most importantly, Carla laid down a record for the future, one that would enable journalists like me to follow in her footsteps.

¤ ¤ ¤

I keep digging and find that during the 1960s and 1970s a variety of Texas government agencies produced dozens of reports on oilfield waste contamination. The Texas creeks, rivers, lakes, aquifers, reservoirs, irrigation wells and even municipal drinking water wells that have been tainted—or based on testing were suspected to have been tainted—by the oil and gas industry's waste form a list that is several pages long and runs across much of the state:

the Red River,
the Wichita and
Little Wichita Rivers,

North Fork Buffalo Creek,
a reservoir on the
Oklahoma border
popular for fishing,
camping, swimming
and sailing called
Lake Texoma,
the Canadian River
downstream from
Amarillo,
Lake Fork Creek,
Hubbard Creek, Socagee
Creek, the City of Hawkins in
East Texas whose "water wells
were charged with gas and salt water"
during the summer of 1961 and actually
"yielded drilling mud when pumped,"
Clear Fork of the Brazos River,
and the general Brazos River
Basin, where it was noted that
"injected brine may move
upward along fault zones and
eventually reach surface streams,"
Paint Creek near Haskell,
California Creek near Stamford,
most of the streams in the Hubbard Creek
drainage, the Leon River near
Eastland, Navasota River near Bryan,
Leon River near Hasse,
Big, Cow and Varner creeks
along the lower reach of the Brazos
River, a reservoir between Newcastle and
Graham called Lake Graham, site of the
proposed Breckenridge Reservoir,
Lake J.B. Thomas on the Colorado
River, the Mission River at Refugio
in the San Antonio-Nueces Coastal
Basin, Chiltipin Creek and
the Aransas River,
and Copano Bay,
the Colorado River

all the way to Austin,
the South Concho River,
the headwater reaches of
Pecan Bayou, Beals Creek in
Mitchell, Howard, and Scurry Counties,
the Frio and Atascosa Rivers, the Nueces River,
the Pecos River between Orla and Girvin, where it
cuts through the heart of the Permian oilfield, the lower
reach of Plum Creek, the San Marcos and Guadalupe Rivers,
Elm Creek and Cibolo Creek near Falls City, streams and groundwater
in the Henderson Oilfield of Rusk County on the property of N.R. Dorsey
and R.P. Yandle, the Ogallala one of America's most important aquifers
which supplies much of the southern and central Great Plains with
fresh water for drinking and irrigation including approximately 48,800
irrigation wells and 805 municipal wells and across 48 Texas counties,
found to be widely contaminated from "the mineral contaminants resulting
from oil-field operations which enter the aquifer through seepage from
unlined surface pits" and "are not removed by the natural processes of
ground-water movement and discharge" and over time as ranching and
communities expand into areas where surface disposal of oilfield brine is
practiced "the presence of additional large areas of contamination will be
revealed," Crab and Cedar Creeks in Navarro County, including the tens of
thousands of barrels of brine daily disposed to these creeks by the Powell
Salt Water Company via earthen trenches and small diameter
drain pipes, and also in Navarro County, Cummins,
Post Oak, Chambers and Richland Creeks,
wells used for watering livestock across
Shackelford County, "several areas of
vegetative kill" and the revelation that
"only a small amount of brine entering
a water supply is necessary to change
significantly the chemical character
of the water," Lake Grand and Gonzales
Creek near Breckenridge in Stephens
County and also in Stephens County
large "kill" areas of salt-impregnated
soil and salt deposits, ground
water and water wells
in the Juliana and
West Jud Oilfields
of Haskell and

Stonewall Counties,
water wells used for
domestic consumptions and
livestock in Baylor County,
Cypress Creek and Buffalo
Bayou subbasins in the San
Jacinto River Basin, water
wells on the Edwards
Plateau and in Reagan
County, extensive soil
damage and vegetative
kill in some areas of
Throckmorton County
near the towns of
Throckmorton and
Elbert and also
contamination in water
wells used for domestic
and livestock supplies
in Throckmorton County,
groundwater contamination
in Archer County and
numerous vegetative
kill areas, groundwater
contamination and dozens
of water wells and also surface
vegetation kills several acres in
size in Young County and surface
and shallow ground waters
throughout the drainage
system of the Brazos
River, vegetative
kill areas and
water wells in
Montague
County,
soils
and “native-
quality water”
in some
areas in

Coleman
County,
also vegetative
kill areas that
included "the
absence of
vegetation,
dead trees,
and...salt-
impregnated"
zones and the
destruction of
a pecan orchard,
Little Cypress
Creek and
Glade Creek
near Ore City
in Upshur County,
White Oak Creek
near Mount
Vernon and
Omaha in
Franklin County,
and in Jones County
contaminated
water wells
and ground-
water.

All this information had been available when Senator Bentsen submitted his crucial testimony in the 1979 Senate Committee on Environment and Public Works hearings, in reports of the Texas Water Commission, the Texas Department of Water Resources, the Texas Water Development Board, and the Texas Board of Water Engineers. And yet none of it was presented.

¤ ¤ ¤

In July 2019, I am just off Main Street in the West Texas oil town of Andrews, having a strong black coffee at Cpl Rays Coffee and plotting to follow up on information I have concerning an interesting site in the desert beyond the city limits. Lotus LLC is situated off a dusty road 19 miles west of Andrews, and just several miles from an extensive solar array financed by Facebook that powers the oil giant Shell's fracking operations—and there are even stranger things happening out here in the desert.

Every single day, hundreds of barrels of oilfield sludge, contaminated soil and pipe-scale and other waste may arrive to Lotus from offshore wells in the Gulf of Mexico, some of the last remaining oil and gas platforms off the California coast, oilfields as far away as Pennsylvania, Michigan, North Dakota, and Alaska, and states like Minnesota and Iowa, which have no significant oilfields but are crisscrossed by pipelines that fill up with radioactive sludge and scale. Files I receive in November 2020 via a records request to the Railroad Commission of Texas indicate that ExxonMobil, BP, Chevron, Cabot (now Coterra), Rice (now part of EQT), Devon Energy, XTO Energy, Occidental, ConocoPhillips, Chesapeake, as well as companies that run pipelines and compressor stations like ONEOK, Enterprise Products and Kinder Morgan have all sent radioactive oilfield waste here.

Lotus has permits from the Railroad Commission of Texas that enables this waste to be unloaded into pits, and crushed and mixed with water to form a slurry that can be more easily injected down a set of injection wells and into a salt cavern. Salt caverns, when properly prepared in a process that involves dissolving natural deposits of salt deep underground to create space, have been deemed by the Department of Energy as an appropriate option for the disposal of radioactive oilfield waste. There is no other site like Lotus in the country, and from 1997, when the site opened, through the beginning of 2021 about one million barrels worth of oilfield waste were brought here.

I spend a year researching Lotus and discover a 2000 letter from "Concerned Citizens of Andrews County, Texas" informing the Railroad Commission of what they believed were inappropriately stored drums and tanks, some "marked as radioactive material, and a great many of them bear no markings at all." The letter, addressed to Ms. Jill Hybner of the Environmental Services Section begins: "We regret to write you" a "letter anonymously, but because of the nature of the individual involved, we fear not only reprisal from him personally, but also from his battery of attorneys." A 2003 Railroad Commission inspection suggested Lotus was only using the facility "for storage," and "metal drums with corroded sides and/or bottoms" had allowed some radioactive contents to escape to the ground.

James Dillingham, Lotus's Global Director of Sales and Operations, insists the operation is being run appropriately and according to the laws and regulations of Texas and the United States. He says the lineup of containers and drums I see in aerial photos of the site are being "securely temporarily stored in a restricted area" and in 2021 tells me, "we are currently investing heavily in new technology that will help us process the more difficult types of waste that are plaguing the industry." The Railroad Commission will not directly answer my questions on whether or not the apparent stockpiling of waste at the Lotus site is legal. But no matter, the most shocking revelation about the place is one that is entirely on the books.

On October 12, 2016, Lotus asked EPA whether or not they could import radioactive oilfield waste from foreign countries into the United States. The agency replied on November 7, 2016, stating: "The waste...is exempted from federal hazardous waste regulations" and "as such...may be imported to the United States without a hazardous waste notification."

A month later the Railroad Commission gave Lotus the go-ahead, recognizing that Lotus's permits with the state do not "restrict the acceptance of offshore (outside US waters) or foreign oil & gas waste." A 2018 letter from the Nuclear Regulatory Commission also okayed the shipments, saying because the federal agency has no regulatory authority over the oil and gas industry's radioactive materials, "it would not meet the...definition of radioactive waste."

Lotus's first international shipment was contaminated soil and sludge from Alberta, Canada in November 1999. Between May 2017 and November 2019, Lotus imported 750 barrels of oilfield waste from Australia. These shipments came to the US by ship. Except for the first one, a drum of radioactive oilfield waste from Australia that entered the United States aboard a Singapore Airlines cargo jet, appropriately packaged in a steel drum, arriving to the Lotus facility in the desert west of Andrews on May 8, 2017, and containing radium at concentrations of 2,095 picocuries per gram, thousands of times above general background levels.

Lotus has established an office in England and has a presence in oilfields on every continent but Antarctica. James Dillingham spent two years living in Kuwait, from 2014 to 2016, working on growing the company's Middle East operations. "It has never been our long-term strategy" to import waste, he tells me, "the long-term objective is to help countries develop local solutions."

When I ask, an EPA spokesperson tells me the agency is not keeping track of how much foreign oilfield waste is entering the US, how it enters the country, at which port it enters, or how radioactive it is.

"EPA has no records," they say, "of Lotus importing oilfield waste."

13
The Sickness of Before

If you want to see the rush and bang of an American oilfield kicking out product at a furious pace in the modern age go to the Permian Basin in West Texas, a desert space of small towns and cities that overlies the remains of a 300-million-year-old set of shallow seas. "An open, empty land," reads one West Texas history. "Its arid surface concealing unseen depths wet with oil." Some of America's most notorious oil towns have blossomed in the Permian, places like Midkiff, Iraan, Odessa, Andrews, Midland, Wink. In late September 1925 oil was struck again among the creosote bushes, this time by Fort Worth oilman George B. McCamey. Within months a town was organized, some leases required construction begin within 60 minutes. "I spent an hour looking over a boom town in its infancy," wrote Oscar Waldo Williams, a Harvard Law graduate who visited in 1926. He described McCamey as "unpainted houses...with tin roofs, no lights and no water." There were drilling tools, tents and men, "working in dust, eating in dust, sleeping in dust."

The Orient Railroad had set up headquarters, and new oilfields, pipelines, and storage facilities were in the works. Humble Oil Company, which eventually became Exxon, planned to construct a refinery. Oil stock was sold on street corners and in hotel lobbies. Fortunes were made and lost overnight. McCamey, recalled the veteran oilman Mack McKinney, was the type of place where "it was not unusual to see a Cadillac parked in front of a tent." There was a certain admiration for the process of extracting the fuel itself. "Drilling was an art as much as a science," reads one book about McCamey. "The driller used equipment evolved from primitive tools" and "developed a 'feel' for the way in which the drilling bit chewed into the earth. Like the cowboy and the riverboat pilot, the driller acquired an individualistic style that was admired in the West." Many McCamey folks believed, as one local driller conveyed, "the future would be bright, the sun would shine forever."

There are photographs in the museum in McCamey of the wide dusty early streets lined with Model Ts, Shell Oil's much celebrated Million Barrel Oil Tank, made from 265,000 yards of concrete, Miss Allie V. Scott's 1937 first grade class, the McCamey Badger marching band in 1940, "outstanding athletes" Dale Reynolds and Rayford McIlhaney standing by the track in buzz cuts looking strong and healthy, cheerleaders in a pyramid, Miss Ethie Eagleton and her junior historian club, the Armendarez family and their 56 grandchildren, and Dr. James Cooper, who arrived to McCamey in 1936, set up an office in the back of Echo Drug and later opened his own hospital. "Dr. Cooper was enthused by oil and wildcatting" reads one pictorial history of the area, and drilled several wells himself. In 1979 he was awarded, by the McCamey Chamber of Commerce, "Man of the Year."

Wandering the streets in the early 2020s, McCamey is a main drag of shuttered stores, side streets of simple homes and cactus yards, oilfield junk still piled around, man camp trailers from a more recent boom hastily installed with sand now blowing in the front door. Inside one is a hot plate stove and beat-up bed. A stray cat, a barking dog, a hot wind, and everywhere, dust. Dust and sand. The dust blows over the history, the dust is the history, the dust blows away. But the story is in our bones. And as the sand grains skip in the wind along the desert surface, and the etchings and outlines of booms past are covered over, and even the structures crumble to dust and are gone, sometimes the strangest thing happens. Sometimes, a story that should be lost to time, gets spilled out onto the face of the world.

¤ ¤ ¤

Sir, my name is Linda Cordes Fox, and I was born in 1947 in McCamey, Texas. Born and raised in the middle of the Permian oilfield. I have endured so much pollution in my life and they keep telling me it is not there. I have spent most of my life with sickness around me. And I have spent my life working. I was working so much that until the last few years I didn't realize how poor I was.

What we had in West Texas and what we still have is poor immigrants. You have the families like mine who came over from Ireland and Scandinavia and Germany and they ended up in Texas and the panhandle of Oklahoma. Here come these oil companies and they start pumping and they need towns, and they put towns right on top of where they are pumping oil and tell us we have to live there. I have ridden on those pumps as a kid, they put me up there and I would turn knobs. Everything out there was built like a wooden mobile home. Homes so thin and walls so thin and floors so thin, they don't even have insulation under the flooring. Homes on wood piers right off the dirt, if you had tornadoes you got under there.

My dad was the master butcher at the meat market in McCamey. And I will tell you something which will help you understand us a little better, my dad was what they call a healer. He worked with animals. We used to feed the wild deer behind our house and if they got hurt they would let him work on them. We always had chickens and ducks and dogs and cats and parakeets and bunnies. There were numerous times I had a bunny behind my chair where I ate my meals.

I remember watching the flares. The flares were gray black, and the actual flame would be in the center. It would just boil out. It didn't go straight up, it boiled out, and the heavy gas would settle to the ground.

And the other gases would rise and it would make a cloud over everything. It would be like a wispy cloud, and it smelled like sulfur, and there was also a different smell, very noxious. It would make your eyes and nose burn and drip. You would get a metallic taste in your mouth.

We wore handkerchiefs in the house. It would even seep through the walls. We had wooden windows, and the pollution would come in through the cracks between the windows and the walls. We put cedar tape on the bottom of windows but the smell would still come in. So we put towels along the door but it would still come in. If you opened the window it would be that air there all the time. There was always oil on everything, we would wipe it down. We were close enough to the oilfield that the clouds would smell of oil.

The animals got horrible cancers, and the people got all kinds of cancers too. And vision problems. The whole time I was growing up my mother had poor health. And the whole town of McCamey and especially the women were very diseased. My mom had thyroid issues, all kinds of arthritis, she suffered all but a few years of my life. My grandparents lived a few miles down the road in Crane. And oil wells ran in front of that two-lane highway that went from Crane to McCamey. Then you turned north and ended up in Odessa and Midland. Between McCamey and Crane and Midland and Odessa you had so much oil. My grandad was Irish and German and he had the lust to get that big rig. He put money on every rig he could when he was a young man. He was going to put that wildcat out there and be the next oil millionaire. He worked for the oil companies a long time and ended up sick like everyone else. But that was the golden dream back then.

Because my mom was so ill my grandmom would stay with her, and from the time I was three to the time I was 13, on weekends and holidays and in the summer, I worked in the oilfields with my grandad. He was a mechanic and checked wells and pumps. We used to go to the top of the tanks and my grandad told me stories. We would be way up there, and you could see through the fumes and it would make everything hazy, and you could make up all kinds of tales on what was over that next tank, that next hill. Anything that flew would land on top of the tanks. We found sparrows, doves. I think it was the gas that killed them. We had a mop and we would bring down the dead owls and hawks. We didn't have bags, we had to put their bodies in cans and carry them back down. In the sand below the tanks, we would clean up bunnies.

The tanks would collect the oil and they would also collect the salt water. Oil is lighter and rose to the top of the tank and trucks would come and draw the oil off. The saltwater collected in the bottom and they would open a valve and let it out into the desert. All this stuff was running out into the desert. They called it saltwater, or brine, but I later learned it is not just saltwater, and it is not just brine, it has heavy metals and radioactivity. What they would do is make a grid out of the dirt, like an open pit in the shape of a swimming pool, or sometimes just a rectangle sketched into the sand with little dykes made of sand. And they dropped the saltwater into the open pit, and into the sand. There was no liner. Eventually that water sunk lower and lower and wider and wider. Sunk down into the sand. They did that for years across the whole Permian, from McCamey and Crane to Odessa and Midland. There were fields of tanks as far as you could see, and they let all that brine run into the desert and no one ever tested our water, or tested our air, or tested our soil, or tested our bodies.

There was sludge that formed in the bottom of the tanks too. What they basically did was take it down into an empty area and dig a hole and dump it, and if there was excess they scraped the excess into that saltwater pit. Another job was cleaning what they call scale out of pipes. There was a metal cap on the pipe and you would take that off and stand to the side and the first thing that came out was any liquid left in the pipe. Sometimes it would come out in a long spurt, five to nine feet. Sometimes it would just run out on the ground, and you had to open the cap then back off quick and let it come out. We had a thin strong flattened pipe with an attachment similar to a spoon and my grandad would push this down inside the open pipe and scrape out the residue, like a caking. Sometimes the pipe was more than half covered in this scale, and we would take a pocketknife and scrape it onto the sand and cover it.

The scale had an oily film, so it always got on you some way or another. That was part of the situation. You always had it on your feet and you always had it in the car floorboard. My grandad wore a pair of tan Dickies pants and I wore my cowboy jeans and my long sleeve cotton shirt. If it was hot I had a Mexican hat. Not a sombrero, a real Mexican hat, because it had my favorite brim and it covered my face better. We never had gloves.

Shell built the million barrel tank in McCamey and the town was so proud. It was the largest oil tank in the world. Something like that had not been attempted. They filled it to the top but what they had not thought about was the base. The weight made the tank break open, and it all went into the soil, and it went through the earth. They saved none of it. The walls of the tank were still there, and the high school kids would go party in the crumpled tank. And the oil is still there too, down in the soil. There was no surface water in McCamey, so the drinking water would have had to come from underground somewhere. These things were never considered.

My mom had a brother and he was quite the man, a chemical engineer and World War II bomber pilot. He was in the group to fly the Enola Gay that dropped the bomb on Hiroshima. When they went out that morning they didn't know who was going to fly the mission, they sent several groups and picked the one. He flew in the backup group. And he is the one whose baby died. His wife was also from the Permian, she gave birth and the baby was born with an encephalitic tumor on the brain. They couldn't do anything for the baby at the hospital, so they told my aunt to take her home. It was horrible. I was maybe five years old, and before she died I saw her.

They didn't expect the baby to make it, but that baby actually lived for four months. They had her in a special room at the house and did the best they could to feed her, to hold her. She just didn't respond. It seemed like there was some type of brain malformation, like it didn't finish developing. I remember going to visit and my mother saying, this baby is very ill. She didn't have horrible pain, most days I was there it was like she was asleep. And they were just trying to give her some sustenance. They took care of her the best they could. Later, my uncle's wife died of bone marrow cancer. After that my uncle took a brief respite and broke down and became an alcoholic. Then my mom lost my baby brother.

It was totally unexpected. My mother had a very healthy pregnancy and had gone to term. It seemed to be a normal birth coming. She felt the contractions, and right up until her delivery no one thought there was any problem. But when she came home from the hospital she explained the baby had not been born. It died during delivery. No one ever really discussed it. I believe it was probably similar to what happened to my uncle's baby, that it wasn't fully formed when it was born. That was around 1952 or 1953, at the hospital in McCamey. The doctor was Dr. James Cooper. No one ever saw the body. No one showed my mom nothing, and the hospital never gave a reason for the death.

My mother's health got worse and worse and we finally got her to Scott & White Hospital in Temple, Texas. They said her thyroid had withered up and died and they would have to operate on her, and they did. They took her information and made a journal entry and used my mother's case in teaching. The whole time she was there my mother was always very puffy looking. The pictures I have seen of her, when she was a teenager and in her early 20s, she was not puffy, but by the time she gave birth to my brother who died, she had that puffiness and she had that sallow skin.

My mom had been born in Mexia, an oilfield in East Texas. Then they transferred my grandad down to the Crane-McCamey field, and they lived in a house like a wooden mobile home right off the dirt in Crane. My mom spent her childhood going out in the oilfield just like I did. She had symptoms. Joint pain, nasal problems, all different types of arthritis. If she ate she would pass out. If she didn't eat, she would feel so dizzy she couldn't get up. She was only 27 and her bones were already having problems. Every time you went to a doctor they said, oh, that's just what happens here.

I lived in McCamey up until I was 13 and we moved to central Texas. At age 19 I went to University of Texas in Austin. I lived in Bryan, Texas, right off the Brazos River, a lot of cotton fields, cotton pesticides. At night when the moisture came in you could smell the pesticides. I lived along the Gulf Coast, where they had a very large aluminum manufacturing plant and we were told to always filter the water. I lived in Kountze in Cajun Country in East Texas. They had paper mills, they had every kind of pesticide in the world, and herbicides and fertilizers. In Texas we are told constantly, oh we cleaned up, it's good, we don't have any problem, we don't do it like this anymore.

I have said I am not going to talk about Derek's father and I won't. What I can say is that I do not pick men well. The first two people I ever loved and would have loved to spend my life with got killed, not together, but at different times. I met Derek's—ex-father is what I call him—when I was living at Buchanan Dam, Texas. My parents had a small family-run motel, his parents lived in the area and someone that knew me told him I was the right age and he should come meet me. He literally followed me and followed me and showed up at my house so much and I thought he must be a really nice person, and he wasn't. The best thing I can say is he came into my life at a time when I was on a certain pathway, I had no money and I had nowhere to go and I was trying to keep going to school or get a job or something, and I never did understand about falling in love. I thought you learned to love someone and it always got better. He wasn't good with money and he was a very demanding man, an I want all the attention type of guy. And he was a bullshitter. He would lie when he could tell the truth. Basically, I married a conman.

Derek was born in 1981 at St Elizabeth's Hospital in Beaumont, Texas. I had gastrointestinal issues and some things with my immune system and I had off and on arthritis like my mother and my thyroid wasn't working right, but I had never carried a baby or lost one. I was 32, I walked every day, I ate healthy, I did everything I was supposed to. The doctor who was to deliver that day was out so another doctor delivered. I had to have a C-section, so I didn't know about his hand. Doctors just called it a mutation. They said, oh well these things happen, we'll check his feet, we'll check the other things, okay he is fine.

I took him to seven or eight doctors. Even as a baby he had night terrors. The doctors told me he is just having bad dreams. But it wasn't just bad dreams, he would wake up screaming and say what he saw was horrible. The doctors said you shouldn't go in there, you should let him scream. I tried that one night, and I can still hear him screaming. I said, do MRIs, do CAT scans, and they said they didn't need to, they knew what it was. They diagnosed him with all sorts of psychotic problems. We went to all these doctors and they gave all these reasons.

Derek has no circadian rhythm. When he got older, he would go two or three days without any REM sleep. But at that time he was still making good grades and he had friends. He was very talented in school up through high school, always making A's. He was already writing, and his writing was good. Like he was putting commentary out there on TV, like he wanted to tell the world something. Then in high school he had the brain hemorrhage. We believe what happened is his pituitary ruptured. But they didn't even test him, they just decided he had a psychological problem.

First, 1998 and then 1999 was a horrible two years. Derek's health was so bad and going downhill so fast nothing was going to improve it. I was teaching at Lake Travis, which is outside of Austin, and I was trying to help him, trying to think about what I should do. My husband and I were having more and more problems and finally I said, I can't live with you anymore and you are not helping Derek. I tried to look for people who could help and some of the doctors suggested he come out here, and so in 2000 we came to California trying to find medical help.

I had referrals for a school district in Oceanside, California. I thought that sounds really nice. They said they would love to have me and sent papers. We found doctors at Scripps that were supposed to be better than what we had. We got everything ready. We had a decent house but it didn't get sold right away. We had a Chevy Blazer and put everything we had in a U-Haul trailer and started to California. You know, the wild west man who didn't have anything but the clothes on his back, and he came west for him and his family and he made himself better. That is Derek in his heart. I wanted to make Derek better. We were glad to be leaving Texas. We were hoping for something really good.

There is always the unknown. West Texas is like you are just trying to get through it. Driving through New Mexico is alright. We got to Arizona and it was hot. In Tucson the air conditioner in the motel didn't work. The food was bad. Arizona was a disaster. We finally got to El Cajon, California, where we were to leave the U-Haul trailer. We stayed there that night because it was late and in the morning we went on over to Oceanside and got a room in a Motel 6. And it was right beside the ocean.

I was going to be an English teacher at the high school. We went out to meet the people at Oceanside Unified School District and they said they were sorry, but at that point they no longer had a position for me. They went on and on with the reasons. So that was our trip to California, I had always wanted to live by the ocean, but we ended up in the desert.

I tried several different jobs and they weren't very good. I tried substitute teaching, it didn't pay and it wasn't that steady because you didn't get guaranteed work. I needed enough money for Derek and I to live out there and for me to take care of him and his medical expenses. Then I saw an ad in the paper for a casino on an Indian reservation. It paid more than teaching and I went out to apply. I have never gambled and I have never been in a casino. I convinced the man that I was really good with people and I could learn because I had been a teacher. He said, how many years you been a teacher? I said, twenty. He said, how many subjects? I said, more than I can count on my hands.

So, I took the class for six weeks and became a floor supervisor. I was the one who made sure no one was cheating. If there was a problem, I took care of it. If you needed a hotel room, needed food, I took care of it. I am a people person, and this paid more than teaching. I eventually went from the $15-20 tables to the hundred and $5,000 tables. It was definitely the high rollers section. We had blackjack, baccarat, pai gow. Those were the games people liked, they could make the most money. You had lots of different odds, lots of different kinds of bets you can make. Let me put it this way, gambling can be as benign and fun as possible, or really, really lowdown degenerate. It is what the human makes of it.

I would get up at 1 am for work and Derek was still up. We would eat a little bit together. For him it would be his last meal of the day, and for me it was the first. Then at 3am I would go to work. I worked at the casino 17 years. Although I was around people all the time there was no depth to the interactions, you didn't really have time to get close to those people. Still, I was with people out in the world and Derek was spending the time completely debilitated. He has had a lot of alone time. I on the other hand have had almost no alone time. I either had tons of people in front of me at the casino or there was something happening at home and I had to take care of Derek. So, he and I have had a life of opposites.

Here is our situation, we are in a cage. The million barrel tank in McCamey, they filled it to the top and the bottom sank out. And my mother got sick and lost the baby. And my aunt lost the baby and she died of bone marrow cancer at a very young age. And my mom had thyroid problems all her life and died of pancreatic cancer in November 1986. And my father died of cancer in September 1987. And now my son is suffering and I can't get anyone to help. I saw a photo of a young boy in Ecuador where the US oil companies spilled waste everywhere and people drank radiation and this young boy in the photo has the same deformity as Derek. Mr. Jairo Yumbo. Except Mr. Yumbo has two of his fingers fused together and after Derek's surgery his hand has more like three separate fingers. So, if it is here, and there, then it is all over the world, right? They told those people in the Amazon the oil waste had antiaging properties. They told us things like that in West Texas. We have been told lies, and they expected us to believe them.

There are things I am remembering about being by the wells. I am making notes. Derek is making notes. My son is a grown man now and has so many gifts and so many skills and he was able to do almost nothing. My son has the courage. I am sorry, I am crying now and I am not usually emotional. I just need someone to know that we are not anonymous. I look back, it is mainly for Derek, but it is also for me. And my parents. This story has to be told, over and over. I just want people to know how insidious these companies are because the whole world is dying, and their attitude is they keep up the veneer of the cowboy. So that is what this is really all about. This is about Texas.

I want the people in this country to know what has been done for the almighty dollar. And I am so disappointed with these climatology people. They say they are fighting oil and gas, but they do not even know what oil and gas looks like. They know nothing about this industry. Derek is the best example you can have. His own body, his own person, he is all the information you need. There was a case in Oregon where kids sued the government because in the future these kids are going to have all these horrible things. And the judge said, I am not going to make any decisions because you don't have people being harmed right now. He said you need a real person you can bring in and show me their harm. But they are not looking in the right places. We are the harm.

14
The Lawsuits to Come

To see just where the lawsuits are going to come, look to where the oil and gas industry has already expressed concern. In 1982, the Committee for Environmental Biology and Community Health of the Department of Medicine and Biology of the American Petroleum Institute generated an incredible report entitled, *An Analysis of the Impact of the Regulation of 'Radionuclides' as a Hazardous Air Pollutant on the Petroleum Industry*. It states, "almost all materials of interest and use to the petroleum industry contain measurable quantities of radionuclides," and says regulation of this radioactivity "could impose a severe burden" on companies.

The American Petroleum Institute explains that oil and gas development brings some particularly worrisome radionuclides to the surface. There is radium-226, "a potent source of radiation exposure, both internal and external." There is radon-222 and its immediate daughters of radioactive lead, bismuth and polonium, which with swift half-lives fire off radiation within seconds or minutes and "deliver significant population and occupational exposures" to the lung and pose "the most severe impact to the public health." And there is lead-210 and polonium-210, which are sometimes referred to as the longer-lived daughters of radon. They have longer half-lives and stick around for weeks and years and carry special risks to workers.

This radioactivity, the American Petroleum Institute report warns, is incredibly hard to get out of the industry's waste. Treatment systems, "must recognize the fact that radioactivity can not be modified or made inert by chemical means." Attempts to remove radioactivity risk transforming, "a very dilute source of radioactive materials into a very concentrated source." Meaning even if some operation succeeds in removing the radioactivity, they have inherently concentrated it and now face a new problem, because what are they going to do with that?

And yet, these days the oil and gas industry has been boasting of their ability to treat, recycle and reuse oilfield waste. The most ambitious example may be a $255 million facility called Clearwater, located in Doddridge County, in northern West Virginia, and developed by the Colorado oil and gas extraction company, Antero Resources, and the multinational French waste, water and energy company, Veolia. At one point Yale University had nearly a quarter of a billion dollars invested in Antero, while Veolia is a $23 billion company and has branded itself as a compassionate corporation, fighting climate change and cleaning up pollution. They began as Compagnie Générale des Eaux, founded in 1853 by an imperial decree from Napoleon III, and have global headquarters in the Paris suburb of Aubervilliers in a building known as *Le V* that contains multiple interior gardens and is certified by various sustainable architecture alliances. Clearwater was built to process 600 trucks of oilfield brine and flowback each day.

"It's the best project like this in the world. Bar none. Period," one Antero official told a West Virginia newspaper in 2019. Project descriptions said Clearwater was going to transform 98 percent of the incoming fracking wastewater, "into clean products: salt and freshwater." The water would be reused to frack new wells and the salt, said Antero engineer Conrad Baston at a 2015 community meeting in the Doddridge County courthouse, could be used as a deicer on roads, or even for food.

"If anybody wants some I can get you a big bag of it," he told residents. "I thought about calling it, *Taste of the Marcellus.*"

"This plant, if it works, it would be great," stated the retired industrial electrician and self-taught radioactivity sleuth, Bill Hughes, at the 2015 meeting. "If it's done poorly, if it's not perfectly designed, installed the way it's designed, operated in accordance with standard operating procedures, with a lot of failsafe features, we risk a massive amount of potential water contamination." He reminded Baston, the Antero engineer, that he never addressed "the highly radioactive Marcellus Shale" and asked if this sort of project has "ever been done with Marcellus Shale quality produced water, ever, anywhere?" Baston did not directly answer the question. "Don't lie, don't shove it under the rug," cried another resident. "We don't want another Chernobyl."

The balmy April morning in 2019 I visited Clearwater with Felicia Mettler from Torch CAN DO and Peter, the Ohio brine hauler, we approached the facility from the west on U.S. Highway 50 and immediately noticed a tremendous plume of grayish white steam rising off the plant's cooling towers. It drifted over the highway and became one with the sky. Peter suggested flying through a drone or helicopter outfitted with a Geiger counter. This would have been a good idea, as Clearwater, which began operating in November 2017, by September 2019 had been idled. Whether or not the facility, during its 22 months of operation had drifted a curtain of radioactivity over the West Virginia countryside and locations downwind, like Baltimore and Washington D.C., remains an open question.

When I ran the question by the Vermont-based nuclear physicist and radioactive waste specialist, Dr. Marvin Resnikoff, in 2019, he said the "steam should contain radioactive elements" and may "potentially mix with the hydrologic cycle and fall out as radioactive rain." Bill Burgos, the Penn State environmental engineer, has published several academic articles on Marcellus fracking waste and said the complex chemical makeup of oilfield brine and flowback, including the extraordinarily high salt levels, make it very difficult to treat, and very difficult to remove the radium. "The waste can be filtered with certain types of membranes," says Burgos, but to do this successfully can be expensive, and still may leave operators with a waste product, "rich in radium."

When I ask Carrie Griffiths, Executive Vice President and Chief Communications Officer for Veolia North America, in 2023, if radium from oilfield brine and flowback would have been released in the steam, she tells me, "Air testing was under Antero's responsibility." When I ask her if the steam was ever tested for radioactive elements commonly found in oilfield wastewater, such as radium, she says, "As previously stated, air testing was under Antero's responsibility." Antero has not replied to any of my questions, and I have been asking them questions on Clearwater since 2019.

When I ask the West Virginia Department of Environmental Protection, in 2019, whether Clearwater had a permit to release radioactivity into the air, and whether or not the agency was testing the steam being released for radioactivity, spokesperson Casey Korbini says the agency issues permits in accordance with federal and state air quality statutes, "and radionuclides are not a regulated pollutant under these statutes." He adds, "this does not mean that radionuclides are prohibited; they are simply not regulated."

Clearwater, and what really happened there, remains on my mind, and soon enough more information emerges. On March 13, 2020, Antero filed a lawsuit against Veolia in the District Court of Denver County, Colorado, accusing the company of fraud, breach of contract, gross negligence, willful misconduct, and demanding at least $457 million in damages. "Clearwater was a failure," reads the complaint, the legal document that lays out the lawsuit's allegations. "Veolia promised, a 'turnkey' facility" where Antero would "simply 'turn the key' and have everything function as intended" but "Veolia failed at every turn," the complaint alleges.

According to the complaint, the idling of the plant in September 2019 had nothing to do with a drop in natural gas prices, as Antero told the *Pittsburgh Business Times*, more, as the complaint alleges, "the facility simply did not work." Griffiths tells me: "Veolia has and continues to strongly disagree with Antero's allegations" and "in particular, Veolia emphatically denies that it committed fraud."

When I ask Griffiths in 2023 how radium was removed from the incoming waste, she said Clearwater's treatment process had three parts, a pretreatment system that treated solids and dissolved metals, a thermal system where salts were crystallized and separated from the water, and a post-treatment system where the remaining organic compounds were treated by a biological process. "The pretreatment process precipitated radium-containing constituents through a physico-chemical settling process," she tells me. "The radium-containing constituents exited the stream through the pretreatment system's sludge waste."

In reviewing project permits I learn that Clearwater, during its 22 months of operation, may have produced as much as 144 million liters of waste sludge, and 2.8 billion pounds of waste salt. Where did all this waste go? "The sludge was transported to several disposal sites in the United States," Griffiths tells me. And were salts drawn from the fracking waste ever made into road salts or food? "To Veolia's knowledge, all the salt was disposed of in the landfill adjacent to the Clearwater facility" and "Antero never produced commercially marketable salt," says Griffiths. The West Virginia Department of Environmental Protection has not responded to my repeated questions on the whereabouts of this waste.

In early 2024 I hear from Nick Fischer, who had stumbled across my reporting. He operated a bulldozer at the Clearwater landfill, starting just after the plant came online and working through the day it was idled, burying the loads of soupy salt produced by Clearwater's fracking waste treatment operations. This material, he says, was mixed with fly ash and delivered to him by dump truck. Nick tells me the Clearwater plant never really worked right, no one wore respirators and he was told radioactivity was not a problem he had to worry about. Recently, he has been having breathing difficulties, trouble holding down food, and is losing weight. "I am falling apart, I don't know where to begin," Nick tells me. "The companies are just fighting over the money, I'm stuck holding the radioactive bag at the end of this thing."

Indeed, international and American corporations may battle it out in court over who is at fault, but nowhere does the complaint specifically mention the people and communities of West Virginia who were exposed to the plant's emissions, and the workers who were exposed to its waste. "The oil and gas industry has succeeded in taking this enormous aspect of their operations and making it vanish," says Carroll Muffett, President of the Center for International Environmental Law, a nonprofit legal organization based in Washington, D.C. and Geneva, Switzerland. "Is this recognized in the European public? Almost certainly not, because it is not even recognized in the places where it is happening."

¤ ¤ ¤

In February 2021, a fracking waste treatment facility in West Virginia operated by a company called Petta Enterprises caught fire. A video shows a raging nighttime inferno billowing out of the collapsed building, yet an emergency management official tells me he does "not necessarily" have concerns about radioactivity "because there was no release to the atmosphere." In June 2023, I am back in West Virginia with Jill Hunkler, Executive Director of Ohio Valley Allies, a grassroots group active in communities threatened by fracking across the Marcellus-Utica, a local filmmaker, and Dr. Yuri Gorby, the former Department of Energy scientist. I learn of another fracking waste treatment plant that had recently exploded, Fairmont Brine Processing, and we stop by to check it out. There are no gates, no "No Trespassing" signs and we waltz right in. The plant is set on a hilltop overlooking the city of Fairmont and has been abandoned. It is littered with random debris, including a mattress and also a speed boat, half-sunk in a moat of radioactive water that surrounds part of the charred main structure. A spew of odd brownish dirt has leaked or been ejected out of the burned-out building. We return with protective gear.

"This is all hot," Gorby exclaims, as he explores the site with a Ludlum 3000 Digital Survey Meter. As he approaches the brown dirt the unit issues a terrifying alarm—at around 2 milliroentgens per hour, and EPA later finds levels as high as 3 milliroentgens per hour. This is disturbing, as the facility's empty buildings are covered in graffiti and littered with beer cans and used condoms, indicating the place has become a local party spot. A man in town tells me scrappers have been visiting too, to swipe copper. "They would have been getting dosed," says Gorby. Behind a barbed wire fence, with gaps in it, is a pool of radioactive wastewater that in big rains spills right over the hillside and down toward town. And we find a bathing suit in the parking lot. "Oh my god, did they go swimming?" asks Jill. We take samples across the facility and Gorby and Jill have them tested at a radiological analysis lab and discover the radioactive element radium to be 5,000 times general background levels, making these parts of the site more deeply contaminated with radioactivity than over 99 percent of the present-day Chernobyl Exclusion Zone.

In September 2023, Jill calls me. A former Fairmont Brine worker has gotten in touch with her and would like to speak about their experiences. A few weeks later I head out to southwestern Pennsylvania and meet Sean Guthrie. "I had been working in a state prison 12 years as a contract employee, and they lost the contract," he tells me. Guthrie knew nothing about the oil and gas industry, but local employment had dried up and in 2009 he accepted an entry-level position at a Fairmont, West Virginia fracking waste treatment facility called AOP Clearwater. The year after he took the job the plant shuttered, and in 2013 it reopened as Fairmont Brine, under the ownership of a Pennsylvania firm called Venture Engineering & Construction and Guthrie signed on.

"I felt good about the job and thought we were doing something beneficial for the environment," he says. He was promoted to operations manager but by 2017 the company was having trouble paying debts, and the following spring Fairmont Brine was shuttered. Two co-workers are now dead from cancer—stomach and brain—and Guthrie suffers a range of health issues that have sidelined him from manual labor jobs, led him to sell his possessions to pay expenses, and left him wondering if he has unknowingly clipped his own life short. "I would like to see some accountability," he says.

"The facility was designed in accordance with the codes and regulations at the time," Venture Engineering President and CEO Dave Moniot later tells me. "To our knowledge Fairmont Brine followed all regulations." He says employees received a six-page explainer on radioactivity, but Guthrie and three coworkers I speak to deny ever receiving this document and say radiation hazards were not mentioned, and no one wore dosimeters, the simple radiation safety devices required in the nuclear industry and radiation medical field that measure a worker's accumulated radiation dose. "Venture was very nonchalant," says Guthrie. "They told us while there was radium in it, we weren't concentrating it enough to have it be any kind of a danger."

His story of what happened at Fairmont Brine is remarkable, and an important inside look at what may be awaiting workers and communities at dozens or even hundreds of fracking waste treatment facilities operating across America (amazingly, no agency or group I know of has accurately added them all up). Upon entering the Fairmont Brine facility brine trucks unloaded fracking wastewater, namely oil field brine and flowback, into a large pit—where we had found the half-sunk speedboat and soiled mattress. Workers would mix in material to help sediments in the brine clump together and settle as a sludge at the bottom. The leftover liquids went through a filtration system before being piped underground into the "brine pond"—that pool of wastewater we were worried people had been swimming in—then into the main processing building, where they went through a series of specialized tanks called vapor liquid separators that helped separate the salts from the water, which was piped into a second impoundment and after testing for certain contaminants under permitting known as the National Pollutant Discharge Elimination System or NPDES, discharged through a pipe into the Monongahela River.

But problems, Guthrie and his coworkers tell me, were many. Sludge that accumulated in the pits where brine trucks dumped their wastewater was too radioactive to take to local landfills. This led to a situation, reported in 2016 by the Kentucky Department of Environmental Protection, where sealed containers of radioactive oilfield waste were illegally disposed at a landfill across the road from an eastern Kentucky high school and middle school. The brine pond experienced issues too, Guthrie recalls an incident when a rip was detected in the liner and a worker was tasked with diving down to the bottom to make the repair. "They had to put weights on him to get him to go down," says Guthrie, because the man was having trouble descending through the dense salty water.

In the main processing building the salt slurry being transported on conveyor belts between vessels routinely fell off and accumulated on the floor. This mess had to be shoveled away, and the task soaked workers in the material. Salty dust in the air was so thick, they recall, the workspace often appeared as if trapped in a haze. With no face masks or respirators, the men were forced to breathe it in. "The ventilation in that entire building was shit," says Guthrie. "Your clothes got encrusted in salt and it would eat through your boots. When I came into my office and sat down, I could taste salt in my beard. If you licked your lips, or took a drink, you could taste salt in your mouth." This part of the facility was also uncomfortably hot, with temperature in some areas hovering "around 120 degrees," he says.

The vapor liquid separators frequently broke down, which occasionally resulted in salty water that had not been fully treated being discharged to the Monongahela River. Guthrie alleged two more examples of waste being dumped into the river or local environment. On a Friday in 2017, he recalled, the brine pond had filled up with wastewater and Venture Engineering President and CEO Dave Moniot told him to take the weekend off and he'd fix the problem. Guthrie was suspicious. When he came back Monday the brine pond was significantly lower, but he saw no evidence of the 40 trucks Moniot claimed had drawn off the wastewater. What he did see was evidence someone had unhooked a hose, enabling wastewater from the brine pond to run directly into the Monongahela. "It looked like he hooked up the impoundment to run straight through the weekend," says Guthrie, "and discharge the whole frigging thing into the river."

In a second incident, Guthrie says, he was asked to dump fluids from a set of frac tanks into the parking lot. "I wouldn't do it, so they got some knucklehead on the nightshift to do it," he says. There was a pond rich in waterfowl, turtles and fish located downhill from this location. After the incident, "fish in the pond turned up dead," remembers Guthrie. Still, proud of the facility and the energy he put into trying to make it run right, Guthrie insists that "under normal day-to-day operations, the standards for the NPDES permit were met." Moniot has not replied to specific questions about these alleged incidents. He had previously told me: "All waters that were discharged were processed through the evaporation plant, according to the NPDES permit requirements." The permit does not require testing for radioactivity.

Guthrie connects me, at the end of 2023, to Shannon Lutz, whose husband Michael was the worker who passed away from brain cancer. It was an aggressive form called glioblastoma, she tells me. Shannon remains convinced the causes were environmental and says Michael had his body donated to the West Virginia University School of Medicine's Human Gift Registry, "so they could try and figure out what the problem was and keep this from happening to other people in the future." She lost Michael earlier in the year and is still grieving. "This is not the plan I had for my life, to lose my husband at 45," Shannon says. She and Michael both grew up in northern West Virginia and met in the mid-1990s at a mall kiosk that sold batteries, Michael had helped interview her for the job, then fell in love with her, then she fell in love with him. "The movie *Mallrats* was our life," says Shannon. They moved to Pennsylvania, taking office jobs in the same communications company, and followed the company to Buffalo, where they lived together in a large city for the first time and loved it. Then the stock market crashed, they moved back to West Virginia and in with her parents. They had a young child, and Michael got a job in fracking waste at AOP Clearwater to pay the bills.

"I just knew there was exposure," she says. "His shoes and clothes got damaged, the bottom of his pants were crunchy and hard form the salt and chemicals, and the dust, the dust was crazy! Then there was the sludge pond. He would come home filthy and I would have to wash his clothes, I mean it was disgusting. I was like this can't be good. We were educated enough to know there was something definitely not right. Michael wanted to get out as quick as possible, and he only worked there a year or two, but he made some of the best friends he ever had. They had a grill that stayed right there at the site, Michael liked to cook and would take a crock pot full of pork barbecue and feed everyone at work. They would bring rolls for sandwiches or Styrofoam bowls for soups. I know Michael grilled ribs at many different times. My son and I would drive up there and drop off dessert. Now when I look back I am like, Oh my god."

I connect with the University of Pittsburgh geochemist, Dr. Daniel Bain, who interviews Sean Guthrie about the details of his job. Amount of hours worked, type of clothing worn and level of exertion are all critical details in building a model to convey just what the radioactivity dose is that he and his coworkers would have received.

Bain's research could potentially challenge studies done by the Pennsylvania Department of Environmental Protection and Argonne National Laboratory, which conclude oilfield workers don't receive enough exposure to cause cancers. But these studies have failed to interview workers and truly understand the incredibly sloppy nature of the facilities where they work. The fallout from scientific evidence demonstrating that those working in oilfield waste indeed receive enough radiation exposure to cause lethal cancers would be explosive, as even if the industry keeps its exemptions, decking men out in hazmat gear and Geiger counters would make it a lot harder to put fracking waste treatment centers near homes and schools and in the heart of communities. And no worker I've met so far, no matter how much they love their country and believe in energy independence, wants to unknowingly be contaminated with radioactivity then get taken out by cancer and leave their spouse, perhaps a very special woman met decades ago at a kiosk in a mall, a widow.

¤ ¤ ¤

In 2020, researchers at Harvard's School of Public Health published a groundbreaking study in the journal *Nature Communications*. They found that the components of fracking—wellhead emissions, wastewater impoundment emissions, pipeline and compressor station emissions, drill cuttings, and brine spills—add to the atmosphere's load of radioactivity at levels that "could induce adverse health effects to residents in proximity." Co-author Dr. Petros Koutrakis told a British newspaper: "If you asked me to go and live downwind [of fracking sites], I would not go." When I question lead author Longxiang Li on whether communities and people across Pennsylvania, Ohio and West Virginia oil and gas country that live in steep valleys, where emissions are known to settle, might be particularly at risk, he says it is "a reasonable" theory.

The year before, in 2019, an oil and gas industry consultant named Alan McArthur gave a presentation on radioactivity to a group of radiation professionals called the Conference of Radiation Control Program Directors. McArthur was born on Lamlash, a community of about 1,000 people on the Isle of Arran, off the west coast of Scotland. He studied business and engineering at the University of Strathclyde in Glasgow, and later worked in Canada building and managing hydroelectric power stations before returning to Scotland and co-founding a North Sea drilling company called Drilex.

"We first found radioactivity by happenchance," he tells me, on a North Sea oil platform in 1981. When they actually searched for it, McArthur and his colleagues found it everywhere, "from the wellhead to the refineries." He became one of the industry's most knowledgeable experts on the topic and has consulted for some of the world's largest oil and gas companies. This access has allowed him to do something pretty much no one else has been able to, look inside pipelines and take measurements.

In his 2019 presentation, McArthur explained that radon comes to the surface with natural gas and follows it through the pipeline system, with some of its radioactive daughters, including the highly lethal polonium-210, concentrating in pumps, valves, filters and the inside of the pipeline itself, and accumulating to the extraordinary level of 1.2 million picocuries per gram, around half a million to two million times general background levels.

The British journalist Luke Harding's book on the murder of former Russian security officer Alexander Litvinenko is titled, *A Very Expensive Poison*, because, as Harding explains, even though the lethal dose swallowed was just 26.5 micrograms, the only way to gather this much polonium-210 was by irradiating a large quantity of bismuth-209 in the core of a powerful high-flux nuclear reactor, and the only one on earth capable of doing that was located at a Cold War nuclear weapons and fuel production site called the Mayak facility, in the remote Russian interior. McArthur's data, presented in 2019 to the Conference of Radiation Control Program Directors, indicates that 218 pounds of sludge scraped from the filters of a natural gas pipeline would contain the same amount of polonium-210 as the dose that killed Litvinenko.

This may seem like a lot of pipeline sludge, but consider the United States has at least 321,000 miles of natural gas gathering and transmission pipelines. They run beneath fields, rivers and under countless small towns and cities, and they all may be accumulating radioactive scale and sludge, and this material must be cleaned out. How much is out there? No government agency, including the two main ones that regulate natural gas pipelines, the Federal Energy Regulatory Commission and the Pipelines and Hazardous Materials Safety Administration have been able to answer the question for me.

Even the person who knows more than anyone, Alan McArthur, doesn't know. It's a "GREAT QUESTION," he tells me when I ask via email in 2021, though "I have no data not even an estimate." But his work shows each natural gas pipeline may pose a terrorism threat. Not just because of the fuel it carries, but the polonium building up inside. Cleaning out this toxic radioactive waste falls to a group of industry workers called piggers. The name refers to the steel, plastic, or foam Pipeline Inspection Gauges, which are the tools piggers use. These pigs are often shaped like bullets or missiles and typically contain a series of bristles and protrusions that scrape and scour sludge and scale off the inside of the pipeline. The pigs are dragged through by cables or pushed along by pressure and enter and exit the pipeline at points called pig launching stations, then piggers clean off the radioactive waste by hand.

"We set up this big tarp containment system with three walls and a floor and made sure it was slightly downhill, so all the water would collect on the bottom," one former oilfield worker who has done the job tells me. He says they were aware of the radioactivity dangers and dressed in full-body Tyvek, rubber gloves, rubber boots, hardhat, a face mask with a breathing apparatus and goggles, and they wore dosimeters. "We lay the pig inside the containment using a forklift and tested it with a Geiger counter and registered what was hot," the man tells me. "Then we sprayed the pig down with a high-pressure hot water sprayer, a cleaning liquid available at Lowes, and long-handled brushes. We would Geiger counter the pig again, spray it down again, and continue the process until it was no longer hot."

Dirty water was vacuumed up into drums, sludge was shoveled into different drums, a lock seal was placed over the top, and drums were loaded onto a flatbed trailer then hauled back to Andrews County, Texas, where the waste was to be injected into the salt cavern operated by Lotus LLC. This may sound satisfactory, but because no government agency closely monitors or regulates the job, it's impossible to say for sure where all the nation's polonium-rich pipeline waste is being disposed, or whether all the country's piggers are being appropriately protected against radioactivity. Pigging waste, no matter how much deadly polonium it contains, is considered nonhazardous thanks to the Bentsen and Bevill exemption.

Alan McArthur, in his 2019 presentation, warned that the inhalation of radioactivity generated in pipeline cleaning operations would alone put an unprotected worker above yearly thresholds set by the Nuclear Regulatory Commission for nuclear workers—although for purposes of regulation piggers are considered members of the public with radioactivity thresholds that would be significantly lower. McArthur also said "public air monitoring" should be required on all natural gas pipeline projects.

Radon comes to the surface with crude oil too, as the Canadian graduate student Eli Franklin Burton first discovered in 1904. And some radon inevitably follows in oil pipelines, oil tanker trucks and railway tank cars. Whether or not there is any radioactivity left in one of crude oil's final end products, gasoline, is an interesting question, and one that there does not appear to be much research on. Though, the radioactivity would be expected to have settled out long before reaching the neighborhood gas station, as radon in the crude oil decays during the stages of oil transport and refining, forming a radioactive scale or sludge inside pipelines, oil tanker trucks, and railway cars. Radioactive emissions, however, would be expected at oil refineries.

There are 129 in the United States, and many are located within communities. The atmospheric scientist Dr. Detlev Helmig, who has worked at University of Colorado Boulder and also in the Arctic and

Antarctica, runs a group called Boulder AIR that monitors air pollution in northern Colorado, with an emphasis on oil and gas emissions. In 2023, at Commerce City, a community on the north side of Denver located beside an oil refinery, Detlev's team added radioactivity to the list of contaminants they measure for. Their findings indicate radioactivity levels are two to three times higher when the wind blows from the direction of the refinery. This is a significant revelation, and I'm helping him write it up for publication. "Rarely do we have something in our hands that seems so exciting," Detlev tells me recently, "that's so clean and clear and novel."

He is presently working with community and nonprofit groups concerned about air quality and is interested in trying to set up radioactivity monitoring at other oil and gas infrastructure. There are more than 1,200 compressor stations across the country, located in almost every US state, and regularly beside parks, busy roadways, and communities. Because of the radon in natural gas, radioactivity would be expected to be released at locations along the pipeline system where emissions occur, like compressor stations, and also natural gas processing plants, plastics plants, and pump stations, which keep material in natural gas liquids pipelines flowing.

A plastics plant may seem like an unlikely place to look for radioactivity, but for interesting reasons of physics and chemistry, they can be highly contaminated. At a natural gas processing plant, gas from all wells in a general area is brought via gathering pipelines. Methane, the fuel we call natural gas, is separated out from natural gas liquids, which include common fuels like propane, used in the backyard barbecue, butane, used in lighters, and ethane, critical in plastics production. To carry out this separation the gas stream is cooled then reheated. While some radon follows methane into the natural gas pipeline system upon reheating, even more of it, due to radon's boiling point being closer to the boiling points of propane and ethane, follows these fuels.

Radioactivity in propane in the United States appears to be unexamined. In Canada, in 1994, the National Energy Board issued a safety advisory that warned of "possible inhalation" risks to workers and recommended the petroleum industry "measure the concentration of radon in propane prior to release to the open market." When I ask the National Energy Board's current iteration, the Canada Energy Regulator, if this ever happened they tell me, "this is outside" of their jurisdiction.

Ethane is taken by pipelines to large petrochemical facilities called ethane cracker plants and superheated to form a compound called ethylene that is transformed into polyethylene, from which much of the world's plastics are made. Radon follows ethane into a cracker plant, and the longer-lived daughters, lead-210 and polonium-210, end up coating the inside of pumps and valves, which can become highly radioactive. In Argentina, the country's nuclear regulatory agency found radioactivity levels at a pump in a plastics plant of 40 millirems per hour, on par with present-day radiation levels lingering in the basement of the hospital at Chernobyl, still littered with the clothing of the nuclear disaster's horrifically irradiated first responders.

Shell has just built an ethane cracker plant in Monaca, Pennsylvania, northwest of Pittsburgh. The facility came online in November 2022, and at full capacity will annually produce 3.5 billion pounds of plastics. Within months of opening the plant was exceeding pollution limits and the following year the Pennsylvania-based Clean Air Council filed a lawsuit against Shell, alleging the plant was putting residents' health at risk by persistently violating air quality standards. I ask Shell if this plant is emitting radioactivity, but the company has not responded.

Shell also doesn't answer my question of exactly how much radioactive sludge and scale is cleaned out of their Pennsylvania ethane cracker's pumps and valves each year, how radioactive it is, and where it all goes. Another interesting question is how much polonium makes it through all the pipes and pumps of these facilities and into the plastics themselves? While I am not aware of any distinct research on the issue, one expert I speak to says they wouldn't expect much. The problem, I learn firsthand, is in the cracker plant's pumps and valves.

¤ ¤ ¤

In 2005, Dennis Schum began working for a company called John Crane in a beige building in an office park in Golden, Colorado, cleaning mechanical seals from oil refineries, petrochemical plants, and oil and gas industry pipelines.

"They would literally take the seal off a pump, stick it in a box, and ship them to me," says Dennis. "Usually, seals came in dirty, and we routinely got seals leaking right out of the box."

Any liquid being moved at high pressure from place to place invariably involves pumps. An oil well often uses a pump to pull oil to the surface. A pipeline carrying ethane may require dozens of pumps. And an oil refinery or petrochemical plant, which is really just a vast network of pipes and tanks processing various liquids and gases at different pressures, may have thousands of pumps. Mechanical seals are an essential part of a pump, holding the pressure as liquids are transferred from one spot to another. Each side of a pump has a seal, and each seal is about the size of a lawn mower engine and can weigh more than 80 pounds. "I did around 200 seals a month from the oil and gas industry—I was the man," says Dennis.

The Oklahoma industry consultant, Peter Gray, in his 1993 report on oilfield radioactivity published in the Society of Petroleum Engineers' *Journal of Petroleum Technology* noted pumps are one of the oilfield's most highly contaminated pieces of equipment, even though these items are often cleaned far from the oilfield. "Contamination inside a pump is often chemically bonded to the pump structural metal and cannot be easily removed without scraping and grinding," wrote Gray. The act of cleaning "may generate significant quantities of radioactive dust that can contaminate personnel as well as the shop facility. This can pose a very serious problem." Gray said in order to prevent exposures employees must exercise precautions in opening equipment and vessels, and he advocated "the use of respirators and good hygiene to prevent inhalation of radioactive dust."

Dennis says he worked in a room roughly 25-feet-long by 15-feet-wide with no windows or proper ventilation. The scale was often a tan or white color, existed on the seal as a thin glaze, and was very difficult to remove. Dennis used a special worktable intended to suck up dust called a downdraft table but says instead of being connected to proper ventilation the table "would just blow back into the room." He says the sandblaster he used to clean and smooth parts was not connected to appropriate ventilation either and dusted the shop, and his hair, with a fine debris, "as if I've been at the beach in a windstorm." For most of the time he worked there Dennis had no respirator, no face shield and no Tyveks. He had glasses to cover his eyes, disposable rubber gloves for his hands, and a cotton shop apron for his body. John Crane eventually got employees standard button-down blue work shirts and khaki work pants, says Dennis, but before that he says he typically wore Levi's jeans and a T-shirt.

"You ended up covered in the filth of the seal, and John Crane had no changing room or locker room, so I would bring home my work clothes and have shit all over me and wash everything in my family washing machine," says Dennis. He says he worked at John Crane for five years before a set of seals arrived, in 2013, from a natural gas liquids pipeline in Utah and happened to be labeled as radioactive.

In 2000, John Crane merged with Smiths, a storied British company founded in 1851 that, among many other things, made the watch worn by Sir Edmund Hillary who with Tenzing Norgay, in 1953, recorded the first summit of Mount Everest. Smiths presently makes airport security scanners and antenna systems for aircraft and satellites. Many of the oilfield pumps Dennis cleaned were made by Sulzer, a Swiss engineering firm founded in 1775 that today defines themselves as leaders in climate and sustainability. They have 180 facilities worldwide and headquarters in Winterthur, a Swiss city known for its museums and gardens.

At the John Crane company library Dennis discovered a report on oilfield radioactivity bearing the logo of John Crane and Smiths. It appears as if the firms knew their technicians were being exposed to radiation but never bothered to tell them—or at least they never bothered to tell Dennis. "The greatest hazard… is not from external exposure, but from inhalation, ingestion or absorption," the John Crane/Smiths report states. Radioactive particles can also enter through "broken skin" and "may be absorbed into the bones."

Dennis says two engineers he worked with passed away from aggressive cancers, "we are talking six months from diagnosis to death, it just ate them alive." And these workers did the same job he did. "It kind of makes me nervous what I have inside of me," he says. "Huge lumps started to grow on the back of my ears that no one was able to explain and I developed this condition where I had way too much iron in my blood and the teeth in my bottom jaw started falling out. I am in pain all the time, and I am scared. I know how this stuff is, I know how it gets in your body and accumulates. I know it is not like you go in to work and touch it and you're dying the next day, sometimes it takes 5, 10, 15, 20 years, then all the sudden you have these cancers eating you alive."

Dennis says that at some point in 2013, his final year at the company, John Crane began to supply workers like him with respirators, face shields and Tyveks. He says they also repaired the downdraft table and ensured that it and the sand blaster vented to the outside—and into the space of the surrounding office park. The Swiss company Sulzer has a service center east of Denver, located in a business park setting. Neither John Crane, Smiths, or Sulzer have replied to any of my questions. Dennis, like most oilfield workers I'm in touch with who believe they've been contaminated, has had difficulty finding a good lawyer willing to take his case.

¤ ¤ ¤

The Louisiana attorney Stuart Smith, after his Mississippi pipe-cleaning cases, built a booming business around oilfield radioactivity, previously unexplored legal terrain. It was not just workers directly connected to the waste who had to worry about radiation, such as pipe-cleaners and those who shovel sludge. Many of the oil and gas industry's most common jobs, his legal team argued, face radioactivity risks that pile up over time and may have serious health impacts. This included roughnecks and roustabouts, who serve as the common oilfield laborers and can get repeatedly drenched with brine and sludge as they pull pieces of oilfield pipe from a well or face exposures in cleaning out wellhead equipment. Stuart also represented truck drivers who hauled pipes or sludge, derrickman, and welders.

The workers, mostly from Louisiana, were diagnosed with a number of cancers, including colon cancer, lung cancer, liver cancer, non-Hodgkin lymphoma, multiple myeloma, and several different types of leukemia. Stuart's legal team used an analysis program developed by the Centers for Disease Control and Prevention called the Interactive RadioEpidemiological Program, or IREP, initially intended to analyze the exposures of nuclear weapons workers. In many instances, IREP showed with over 99 percent certainty that these men's cancers came from exposure to radiation in their oilfield work. "I can tell you this industry has tremendous resources and hired the best people they could, and they were not successful," Dr. Marvin Resnikoff, one of Stuart's radioactivity experts tells me. "Once you have the information, it is indisputable." "These men," Stuart tells me in 2020, "are guinea pigs."

And where are all of the oilfield worker cancers from states where Stuart did not bring lawsuits? Oklahoma and Texas, North Dakota and Montana and Michigan, Pennsylvania, West Virginia and Ohio. It is possible cancers have developed but workers have scattered back to their home states or other oilfields, making the emergence of a cluster hard to spot. Liver cancer and lung cancer can take a decade, or several decades, to emerge, and in the Marcellus/Utica it is just getting to the point where many workers would have been at the job for that amount of time. Cases could also be lingering in the population, and because workers don't know their job had radioactivity risks don't think to connect them to oil and gas. Or are hesitant to make the link to an industry that has provided for them. Or have made the link, but can't find doctors, or lawyers, willing to listen.

I once asked Stuart—who passed away in 2022—given all his success, and the industry's vulnerability on the issue, why no other attorneys have brought cases on oilfield radioactivity. "The learning curve on a case like this is tremendous," he told me. "Your average attorney is not going to be able to handle it." But that may be changing.

Paula Bliss's female-run firm helped take down the disgraced Michigan State University gymnastics coach Larry Nassar, among other sex offenders, and has battled Big Tobacco on cases that involve campaigns to get cigarettes into the hands of children. In 2021, Paula brought a complaint in the United States District Court for the District of Massachusetts against the powerful pipeline company, Kinder Morgan, representing a group of men involved in work on the Tennessee Gas Pipeline, in western Massachusetts. "This is a civil action" for workers "exposed to dangerous levels of radiation during the course of their employment causing them to be at an increased risk for developing cancers," it reads. One worker developed blood cancer, a separate personal injury case that was settled, although the case involving the group of workers was thrown out. Kinder Morgan has not replied to my questions, and Paula vows to bring future lawsuits on the issue. When I speak to her in 2022, she tells me: "We don't think the next big area of law involving corporate greed will be going after pharmaceuticals, and we don't necessarily think it is going to be tobacco—we think it is going to be this."

In the heart of southwestern Pennsylvania fracking country is another attorney that has entered this world. Lisa Johnson grew up in a military family in the rural northeast part of the state. “I always wanted to help, but not coming from means and not having access I didn’t know how, and I didn’t know anything about the law,” she tells me recently. “I was going to a university in Pittsburgh and waiting tables.” In hearing of an innovative way to get tuition for law school partly paid for, she went through the Allegheny County Police Academy and became a police officer. “I had a blue uniform and a Glock 40,” says Lisa, “but all the time with law school in mind.” Lisa is presently representing a rural Pennsylvania landowner named Bryan Latkanich and his sons in a case against the oil giant Chevron, where a spokesperson once famously stated, regarding oilfield contamination in Indigenous communities in the Ecuadorian rainforest: “We’re going to fight this until hell freezes over. And then we’ll fight it out in the ice.”

In June 2023 I see Lisa in action at the Washington County Court of Common Pleas, in Washington, Pennsylvania. People I know from across southwestern Pennsylvania have gathered outside the courthouse. “Everyone here was impacted by the Marcellus Shale,” a participant named Cat Lodge, who works with a watchdog organization called the Environmental Integrity Project tells me. “They’ve been fracking here for 20 years, and this is the first time we have had our day in court.”

Inside the second-floor courtroom I take a seat on a wooden bench in back, noticing the ornate white flower patterns on the ceiling, the naked light bulbs, the stenographer’s electronic clock, where time ticks away in pixelated red bars. It is strange to think in this large clean space the complex and hazardous chemistry of the oilfield is decided upon. “When Chevron Corporation came into this state,” Lisa argues. “They profited off these holdings and frankly left a legacy of contamination that Pennsylvanians are going to have to live with.”

Lisa’s complaint alleges that Chevron discharged hazardous chemicals, industrial waste and radioactive waste onto the Latkanich’s land when they developed it for oil and gas in 2011 and 2012, and that Chevron and its employees knew or should have known that drilling and fracking there could result in the release of radioactivity. “If you argue that certain chemicals used in the fracking process are abnormally dangerous, the industry can always argue they do not necessarily need to use those chemicals,” Lisa had explained to me when we spoke before the hearing. But to argue that the radioactivity the oil and gas industry brings to the surface is abnormally dangerous is different. “Because they can’t escape the radioactivity,” she says, “it is inherent, it is always there.” And this revelation, she believes, could change everything, and open up an entirely new legal front across the country against the oil and gas industry.

15
How to Start a Cancer Cluster

There is a bad joke I have heard in oil and gas country—what's the final stage of the fracking process?

First come the landmen, to convince you the process is harmless and you will get rich. The land is cleared, the well is drilled, the well is fracked, the well is put into production, and pipelines must be built, along with natural gas processing plants and compressor stations. Then comes the plastics plant, to transform fuel into plastic pellets to make the products of our world. But, as the joke goes, there is still one more step. What, after all of this, is the final stage of the fracking process?

¤ ¤ ¤

Cecil. A suburb on the southwest edge of Pittsburgh. There is a gurgling creek beside a baseball field, and in a house on a hill above are the grieving parents. Kurt and Janice Blanock have lost their son, their human boy, Luke, to a rare type of bone cancer called Ewing sarcoma. He played on that field as a child with the Cecil Township Youth Baseball Association, slid into first and smelled the infield dirt, in summers mowed the field and smelled the freshly cut grass. Inside the home, lights are dim. A smiling portrait of Luke is embroidered onto a sofa chair. Is stitched, in fact, onto everything in the home. Because how could it not be. How could it not swell up? How could it not pour out? Every dying child becomes a god. Kurt and Janice speak, as if their voices are rising up out of a long deep hole. They slowly cry, slowly smile, slowly share the story of their son.

"I first noticed something was wrong in 2013 right after Thanksgiving," says Kurt. "One day Luke came in and had ice on his back. He went to basketball practice and said he'd talk to the trainer. By that evening he couldn't move his legs and we went to the hospital. They were writing up papers to discharge us, because they couldn't find anything wrong, when it happened again, his legs locked up. An ambulance took him straight to Pittsburgh's Children's Hospital for an MRI. They said a tumor was crushing his spine. It was the worst night of our life."

"The surgery was Thursday," Kurt continues, "and I remember just a few days later Luke jumped up and touched the ceiling. He went to his basketball game that Saturday, he was fine. But it came back. Ewing's is a freaking killing machine. If it's in the spine and has already spread when they catch it, the survival rate is 10 to 30 percent. For him, it was in the spine and had spread to his pelvis. So, right away, he went from a perfectly healthy kid to a kid who was likely going to die."

"The treatments are brutal for this cancer," says Kurt. "The first round of Ewing's has a protocol, but after that there is no book, they are still using the same drugs they did in the 1960s. He went through more than 100 radiation treatments, and 24 rounds of chemotherapy. Luke always said, I don't want to get known as that kid with cancer. He kept playing sports, baseball, basketball. Jan would make him do his bed. You needed normalcy. And there were a lot of amazing times. Through two and a half years of cancer completely wrecking his body, I could probably count on one hand the really bad days. But in the back of my mind there was this cloud, it is going to kill him."

Luke was seeing Dr. Peter Anderson at the Cleveland Clinic, and in the fall of 2015 flew to MD Anderson Cancer Center in Houston where they removed pieces of his hip bone and the upper part of his femur. Luke would be shorter, walk differently, though he would still be able to lead a life. But the surgery didn't stop the cancer and later, back at Children's Hospital in Pittsburgh, doctors told the family his condition was terminal.

A child is born of nutrients in blood. Grows from cells. Develops a brain. Develops bones. Develops a face. Wishes, wants. Develops cancer. Still, it loves. "I think," Luke had said at one point, "any young person dealing with cancer has to mature at a pretty fast rate."

"Right after Christmas," continues Kurt, "he talked about getting married to Natalie, who he had known since middle school. And on February 19, 2016, they had a wedding. It was unreal how much attention he got. News stations in Japan and Russia, and Germany's version of *Good Morning America*. Katie Couric wanted to fly him to New York. But every month the pain came back quicker, and he had trouble going back to his life. In the summer of 2016 we went to the Cleveland Clinic and stayed at a family campground in Ohio. He liked doing grilled pizza. We planned to spend that whole summer there, but by July he couldn't walk."

"There was cancer on every vertebra in his body," says Kurt, "and he had countless tumors, on his brain, skull, pelvis, jaw. He only had one week left of life. But even then he hadn't given up. He was learning Spanish from an app on his phone, and he wanted to take classes at the community college. And for some reason, because of the brain tumors, he talked in an English accent. He wanted to do an English accent cooking show. Even as he was dying, he reassured us he was okay. He reassured us how much he loved us. He was the one comforting us."

Janice has been listening to her husband tell the story of their son. Now she is crying. Now everyone is crying. How can you not cry? "He was," says Janice, "an amazing kid." It is all she can say at the moment, there is really nothing else to say.

Kurt explains there is one more piece to the story. "Luke's handwriting was shaky," he says, "but he continued to keep a journal. Right at the end he wrote:

What you have once loved you never lose.

He wrote it over and over. And that same day he died."

¤ ¤ ¤

In 2019 investigative reporters at the *Pittsburgh Post-Gazette* revealed that in the community of Cecil, where Luke had grown up, in Washington County, five cases of Ewing sarcoma had been diagnosed since 2008. And across the four counties in the southwest corner of Pennsylvania, Washington, Greene, Fayette and Westmoreland, heart of the booming Marcellus Shale, from 2008 through 2018, 27 cases of Ewing sarcoma had been reported.

Six cases of Ewing's were diagnosed within the Canon-McMillan School District, the article reported, and several kids had attended the local high school together, known as Canon-Mac, in Canonsburg, Pennsylvania. One of them was Luke Blanock. Another was Mitch Barton, in 2018 he experienced pain in his right shoulder and a chiropractor found an unusual set of small bumps. An X-ray later revealed his clavicle had been mysteriously fractured. As kids, Mitch and Luke played baseball together. At Canon-Mac Luke was pitcher, and Mitch catcher.

Curtis Valent, also of Cecil, also a baseball pitcher, also played as a kid in the Cecil Township Youth Baseball Association was diagnosed with Ewing's in mid-2008. For him the cancer also began with a hurt shoulder, as well as a fever and chest pains. The disease spread to his lungs, liver, lymph nodes and spleen, and in 2011, at the age of 23, he passed away.

Alyssa Chambers of Cecil was diagnosed with Ewing's in late 2008 as an 18-year-old Canon-Mac senior. She survived.

Kyle Deliere was diagnosed in 2011. He had played in the Cecil Township Youth Baseball Association, and lived about a mile from Luke Blanock in Cecil. Kyle, according to the *Pittsburgh Post-Gazette*, "lost weight, had night sweats and fevers, and developed large tumors on his hip, femur and lungs," and died on November 15, 2013, at the age of 27.

There is also the case of David Cobb, diagnosed in June 2018 at the age of 37. "He found this cancer from a simple nose bleed," his wife Alison wrote on a patient support site. "And days later they were removing a tumor from his sinuses." It's a less common place for Ewing sarcoma to show up, but has been documented. At the time David was living in Cecil.

The *Post-Gazette* article described ten other cases of unusual cancer that were afflicting or killing the children and students of Cecil and Canon-Mac. They included one astrocytoma (brain and spinal cord); two osteosarcoma (bone); one liposarcoma (joint); one rhabdomyosarcoma (muscle); one Wilms tumor (kidney); one liver cancer and two cases of leukemia (blood).

David Spigelmyer, in 2019 president of the Marcellus Shale Coalition, the trade group representing fracking interests in Pennsylvania, had told the *Post-Gazette* that attempts to link the incidence of Ewing sarcoma to the industry were without scientific or medical support. His group cited a review of medical data by the American Cancer Society that had found "no known lifestyle-related or environmental causes of Ewing tumors."

Indeed, the medical profession supports this conclusion. "Doctors have not identified any risk factors that make one child more susceptible than another," says the American Academy of Orthopaedic Surgeons. "Parents should know that there is nothing they could have done differently to prevent their child's tumor," says the Academy, and the disease "does not develop as a result of any dietary, social, or behavioral habits." There are about 75 million children and adolescents in the United States, and according to John Hopkins University School of

Medicine, about 225 of them are diagnosed with Ewing sarcoma each year. “The exact cause of Ewing sarcoma,” says John Hopkins, “is not fully understood.”

But certain information is firmly known. Ewing’s primarily occurs in children and young adults. More males are affected than females. Ewing’s can develop in tissue near bone and also the sinus cavity but most often occurs in bone, and most regularly in the shin bone (tibia), thigh bone (femur), upper arm bone (humerus), hip bones, ribs, spine and skull. Initial symptoms include swelling and tenderness, a lump that may feel warm and soft, or a bone that breaks for no apparent reason. Parents may mistake Ewing’s for a sports injury. And while Ewing sarcoma can occur at any time during childhood, it most commonly develops during puberty, when bones are growing quickly.

“In adults things sort of go in slow motion, but in children everything is rapidly replicating,” says Dr. Larysa Dyrszka, an upstate New York pediatrician and co-founder of an advocacy group called Concerned Health Professionals of New York, which has repeatedly raised alarm about the health risks fracking poses to children. “Because children’s organ systems and bones are still developing there is a lot more turnover of cells,” says Dyrszka, “making them more likely to develop, say, a tumor.” Every year her group, together with Physicians for Social Responsibility and the Science & Environmental Health Network, publish an epic report entitled, *Compendium of Scientific, Medical, and Media Findings Demonstrating Risks and Harms of Fracking and Associated Gas and Oil Infrastructure*. The latest volume cites from over 2,000 scientific studies and informs that radioactivity releases represent only one of the significant harms posed to workers and nearby communities. The release of benzene, heavy metals, and toxic drilling chemicals all pose cancer risks too.

In an area where a new toxic contaminant has been introduced to a community, children would naturally serve as the canary in the coal mine. And the first cancers expected to emerge would be the ones that tend to develop more quickly, like cancers of the blood, and bone.

¤ ¤ ¤

The cancer that grew inside the kids of southwestern Pennsylvania was named for Dr. James Ewing, a pioneering American cancer researcher of the late 1800s and early 1900s. Ewing happened to have grown up in Pittsburgh, the city closest to the communities where more than 100 years later an outbreak would develop of the disease that bore his name. He helped found the American Society for the Control of Cancer, which became the American Cancer Society, and also helped establish a clinical cancer research unit at Memorial Hospital in New York, now Memorial Sloan Kettering Cancer Center, one of the world's most prestigious cancer research institutes. In 1919, he published *Neoplastic Diseases*, his epic textbook on tumors, which systematically organized every known cancer to afflict humans and provided a methodical way to diagnose them all.

Two years later, at a 1921 meeting of the New York Pathological Society, Ewing spoke and mentioned the case of a teenage girl who while pulling on a rope spontaneously fractured her ulna, the longer of the two bones of the forearm. She was diagnosed with an osteogenic sarcoma, at that time the name used for the most common type of bone cancer. But Ewing noted key differences in this tumor's structure and cells, and the influence the tumor had on its surroundings. Bone production had stopped, and "some of the bones appeared honeycombed." Ewing had spotted the novel disease in six other teenagers, and hereby manifested a new type of tumor to the world, the Ewing sarcoma.

James Ewing was part of a group of cancer researchers who adamantly believed that radium, at the time a newly discovered radioactive metal, was not the cause of cancer, but the cure for it. He had followed the wealthy mining magnate James Douglas to Europe to investigate the use of radium as a therapeutic agent in cancer and made sure his New York hospital was stocked with a precious supply, about 9 grams worth. During his 1921 presentation to the New York Pathological Society Ewing declared that Ewing sarcoma, unlike the more common form of bone cancer which "resists treatment," was "highly susceptible to radium." Unfortunately for the young woman he treated with "a radium pack" applied to the arm, her tumor initially showed signs of healing but eventually returned, along with other tumors in the skull. "Death occurred on December 23, 1920," said Ewing. Still, a decade later, in January of 1931, Ewing's picture appeared on the cover of *Time* magazine, bony face, mustache, jacket and tie: "Cancer Man Ewing."

He also examined the radium girls. After five of the women won their case against their employer, the United States Radium Corporation, the company continued to deny radium was hazardous and made sure a medical board appointed by the court to monitor the women was stacked with a pair of industry-friendly scientists. Ewing was one of them. He quibbled at the medical expenses the women were racking up, which US Radium had to pay for, and still doubted radium had seriously harmed them. After conducting what's known as a "breath test," which measured the amount of radioactive air being exhaled, he discovered the women were indeed harboring an internal source of radioactivity. But rather than take this as conclusive evidence their bones were full of radium from the radium-enriched paint ingested on their paintbrush tips, an already proven pathway, Ewing, writes Kate Moore, in her book, *The Radium Girls* suspected the disabled women were up to some sort of mischief. "To make the tests absolutely trustworthy," Ewing said, "we think it will be necessary to carry them out at some hotel where the patients can undress."

There was someone who from the beginning believed the radium girls, autopsied them and found radium in their bones, administered breath tests and determined that the women were indeed venting radioactivity, and had even searched through their ashes to discover they were radioactive. That was the Newark, New Jersey medical examiner Dr. Harrison Martland. His 1931 article in *The American Journal of Cancer* contained an illustration of a skeleton for each woman detailing the location of their tumors. There was a distinct pattern. Tumors developed at "bones that are subject to weight, pressure, and trauma, such as the head of the femur, the acetabulum, the spine, the pelvis, and the tarsal scaphoid," a small weight-bearing bone in the foot.

These locations mirror some of the spots where Ewing tumors had developed in the kids of southwestern Pennsylvania. In the 1931 article Martland says he didn't think the women's cancers were Ewing sarcomas, noting that, "[Ewing's] lesion never showed...the intense inflammatory character seen in the dial painters." Indeed, there was a difference between Ewing sarcoma and osteosarcoma, the more common form of bone cancer. But the latter, Martland's research with the radium girls definitively showed, could be caused by unknowingly ingesting radium.

The instrument Martland used in his breath tests is called an electroscope, which detects the presence of an electrical charge, such as is generated by the decay of radioactive elements. Radium-226 decays to radon-222, which means the radium girls, with radium-filled bones, were continuously producing radon, some of which would inevitably escape the body out through the mouth. Essentially, a human being becomes a radioactive chimney. An early version of the electroscope was invented by a British schoolmaster in 1754 and is called the pith-ball electroscope. It resembles a toy pendulum and consists of a stand with a tiny ball of lightweight nonconductive material, such as pith, suspended by thread. When an electrically charged object or material, such as a stream of radioactive air, moves past the pith ball it is drawn toward the stream. I easily find one on a school science supply website, for $6.95.

¤ ¤ ¤

If radium somehow did happen to be behind the Ewing sarcoma cases, then what exactly had gone wrong in southwestern Pennsylvania that could have led to the radioactive element entering the bones of teenagers?

"The corruption here was pathetic, there was major conflicts of interest," says Ron Gulla, whose Washington County farm was one of the first places fracked in the entire state, in late 2004 and early 2005. He worked for a large company that supplied tools and equipment to the oil and gas industry. While initially enthusiastic about money and business the boom would bring, working in oil and gas and having wells on his farm enabled him to see the industry up close, and Gulla quickly became alarmed.

"The industry planted people on the county chamber of commerce, they hired off-duty police officers to work security, they showered gifts on the local fire departments, and they even wormed their way into agriculture," he says. "I was like these motherfuckers are going to infiltrate everything, and they did. I told people, they are killing us without firing a bullet. And I said, Jesus Christ, this is going to cause cancer. Not because I am a scientist or Mr. Educated Scholar, it's common sense"—a few years after Gulla and I first spoke, his wife was diagnosed with acute myeloid leukemia.

He describes how southwestern Pennsylvania, a patchwork of forests, industry, and sweeping fields and family farms, each with their own streams and cow ponds, and all of it woven together by larger creeks and rivers, became completely overrun by the oil and gas industry and its seemingly endless collection of tanks, trucks and impoundments. "People are going to fall over when they see how much waste this industry has produced," says Gulla. The amount of chemicals necessary to drill and frack became apparent too, as residents saw vats and containers hauled regularly on their roads and set up at well pads. "I spoke to one trucker who hauled fracking chemicals and I was legitimately freaked out," says Gulla. "He said to me, you have no idea how much acid we dumped in these wells."

Among Gulla's biggest concerns were what it all meant for the creeks, and also the wild food many in southwestern Pennsylvania rely on, such as deer and fish. Early on, the son of a local science teacher he went hunting with was diagnosed with Ewing sarcoma. "Kyle Deliere was 25 years-old when he got it," says Gulla, and 27 when he died, in 2013. "Kyle suffered for two years," he continues, "it was a heart-breaking story, I went to the funeral. He played football, was on the wrestling team, and his father hunted on my farm, and Kyle liked to eat deer meat." That small things at the bottom of the food chain may take in minor amounts of an environmental contaminant, concentrate it in their bodies, and pass on much greater and potentially toxic concentrations to things that eat them is called biomagnification, and the concept niggled away at Gulla.

"Remember all the dead cattle," he says. "I know a lot of farmers who said they drilled on my farm and all is fine. Bullshit, who the hell went and did testing? These animals and wild game are exposed 24/7, and that's our food, so what the hell are we eating?"

Following radium from the fracking industry into things that can serve as food for humans has not been closely examined across Pennsylvania, but there has been some research. Dr. Nathaniel Warner, an environmental engineer at Penn State University, and his colleagues investigated freshwater mussels, which are common in Pennsylvania creeks and make their shells out of minerals pulled from the water. They found that in certain heavily drilled parts of the state, downstream of facilities that process oilfield wastewater and discharge back to waterways, the animals had taken in oilfield waste contaminants, including radium. "The mussels," says Warner, "brought the radioactivity into their hard shells."

He is currently assessing whether or not radium builds up in the organism's soft tissue too, which would be worrisome, as most creatures eat the meaty part of the mussel and not the shell. This would suggest a route for the oilfield's radium to travel out of creeks and up the food chain. Warner points out that catfish, muskrats, and humans all eat mussels—and humans eat catfish. "Unfortunately," he says, "the literature is all over the place about how concerned we should be."

Pennsylvania's creeks have floodplains, and the floodplains hold things like baseball fields and town parks, and the creeks flood regularly. Videos of these events show violently rushing water and inundated fields. Everything ends up in the creeks, and when the creeks flood they can bring contaminants with them. Even good operators could lose material in an accidental spill. But early on in the Marcellus boom in southwestern Pennsylvania there was evidence emerging that massive amounts of waste were being spilled intentionally.

In Greene County, it was found that a company called Allen's Waste Water Service had illegally dumped millions of gallons of fracking wastewater. They used dastardly methods, including discharging waste at night, in rainstorms, and pouring waste down a drain in the company garage that led into a stream that ran eventually to Dunkard Creek, a popular fishing hole. One local fisherman says a front of rusty brown contamination invaded the creek, and he observed thousands of fish die and stressed fish jumping out of the water—"you could tell they were being poisoned." Allan's Waste Water Service also dumped waste into an old coal mine shaft. "My theory," one Greene County environmental leader told a reporter in 2013, in trying to describe the industry's mindset, "is, whenever there's a hole, you can use it. It's open season down here."

In adjacent Fayette County, it also must have been open season. In 2017, the Office of the Attorney General investigated local businessman John Ashley Joseph, who allegedly directed employees of a landscaping company he ran called Perry Stone and Supply to dump truckloads of fracking waste at locations across the county, including along a rural road just 50 feet from a cattle field, behind a Dairy Queen, and at a makeshift landfill on Joseph's own property that came to be known as the "Perry Pit." Investigators tested each location and detected diesel fuel, barium, and strontium, contaminants indicative of drill cuttings. Perhaps most outrageously, fracking waste was also allegedly dumped at the courthouse where John Ashley Joseph was eventually to appear. "A large former foundation and the parking lot," one driver testified, "are completely filled with drill cuttings."

The ecosystem was ripe for shady operators. An investigation in the early years of Pennsylvania's fracking boom conducted by *ProPublica* described spills of fracking fluids, drill cuttings and hydrochloric acid. In one 2009 incident, Texas-based Range Resources spilled nearly 5,000 gallons of waste—the equivalent of an entire truckload's worth—into a tributary of Cross Creek, a protected watershed. While the state reported numerous fish and other wildlife dead, Range Resources spokesman Matt Pitzarella said it amounted to less than a pound of minnows.

The U.S. Geological Survey research team that assessed the brine spill in Blacktail Creek in the Bakken oilfield in North Dakota found radium had traveled 4.5 miles downstream and built up in creek sediments and also the floodplain. Radium in the floodplain could be blown about by the wind and also indicated "a potential for animal exposures," the authors noted, and "radium exhibits characteristics similar to calcium and therefore can be deposited in bone and connective tissues surrounding organs."

The idea that Pennsylvania creeks could have ferried a discharge of fracking waste downstream and spread the waste onto floodplains that residents interact with is certainly plausible. In Cecil, two youth baseball fields are in the floodplain of a creek that floods regularly called Millers Run. The fields, among other things, are downstream of the truckyard of Weavertown Environmental, a local oilfield waste hauling and environmental services company, and satellite images show the yard to be filled with, what appears to be, all sorts of waste trucks and containers. "In 2003, when Marcellus Shale discovered a promising flow of natural gas in Washington County, PA," our business "jumped on the opportunity," says Weavertown Environmental Group President Dawn Fuchs Coleman in a book she wrote about how to succeed in business. "We did not sit on the side lines like some companies did," writes Coleman, and wait to "see if the Marcellus Shale opportunity was a winner, winner chicken dinner." Her company, "seized the opportunity."

I ask Weavertown Environmental about radium in the oil and gas industry waste they had hauled and disposed, just how much waste was kept on their site above Millers Run, what safeguards they installed to ensure runoff didn't flow offsite, if they had ever tested this runoff for contaminants, and if any significant floods had occurred at the site, but I have not heard back.

The investigative journalist Joshua Pribanic, at *Public Herald*, the Pittsburgh-based journalism outfit, suggested a novel pathway of exposure. Many of the kids diagnosed with Ewing sarcoma played baseball, and at least two of them were pitchers and one was a catcher. Pitchers must hold a dusty ball and regularly lick their fingers, reminiscent of the radium girls' exposure path. Catchers squat on the ground constantly breathing in clouds of dust, bringing to mind the oilfield pipe-cleaners exposure path. Pribanic suggested the infield dirt the kids had played on could have become tainted with radium. Either from dirt contaminated with fracking waste being used on the sly to lay the fields. Or creeks flooding fields with radium-laden waste from oil and gas operations. Baseball infield dirt is typically 15 to 30 percent clay, and clay is known to form bonds with heavy metals and could potentially have acted to trap radium flooded onto the fields by the creeks and accumulate it over time in the infield.

Samples Pribanic brings to University of Pittsburgh geochemist Daniel Bain show levels of radium in the ballfields to be around background, and in sediment drawn from Millers Run, the creek that flows beside them, to be around two times general background. "There is cause to conduct a full investigation with soil bores at the creek beds to discover how much TENORM was released and how far it traveled," says Pribanic, referencing the term industry and regulators use in referring to radioactivity that has been concentrated by oil and gas operations (Technologically Enhanced Naturally Occurring Radioactive Material).

In the spring of 2023 I connect with Kate Blanock, Luke Blanock's sister, who at the time is doing research at the University of Pittsburgh and on her way to becoming a geologist, and we take additional samples at the ballfields, finding radium levels to be highest not in the infield clay, but the outfield, closest to the creek—one reading, in the outfield of the Cecil Elementary Baseball Field, showed radium levels to be 4.24 picocuries per gram, not above EPA's radium limit for topsoil at toxic waste dumps, but not that far off.

There is also the site of an old uranium mill located less than half a mile from Canon-Mac, a creek flows by it, and Pribanic and I tested its sediment. Between 1911 and 1957 uranium and other ores were processed here to, among other things, extract radium. Early on, according to one history, the plant produced "radium fertilizer" and "uranium steel." Later, uranium was processed for national defense programs. These operations, according to a Department of Energy fact sheet, generated radioactive tailings, "a predominantly sandy material." A large amount was buried on site in a six-acre disposal cell that's covered with several feet of compacted clay, crushed rocks, and topsoil and seeded on top with grass. This disposal cell was closed in 1985 and contains 226,000 tons of contaminated material, including an exceptional amount of radium-226. Government reports from the 1990s indicate the site has leaked radioactivity into groundwater, but say controls instituted at the site prevent this radioactivity from exiting into the greater environment at levels that would be of concern. Pribanic's samples drawn from the creek next to the former uranium mill site showed radium to be around two times general background levels. Not a smoking gun. But, there are other ways radium entered into the Pennsylvania environment.

¤ ¤ ¤

It is not yet noon, and Ray Kemble has already taken shots of whiskey. He retreats to a chair at the head of the wooden table in his dining room, lights up a corncob pipe with Smoker's Pride Black Cavendish tobacco, then pulls from beneath the wooden table a powerful handgun, which he has nicknamed the executioner, and shows it off to a visiting documentary filmmaker.

Ray lives in Susquehanna County, in northeastern Pennsylvania, directly atop a sweet spot of the Marcellus formation. "They've tried every possible way to shut me up," he says. The former oilfield waste truckdriver has a long yellow beard and Harley-Davidson cap and holds what may possibly be an important clue to the Ewing sarcoma cases.

"All I know is we used to deliver to these wastewater treatment plants right on the river," says Ray. "These places were slamming, they would take four brine trucks at a time. We hook up our hoses and are dumping 5,000 gallons of fucking frack waste into some vat, and I see it gets stirred around, and it gets rolled around, then it goes through the treatment plant and right into the river, *schwoop!*"

Oilfield brine in Pennsylvania was initially discharged to pits and streams. These practices were banned in the 1980s and more sophisticated options developed, such as spreading the waste on public roads to try and melt snow and ice or reduce dust. Pennsylvania has far fewer injection wells than other oilfield states, such as Ohio, which has hundreds, or Texas, which has thousands. Before the state's fracking boom began, around 2005, Pennsylvania was still producing tens of millions of gallons of oilfield wastewater a year. Another tactic was needed for disposing of oilfield brine, and a custom developed of bringing this waste to sewage plants and places the state called centralized waste treatment facilities. They accept the waste, treat it in some way to remove contaminants, then discharge the treated waste back into a creek or river. In order for this discharge to be legal, the facilities need a National Pollutant Discharge Elimination System—NPDES—permit, which is supposed to ensure worrisome toxic elements aren't being shot back into rivers and the environment.

There was a problem with this system. According to the U.S. Geological Survey National Produced Waters Geochemical Database, even brine from conventional oil and gas wells in Pennsylvania can have levels of radium above 20,000 picocuries per liter, thousands of times higher than EPA's safe drinking water limit for radium, which is 5 picocuries per liter. But NPDES permits for centralized waste treatment plants didn't require operators to check for radium in the discharge they were putting back into Pennsylvania creeks and rivers.

"The problem started in 1859, with the first oil and gas well drilled in Pennsylvania," says David Hess, who led the Pennsylvania Department of Environmental Protection in the early 2000s and now runs the PA Environment Digest Blog, an invaluable site that keeps tabs on oil and gas and other environmental legislation in the Pennsylvania statehouse. "Every well from the time it is drilled until it is plugged produces brine/wastewater, day in and day out, and it has to be dealt with," Hess tells me via email in 2023. "Conventional well drillers never wanted to pay anything to get rid of this water so they just dumped it wherever, streams, holes they dug, spread it on roads they said to control dust (it doesn't, it's disposal)." He continues, "no one watches what's being shipped, what's being accepted, what's being cleaned up and reused, what's being discharged from these facilities. It's the wild west!" And while in 2010 the Pennsylvania Department of Environmental Protection added stricter discharge limits for salts and some metals at these treatment facilities, there were still no rules for radium.

By 2010, with the Marcellus Shale being intensively developed with the techniques of modern fracking, a massive new wave of oilfield wastewater was headed for the plants, 232 million gallons a year, according to a presentation by an oilfield wastewater treatment plant operator named Paul Hart. It included Marcellus flowback, with its largely unknown toxic cocktail of resurfaced frack chemicals, as well as Marcellus oilfield brine and all its salts, carcinogens, heavy metals, and radium.

In 2015, the environmental engineer Bill Burgos, along with a team of other researchers set out to examine whether they might be able to find places in Pennsylvania's environment where this oilfield radium was accumulating. They realized that 12 miles downstream of Paul Hart's oilfield wastewater treatment plant, on Blacklick Creek, was a reservoir called Conemaugh River Lake. Another oilfield waste treatment plant discharged into Blacklick Creek at a distance of six miles from the lake.

Burgos, and Penn State's Nathaniel Warner, the same geochemist studying the accumulation of oilfield radium in mussels, hypothesized that oilfield contaminants might be flowing all the way down the creek, to where it joins the Conemaugh River, then into the reservoir, which was formed by a dam. Because sediments accumulate regularly every year at the bottom of lakes, and a dammed lake is particularly good at trapping sediments, these mucky bottom layers can provide a detailed window into an area's pollution history. Indeed, the researchers found that coring down through layers of lake muck was like tracing back the years of the Marcellus Shale boom. A paper they published in the journal *Environmental Science & Technology* in 2017 reported that "sediment layers corresponding to the years of maximum" oil and gas wastewater disposal contained higher concentrations of salts and chemicals with the signature of oilfield waste.

Dr. Avner Vengosh, the Duke University geochemist who had studied brine spills in North Dakota and the liquid deicer AquaSalina in Ohio, sampled the point where an oilfield wastewater treatment plant discharged into Blacklick Creek, in western Pennsylvania. His research team found radium levels in the stream sediments at the point of discharge were about 200 times greater than the levels in the upstream and background sediments. The levels were so high, the researchers reported in 2013 in *Environmental Science & Technology*, that in certain states, Michigan for example, they "would require transportation...to a licensed radioactive waste disposal facility." Oilfield wastewater treatment plants were clearly incapable of removing all the dangerous contaminants from the waste streams they were taking in.

The EPA knew this too, and in a little-publicized 2018 report on oilfield wastewater treatment plants in Pennsylvania, Ohio, and West Virginia, said there were "documented and potential impacts to both aquatic life and human health related to discharges from...facilities treating oil and gas extraction wastewater." EPA pointed out that, "multiple drinking water intakes are situated downstream of" these treatment plants. The Department of Energy also examined the issue, with a fieldtrip made by an Argonne National Laboratory scientist, and a report published in 2010. "As the Marcellus Shale development grew in popularity, operators sought permission to bring more truckloads of salty flowback and produced water to the treatment plants," they reported, resulting in an increased discharge of salts from the oilfield wastewater into waterways. Argonne is one of the nation's most sophisticated labs for analyzing radioactivity, but the report never once mentioned the word. I have asked Argonne why not, and not received a reply.

In 2016, the Pennsylvania Department of Environmental Protection published an expansive report on oilfield radioactivity in the Marcellus. The conclusion was, "there is little or limited potential for radiation exposure to workers and the public." But the contents of the report revealed facilities treating Marcellus oilfield wastewater had an extraordinary radiological problem on their hands. At centralized waste treatment plants and also sewage plants, the state found concerning levels of radium accumulating in the sludge that settled out of the wastewater, the sediment at the point of discharge, and the treated wastewater the plants were discharging to waterways. Some plants were discharging radium back to the environment at levels thousands of times EPA's safe drinking water limit. Radiation exposure rates for workers were occasionally at levels dozens of times what would be considered a contaminated workspace by US government health agencies, and radioactivity found on plant surfaces, according to the report, presented "a potential inhalation or ingestion hazard." This raised the point that these workers should be treated more like nuclear workers than sewage plant workers.

Brett Jennings, Chairman of the Hallstead-Great Bend Joint Sewer Authority, in northeastern Pennsylvania, tells me he was against accepting the oilfield brine and flowback the fracking industry was seeking to dispose of at Marcellus area sewage plants like his. For one, says Jennings, sewage plants are not meant to process the complicated brew of chemicals, heavy metals and radioactive elements in fracking wastewater. He saw in real time what happened when his plant tried. In 2014, a pair of brine trucks were discovered near an abandoned railroad track, illegally discharging into one of the plant's sewer lines. "They actually lifted the manhole up and dumped it right down," says Jennings. The incident happened in the morning. By afternoon, his plant was dead.

But as the Marcellus boom came on and continued through the financial crisis in 2008 local governments were broke and desperate. In 2009, the *ProPublica* investigative reporter Joaquin Sapien reported that when Francis Geletko, financial director at a sewage treatment plant in Clairton, a city south of Pittsburgh located along the Monongahela River, learned drillers would pay 5 cents a gallon to get their wastewater processed at his plant his first thought was: "Cha-ching!" Pennsylvania had enabled a practice that was discharging a considerable yet largely unknown stream of additional radium into the same rivers Pennsylvanians relied on for drinking water.

And all roads lead to Pittsburgh, the city of three rivers. Here, the Monongahela meanders in from the south to meet the Allegheny, which enters from the northeast to form the Ohio, which exits toward the west. Water for downtown Pittsburgh is covered by the Pittsburgh Water & Sewer Authority. Much of the area north of Pittsburgh in Allegheny County is serviced by local municipalities. "And the whole southern part," a former Pittsburgh Water & Sewer Authority water plant worker tells me, headed south along the Monongahela River and into Washington, Greene, Fayette and Westmoreland counties, the four counties where the Ewing sarcoma cases had occurred, "that's mostly Pennsylvania American country."

¤ ¤ ¤

Pennsylvania American Water is a subsidiary of American Water, founded in 1886 as the American Water Works & Guarantee Company. "Our beginnings were humble," says the company. "A small group of entrepreneurs and innovators spurred the nation's industrial development by bringing a critical commodity - pure, abundant water - to towns and cities across the land." Over the 20th century the company bought up smaller water providers and expanded. By 1999, American Water Works, as it was then called, served 345 billion gallons of water to more than ten million customers. "Today," they say. "We work hard each and every day to supply our customers with something they cannot live without - high-quality water."

But the oil and gas boom in Pennsylvania was so big it didn't just swallow up local governments and fire departments and sewage plants and environmental protection departments, it swallowed drinking water providers too. "Private Water Companies Join Forces With Fracking Interests," reads the 2012 headline of an article in the *Colorado Independent*. It detailed how "two of the country's largest private water utility companies are participants in a massive lobbying effort to expand controversial shale gas drilling." One was American Water. Apparently, because the practice drank up so much water, fracking was good for the drinking water business.

In 2011, Pennsylvania American Water joined the Marcellus Shale Coalition, the fracking industry's powerful trade group. Annual associate membership dues at the time were $15,000. American Water will "continue to be stewards of the environment," spokesman Terry Maenza told the *Colorado Independent*. In 2011 he told another investigative reporter that Pennsylvania American Water had at one point considered leasing its properties for gas drilling, but shelved the idea and instead decided fracking should be restricted to a distance of at least 1,000 feet from a reservoir relied upon for drinking water.

American Water's priorities are laid out in the company's 2012 annual report to investors. "Dear Fellow Stockholder," begins a message from Chairman of the Board President George MacKenzie and Chief Executive Officer Jeff Sterba. "We increased earnings per share from continuing operations by more than 12 percent to $2.11 per diluted share. Revenues, net margin and cash flow all increased, strengthening our balance sheet, while we improved our regulated operation and maintenance (O&M) efficiency ratio to 40.7 percent." And, the report continues, "we entered into agreements with two energy companies to construct pipelines for supplying water to support shale gas drilling operations."

By the beginning of 2012, American Water was selling water to the oil and gas industry at 34 different distribution points in Pennsylvania. We are "remaining vigilant in protecting our water sources," a March 2012 presentation to investors stated. And what exactly were their water sources? The company has three large drinking water intake facilities that serve customers in Washington County and southern Allegheny County, the E.H. Aldrich Water Treatment Plant, the Brownsville Treatment Plant, and the Hays Mine Water Treatment Plant. All three are located along the Monongahela River.

The Monongahela flows from south to north, starting as a series of rushing creeks in the mountains of West Virginia. While the eastern forks begin in largely undeveloped highlands in the Appalachian Mountains, one of the Monongahela's principal tributaries, West Fork River, flows through the heart of West Virginia fracking country before crossing the border into Pennsylvania, where the river continues to draw its water from smaller creeks and streams originating in some of the most heavily fracked land in Greene, Washington, and Fayette counties.

"One thing I think you need to keep in mind is the whole drinking water industry's formation was based primarily on microbiology," says Dr. Mike Domach, a chemical engineer at Carnegie Mellon University in Pittsburgh and also board member of the Pittsburgh Water & Sewer Authority. Initial water providers, he points out, were worried about things like cholera and dysentery, not oilfield salts and radium. "Chemistry and pollutants have been an add on," he says.

Domach also notes that drinking water systems are based on what's referred to as the barrier model. That is, a drinking water provider has a number of different barriers intended to keep contaminants or disease from entering their water supply. This might start with the protection of the water supply's watershed, include guidelines regarding the discharge of harmful waste into waterways, and treatment and disinfection at a drinking water plant before the water is passed on to the public. The establishment of a single industry across the landscape in a way that is pointed yet also diffuse and difficult to assess represents a significant challenge to the barrier model.

Several agencies and initiatives were monitoring water quality as fracking boomed across the area, including the U.S. Geological Survey, the Ohio River Valley Water Sanitation Commission, West Virginia University's Water Research Institute, and a group of water providers called the River Alert Information Network, or RAIN, which Pennsylvania American Water was a part of. But the release of oilfield waste into the Monongahela was so substantial that sophisticated techniques were not necessarily required, it appeared to be gumming up industrial machinery and household appliances, and contamination could even be tasted.

"Workers at a steel mill and a power plant were the first to notice something strange about the Monongahela River last summer," Joaquin Sapien reported in his 2009 article for *ProPublica*. "The water that U.S. Steel and Allegheny Energy used to power their plants contained so much salty sediment that it was corroding their machinery. Nearby residents saw something odd, too. Dishwashers were malfunctioning, and plates were coming out with spots that couldn't easily be rinsed off." In the summer of 2008, people relying on the Monongahela had also begun complaining about a salty taste in their drinking water.

Dr. Jeanne VanBriesen, an engineer at Carnegie Mellon University, along with colleagues warned that the influx of salts from oilfield waste, or other industrial sources such as coal-fired power plants, could substantially raise levels of bromide in the Monongahela. The concern was that when bromide combined with the chlorine used by water plants for treatment substances called trihalomethanes would be produced. When consumed over long periods of time trihalomethanes have been associated with bladder cancer. "Especially during the low-flow conditions of 2008 and 2009," VanBriesen and Dr. Jessica Wilson pointed out in 2012 in the journal *Environmental Practice*, "these loads would be expected to affect drinking water."

A number of concerns with fracking had been documented by Pennsylvania residents and researchers, and in many instances not much seemed to change regarding the industry's practices. But the Carnegie Mellon research had a profound effect, and this concern for drinking water led to action. In 2010 the Pennsylvania Department of Environmental Protection had limited the discharge of salts and heavy metals at plants processing oilfield wastewater, but a loophole enabled the practice to continue at many facilities. In April 2011 the department issued a statement intending to close that and shutdown the practice altogether. "Basically, I see this as a huge success story," Michael Krancer, the Acting Secretary of the Department of Environmental Protection, told the Associated Press. "This will be a vestige of the past very quickly."

"We never thought that it was a good practice to begin with," stated Range Resources spokesman Matt Pitzarella. John Hanger, Michael Krancer's predecessor as Pennsylvania's environmental secretary told the Associated Press that as early as 2008 he had been approached by Range Resources and another operator warning that the state's permissive rules on oilfield wastewater treatment plant discharges had left rivers and streams at risk from the salts in oilfield waste. "They came to me," Hanger explained, "and said, if this rule doesn't change, there could be enormous amounts of wastewater...pouring into the rivers."

Now the rules had changed, but just how much of the oilfield's radium had made it into the area's rivers? In 2010 and 2011, Ian Urbina, an investigative reporter at the *New York Times*, turned his attention to America's fracking boom. The articles he produced were a deeply researched and sweeping indictment on the industry's sloppiness, exemptions, and risks. The very first story he published, on February 26, 2011, focused on Pennsylvania and ran on the front page of the newspaper. It was titled, "Regulation Lax as Gas Wells' Tainted Water Hits Rivers," and lays out an apocalyptic scene.

"Drilling derricks tower over barns, lining rural roads like feed silos. Drilling sites bustle around the clock with workers, some in yellow hazardous material suits, and 18-wheelers haul equipment, water and waste along back roads," Urbina wrote. "The rigs announce their presence with the occasional boom and quiver of underground explosions. Smelling like raw sewage mixed with gasoline, drilling-waste pits, some as large as a football field, sit close to homes."

Urbina had visited oilfields across the nation and discovered many problems, but the lead story of his investigation focused on the issue of centralized waste treatment facilities and sewage plants discharging radioactivity into Pennsylvania's rivers. In memos he unearthed from EPA officials, the pollution the practice enabled was described as "one of the largest failures in U.S. history to supply clean drinking water to the public." Urbina honed in on the radioactive element radium. The oilfield waste being brought to these plants "contains radioactivity at levels higher than previously known, and far higher than the level that federal regulators say is safe for these treatment plants to handle," he wrote. Plants not designed to treat this radioactive load were then discharging right back "into rivers that supply drinking water."

Urbina pointed out plants had discharged not only to the Monongahela, but also the Susquehanna River, which feeds into Chesapeake Bay and provides drinking water to people in Baltimore, and the Delaware River, which provides drinking water for more than 15 million people in Philadelphia and across eastern Pennsylvania. In New York, oilfield wastewater was sent to at least one plant that discharged into Southern Cayuga Lake, in the Finger Lakes region, an area famous for its family-run dairy farms and vineyards.

"There is no way of guaranteeing that the drinking water taken in by all these plants is safe," wrote Urbina. "Sewage treatment plant operators say they are far less capable of removing radioactive contaminants than most other toxic substances. Indeed, most of these facilities cannot remove enough of the radioactive material to meet federal drinking-water standards before discharging the wastewater into rivers, sometimes just miles upstream from drinking-water intake plants." He noted, "the bigger danger of radioactive wastewater is its potential to contaminate drinking water or enter the food chain through fish or farming" and said, "once radium enters a person's body, by eating, drinking or breathing, it can cause cancer."

It was a major newspaper loudly ringing the alarm bell, and Pennsylvanians already skeptical of the industry and trying to hold it accountable now had new material. To quell the concern, the Pennsylvania Department of Environmental Protection and Pennsylvania American Water both conducted water testing.

"The DEP tested water from the Monongahela River at Charleroi in Washington County; South Fork Tenmile Creek in Greene County; Conemaugh River bordering Westermoreland and Indiana counties; Allegheny River at Kennerdell in Venango County; Beaver River in Lawrence County; Tioga River in Tioga County, and the West Branch of the Susquehanna River in Lycoming County," the *Pittsburgh Post-Gazette* reported in March 2011. Radium levels were reported to be at or below normal background levels. "I'm pleased by it, of course, as all Pennsylvanians should be," John Hanger, the former secretary of the Pennsylvania Department of Environmental Protection told the paper. "The results demonstrate powerfully that the concerns raised by The

Times articles were false and Pennsylvania runs a stringent oversight program for the gas drilling industry."

Pennsylvania American Water conducted tests of their own and say they found no radioactivity dangers. The results were widely broadcast across the state's media outlets, and also by the industry. "Following a full battery of tests at Pennsylvania American Water's raw water intakes along the Allegheny, Clarion and Monongahela Rivers and Two Lick Creek, in Indiana, PA, the company found no elevated or harmful levels of radiological contaminants, volatile organic compounds (VOCs) or inorganic compounds (IOCs)," the Marcellus Shale Coalition reported on May 18, 2011. The coalition condemned newspapers, such as the *Philadelphia Inquirer*, which had run editorials based on what they called "the debunked New York Times story," and said, "the results confirmed that the quality of the water supplied by Pennsylvania American Water's treatment plants has not been impacted by radioactive materials."

The EPA has enforceable rules on radium in drinking water. The limit, which adds together radium-226 and radium-228, is 5 picocuries per liter. If radium is detected but remains below 2.5 picocuries per liter, then the facility must check for radium once every six years. If a plant finds radium at between 2.5 and 5.0 picocuries per liter, they must check every three years. If a plant finds no radium in their drinking water, what is known as a non-detect, they are required to test for radium once every nine years.

The ancient Greek philosopher Heraclitus famously said, you cannot step into the same river twice. Any waterway is continuously flowing and thus continuously changing, yet EPA's rules mean that for many drinking water plants, tests for radium were only being done once every 3,285 days, during a single moment of a single day. "To do radium once every nine years is ridiculous," says the former water plant worker from the Pittsburgh Water & Sewer Authority. "That is like you take a dart and shoot it into a huge room, well the radium could be anywhere in that room. It's like shooting blind."

Even without industry putting additional radioactivity back into the environment, many parts of the US have naturally high radium levels in groundwater and drinking water, including parts of Illinois, Texas and North Carolina. But in southwestern Pennsylvania, a new radium-generating industry had established itself across the landscape. In his February 2011 story, Ian Urbina and the *New York Times* reviewed data from more than 65 drinking water intake plants downstream from some of the busiest drilling regions in Pennsylvania. "Not one has tested for radioactivity since 2008," he wrote, "and most have not tested since at least 2005, before most of the drilling waste was being produced."

When in 2021 I ask Pennsylvania American Water Government and External Affairs Director Gary Lobaugh to provide the results for radium testing going back to the beginning of the Marcellus Shale boom, in 2005, for the drinking water treatment plants his company uses to supply water to Washington County, where many of the Ewing sarcoma cancer cases were centered, he tells me: "All radium sampling results were non-detect between 2005 – 2019." Lobaugh has not yet provided me with actual results or details of the testing his company did after the *New York Times* article but in 2024 says: "To reiterate, the company found no elevated or harmful levels of radiological contaminants" and the results "confirmed that radioactive materials...from Marcellus Shale drilling wastewater had not impacted the water quality supplied by Pennsylvania American Water's treatment plants." I point out that in 2009 water in the Monongahela River experienced a large and concerning rise in salts and Pennsylvania American Water was part of an effort to look into this matter. "The source of the total dissolved solids was never determined," Lobaugh tells me.

As for my question of whether or not the company believes a drinking water provider providing water for the fracking industry represents a conflict of interest, Lobaugh tells me, "Pennsylvania American Water has worked with the natural gas industry since its inception in 1886" and state rules dictate “the company cannot discriminate against any water service applicant based on end-use.”

¤ ¤ ¤

If the oilfield’s radium, in its path from wellhead to treatment plant to being discharged to a river could end up being concentrated in mud at the bottom of a reservoir, or the shells of a river mussel, then could the bones of kids who drank water run through the same set of rivers have concentrated radium in a similar manner?

“When I started out with the field of pediatric epidemiology I figured environmental exposures would mostly be the cause of many of these rare cancers, and over the years I have learned that this is just not the case,” says Dr. Logan Spector, who directs the Division of Epidemiology and Clinical Research at the University of Minnesota and is one of the nation’s foremost experts on the distribution, patterns, and causes behind Ewing sarcoma. “It more has to do with genes, and lots of genes together creating a milieu that makes the cells more or less vulnerable. Sometimes people are disappointed to hear that, because we can clean up the environment, though it’s less easy to change someone’s genes—but it is what it is.”

“Ewing sarcoma has some very distinct patterns by your ancestry,” he tells me. “Basically, European kids and also Pacific Islanders and maybe Middle Easterners have the highest rates. It is virtually absent among people with significant African ancestry, and east Asians have less risk too. Latinos have intermediate risk. If you were to map Ewing’s in the US, I have zero doubt you would find lower incidence in the South, and we would find it highest in the whitest states. If a cluster were happening among Black children in rural Georgia that would blow my mind. But the fact that there is an alleged cluster of cases in southwestern Pennsylvania, among a very White population, is not very surprising.”

Spector understands why a community might look to radiation as the cause for the disease. But, he says, “there are physiological hallmarks of radiation induced cancers, certain signatures of mutation, and to my knowledge Ewing's does not really exhibit them. Ewing's is very mutationally quiet, and that makes me think it is not caused by radiation." Still, Spector is concerned enough about the oil and gas industry's releases of radioactivity that he believes a nationwide study should be done to assess incidences of cancers like Ewing sarcoma in relation to the distance people live from oilfield waste treatment or disposal sites.

There is another way to learn potentially valuable information. "Analyzing the tumor of a kid with Ewing sarcoma would not be difficult and could provide the thumbprint for what might have caused it," says Spector. Though there are complications. Even something simple, like washing a tumor after removal could affect results. And profiling tumors is still a relatively young science. "They are good questions," he says, "and to my knowledge, no one is asking these questions, and nobody is looking to answer them. We all concentrate on different parts of the elephant, and these are studies for the young and enterprising who are willing to try something very different."

And yet, for me, the question remains—with thousands of researchers devoting their careers to studying cancer, why aren't more of them dissecting Ewing sarcoma tumors? Why aren't they probing more carefully the possibility that radioactivity may be a cause of the disease? It would seem incredible, Spector tells me, but "it is not incredible. These are not common cancers, and a lot of people don't want to stake their career on studying something rare." But there is one researcher who has.

During the 1990s, the Canadian epidemiologist Dr. Murray Finkelstein published a pair of studies on naturally occurring radium contamination in drinking water and the presence of Ewing sarcoma and osteosarcoma among Ontario youths. He wanted to know if there was an association between the amount of radium in home drinking water and the risk of death from these bone cancers. Finkelstein is still around, and one spring afternoon I reach him by phone.

For decades the radiation health community has abided by what is known as the Linear No-Threshold model. It acknowledges that scientific data points to a direct connection between cancer and radioactivity when levels are high. Turn up the radiation, and across a large population of individuals cancers increase. Although the data at low levels is inconclusive, the Linear No-Threshold model says there is no threshold at which this relationship breaks down, and even small amounts of radiation will somewhere in the population cause some cancer, and that it is appropriate for health officials to enact laws and policies accordingly. There have always been powerful critics of the Linear No-Threshold model, and they remain today. Finkelstein is not one of them.

"If you accept there is no threshold, then it is plausible that a small number of cases will arise at the low doses if the population exposed is large enough," says Finkelstein. The factors affecting any single human individual or community are inherently complicated, and he says the difficulty is that the signal of an exposure may often be hard to find. "You will never have a large enough population for this signal to easily be identified," he says. The work of an epidemiologist is to have a full enough view of the problem and its potential causes to at least be able to propose an elegant and precise way of examining the question.

On this note, Finkelstein was fortunate. While studying Ewing sarcoma he was working as an epidemiologist for the province of Ontario and had access to data. He was able to obtain a computer tape containing the death certificates for Ontario residents between 1950 and 1983 and identify people 25 years or younger who had died of bone cancer during this time. He then linked these people to their birth certificates and was able to obtain the patient's address at the time of death, and their mother's address at the time of birth. This meant water samples could be collected from the same drinking water source presumably used by the patient throughout their youth, and that water could then be sampled for radium.

Finkelstein's paper, published in 1994 in the *Canadian Medical Association Journal* and entitled, "Radium in drinking water and the risk of death from bone cancer among Ontario youths," reported the stunning result that even minute increases in radium in drinking water can lead to an increase in death from bone cancers, including Ewing sarcoma. There is a "statistically significant" relationship between levels of radium in drinking water and Ewing sarcoma, he wrote. Finkelstein co-published a follow-up paper in 1996, which found an association between risk of osteosarcoma, the more common form of bone cancer, and birthplace exposure to radium in drinking water. This paper did not find the same association for Ewing's, but it didn't negate his prior results. "The papers," says Finkelstein, "were generally ignored, and I don't think the research had much impact or influence."

Still, he has gained an extraordinary expertise on this little studied topic, and when I describe to him the Ewing sarcoma cases of southwestern Pennsylvania he is interested and clarifies information others had ignored. For example, Finkelstein provides an explanation on why some Ewing tumors may form in the sinus cavity, as was the case with 37-year-old David Cobb. "The radon gets into the bloodstream from its release in the bones and as the blood passes through the membranes in the sinus cavity radon outgases," says Finkelstein. Sinus cancer is one of the cancers that occurred in uranium miners, he continues. "You need a blood air interface, like the lung—or the sinus."

"I think the only ingestion pathway of any concern is drinking water," he says. To try and crack the case, he says, you would need to get a sample of the water the kids were drinking during the early and middle years of the Marcellus boom, to cover the span of time just as the Ewing's cases were developing and the few years before, and also get a sample of the drinking water well before fracking ever began in the region, then compare the two. "It is most unlikely that anyone has a bottle of tap water from 12 years ago," says Finkelstein. But, maybe, he speculates, somewhere, "there is a water museum." In other words, an old sample of drinking water which would hold a record of the radium signature of that time.

The idea is striking, and I spend weeks with it, months. I ponder wine, and become enthusiastic, because every bottle is dated and there are wineries near where the cancers occurred in Washington County, Pennsylvania. But in my enthusiasm, I fail to remember wine is made entirely from crushed grapes, no water is used. I consider pickling, maybe someone has used tap water in canning cucumbers or bell peppers in dated jars going back decades, but Finkelstein informs me the pickling brine may introduce sampling concerns, and a jar of pickled vegetables would not be the ideal water museum. In September 2022, I connect with Stacey Magda and Ashley Funk, of Mountain Watershed Association, the watershed and environmental justice group, based in Fayette County, and Heaven Sensky of Center for Coalfield Justice, in Washington County. They have lost community members and classmates to Ewing sarcoma and not given up on the possibility that the oil and gas industry's radioactivity may have been a cause. We organize with a local plumbing company to go around the region and remove the P-traps of willing residents.

These are the U-shaped pipes under most kitchen sinks, in place to ensure foul sewer gases can't flow up into a home. They also serve to trap sediment that is washed down the sink, and if there was an elevated level of radium in the drinking water then perhaps these traps would have preserved a record. I send the P-trap samples to Dr. Marco Kaltofen, the nuclear forensics scientist, based in Massachusetts, who once memorably told me: "Everything that we do leaves a microscopic trail. Radiation is complex and difficult to understand but it leaves hundreds of clues, and that data is just there, waiting to be collected."

Kaltofen is a bit like Sherlock Holmes, with a Geiger counter. He has examined fallout from the Fukushima nuclear disaster in Japan, and found it, in street dust, car air filters, home vacuum cleaner bags and the bottom of children's shoes. He has searched for radioactivity in the homes of American nuclear weapons workers and found it there in spades, and in one instance, layered in dust atop a beer refrigerator, drifted off the worker's clothes. He once sifted through the ashes of a uranium worker's dead wife in search of radioactive elements from the nuclear fuel cycle accidentally brought home on her husband's clothes and suspected to have caused the cancer that killed her—and he found these too. He even has an eco-thriller novel protagonist styled after him—"Only Sangamon Taylor, a vigilante who slings a test tube instead of a revolver, can put two and two together," reads a description of the 1988 book, *Zodiac*.

Needless to say, Kaltofen reports back to me that the P-traps "were essentially reading no different from background." I still needed a water museum. Then I find the following EPA document: "A Regulators' Guide to the Management of Radioactive Residuals from Drinking Water Treatment Technologies."

It states that drinking water treatment plants can concentrate considerable amounts of radioactivity as they filter water for drinking. This material builds up as a sludge, which in the drinking water business is called residuals. In parts of the country with elevated levels of naturally occurring radioactivity, or where drinking water treatment plants are located near facilities that could potentially contaminate water sources with radioactive substances, EPA says the treatment of drinking water "will produce residuals containing regulated radionuclides." Meaning these residuals could become so radioactive they must be taken to a special radioactive waste disposal facility. Drinking water treatment plant residuals, I realized, represented a water museum.

To obtain files that I expected to detail what was in the residuals at the three drinking water plants operated by Pennsylvania American Water I setup a formal slot of time known as a file review at the Pennsylvania Department of Environmental Protection's Southwest Regional Office in Pittsburgh. I had already formally requested of the Department of Environmental Protection all of the reports, presentations, letters, emails and text messages sent on state-issued phones containing the words "radium"; "radium-226"; "radium-228"; or "radioactivity problem" from David Allard, who served as Director of the Pennsylvania Department of Environmental Protection's Bureau of Radiation Protection from 1999 through July 2022, when he retired. My assumption was that if there was a radium problem at the drinking water plants, the state's top radiation officer would have known and there would be some record of that knowledge in their emails or reports. But a department official responded a few months later to tell me: "your request is denied." One reason, they stated, is because Allard had retired, his "email account was deleted approximately thirty days from his departure from Commonwealth employment consistent with Commonwealth standard practice."

So, I filed a second records request to the Pennsylvania Department of Environmental Protection, this time also asking for records from Dwight Shearer, who was not retired. He had replaced Allard as the department's top radiation officer and been at the agency for some time. This request was also denied. But at the department's Southwest Regional Office, going through a set of colored folders in the file review room on the first floor of the building one spring day, I discover several important things. For one, I find there was a radium reading taken by Pennsylvania American Water that indicated there may have been much more radium in their drinking water system than suggested by the company's continual radium non-detects.

Documents filed by Pennsylvania American Water's E.H. Aldrich plant, on April 6, 2010, show that out of three samples of water discharged from the plant back into the Monongahela River, one recorded not 0.0 picocuries per liter, the equivalent of a non-detect, but 13.21 picocuries per liter for combined radium-226 and radium-228. The value is well above the EPA's drinking water limit of 5 picocuries per liter. If after treatment on this day there was still this much radium in the water the plant was putting back out to the river, how much was in the water the plant sent through the pipes residents would draw their drinking water from? I do not find the answer to that question in the files I am reviewing, but I find something else.

On November 6, 1996, Pennsylvania American Water sent a letter to the Pennsylvania Department of Environmental Protection requesting that residuals from their Hays Mine and E.H. Aldrich drinking water plants, a combined total of 16,000 tons a year, "no longer" be classified as "a waste" and instead be reclassified "as soil." This soil would "be used as topsoil and in topsoil blends" in residential lawns, ball fields, highway projects, and landscaping activities. The letter, from Randolph Pankiewicz, water quality supervisor with Pennsylvania-American Water Company, to David Eberle in the Bureau of Waste Management, states: "Pennsylvania-American water company appreciates the Department's cooperation in working with us to turn a residual waste into a natural resource."

On November 26, 1996, the Department of Environmental Protection responded with a letter to Pennsylvania American Water's request. Unlike my own requests, this one was not denied. The "department has completed a review," the letter states, and determined the drinking water company "may proceed as proposed." As of January 2019, I know the exemption was still in place, because Pennsylvania American Water reminded the state in a letter that their E.H. Aldrich and Hays Mine plants' residuals "is not considered waste and does not require any permits or tracking."

The takeaway for me was scary. In Pennsylvania, aside from all the other ways in which the oil and gas industry's radium-rich waste was sloppily and illegally handled and disposed, the state allowed hundreds of millions of gallons of fracking wastewater to be legally disposed of at treatment and sewage plants. The plants could not fully remove the radium and shot the bone-seeking radioactive metal into the same rivers many of the state's residents relied on for drinking water. Drinking water plant residuals would hold a clue as to how much radium had been in the water of that time, and given the general radioactive nature of drinking water plant residuals and the oil and gas industry's presence in the area, these particular residuals would be expected to, quite possibly, be reasonably radioactive. And yet, there were no residuals as far as the state of Pennsylvania and Pennsylvania American Water were concerned. They had been, through legal means, transformed from "waste" into "topsoil" and spread on God knows how many home lawns and baseball fields. Not knowing who to call with this information, which to me seemed so devastating and important, I dial up the health physicist source I had met at the DC sports bar.

"That is bad, that is bad, bad, bad, bad," they tell me. "There could be a lot of radium going through those plants, when the filters get disposed they often have to go to a low-level radioactive waste facility." It is not just radium, uranium is naturally in drinking water too and drinking water plant residuals can become so enriched they are considered "source material" by the Nuclear Regulatory Commission. There is the 2016 case from the Charles Allen Water Filtration Plant in Englewood, Colorado, where three workers had died of cancer and coworkers believed the drinking water plant's radioactive residuals were responsible.

"This stuff gets passed around, you can't destroy it, all you can do is get it off your ledger and onto someone else's," the health physicist source tells me. "It is not a good situation—they got away with one."

Gary Lobaugh, with Pennsylvania American Water, tells me their residuals are "typically used for brownfield applications and soil amendments, and none has been used for ballfields." He says, "there are no radiological sample requirements for residuals" and adds that, "there has been no indication of radiological contamination based on safe drinking water radiological analyses."

I am still digging.

And the answer to that bad joke I have heard in oil and gas country—what is the final stage of the fracking process?

It is a cancer clinic.

16
Oversight

In the high desert country of New Mexico a pot of gumbo is cooking on the stove. The adobe house has 16-inch walls and hallways adorned with books of poetry and watercolors. In the richly decorated desert garden are wind chimes and hummingbirds. It is in this place that Dr. Paul Templet, who during the late 1980s and early 1990s served as Secretary of the Department of Environmental Quality for the state of Louisiana has chosen to escape.

"Out my back window I see the Sangre de Cristo, and out my front on a clear day I can see the Pedernal, that flat mountain Georgia O'Keeffe painted," says Templet. The mountains are a refuge for him too. "I am at 7,000 feet," he says, "so all you have to do is open your window and the house cools down. The humidity is low, it's wonderful." And a long way from the hot muggy alligator filled swamps of his childhood.

These days, government officials in oil and gas states charged with safeguarding the environment meet regularly with oil and gas industry lobbyists and often may seem like another branch of the industry, there to ensure permits are promptly granted, plans stamped and approved without too much fuss, industry enabled to run their operations smoothly and make their profits. Meanwhile, the concerns and demands of environmentalists are often treated as unrealistic or impractical. Those who care about Mother Earth appear as thorns in the side of the agency's tasked with protecting her. Among today's environmental regulators, to seriously hold oil and gas accountable for all its violations, and to go even further, and create new rules to curb the industry's practices and probe its secrets seems impossible, even laughable. But it is possible, it just takes courage.

In 1987, Buddy Roemer, a candidate running on a message of reform was elected governor of Louisiana. "There's no question about where we are - we're in trouble," Roemer told a reporter. "The old deal was a deal with the Devil - you send us the jobs and you can foul the air and the water. But now, when you have a lousy environment and the highest unemployment rate in America, something's very wrong." He compared Louisiana to a Middle Eastern oil "sheikdom" and said his aim was to bring the state "tip-toeing into the 20th century." As part of that effort, Roemer did something extraordinary by Louisiana standards—he created a position on his transition team dedicated to environmental issues. And to fill it, he tapped Dr. Paul Templet.

Templet grew up on the edge of Cajun country in a rural community in central Louisiana on the banks of the Mississippi River. As a kid, he swam in the mighty river, maneuvering around the barges that lined the shore, and he hunted alligator gar and snapping turtle in the bayous nearby. His mother taught elementary school, and later became the first female principal in West Baton Rouge Parish. Baton Rouge, Louisiana's capital, was just across the river, and Templet eventually found himself there, departing the swamps for the city and what it could offer. He attended college at Louisiana State University with an interest in science and later earned a PhD there, doing his thesis in the groundbreaking field of quantum mechanics.

During the 1960s he worked as a chemist at a set of Shell oil refineries and petrochemical plants located in the stretch of industry along the Mississippi River between Baton Rouge and New Orleans known as Cancer Alley. Many of these facilities were constructed in the middle of Black communities founded after Emancipation by people that had formerly been enslaved in the adjacent plantations. “That experience was certainly eye opening,” says Templet. “People were beginning to become aware of what was going on, the air was turning brown, the water was not very good, and a lot of people were getting sick.”

Suddenly, a career in the petrochemical industry no longer seemed like the best way to protect the rich wildlife and cultures that Templet had experienced growing up. “I liked my state,” he says, “and I wanted to do what I could to help.”

He eventually took a teaching job in environmental studies back at Louisiana State University, where he helped found the first Earth Day demonstrations on campus and developed a reputation as a professor willing to challenge the status quo. A magazine journalist in the late 1980s writing on Louisiana politics described Templet as a Cajun Robert Redford, “regarded by everyone as brilliant, dedicated and amiably relentless.”

During the transitional period before Governor Roemer took office in early 1988, Templet organized a panel of environmentalists, scientists and industry representatives and setup a series of public meetings. He wanted to learn what the state’s most pressing environmental issues were from the people on the frontlines facing them. One panel member, the Louisiana environmental toxicologist Wilma Subra, told me: “Paul Templet was the only time we had that kind of environmental leadership.”

Another member was Maureen O’Neill, an official with the New Orleans Sewerage and Water Board who had an expertise in water quality. It was O’Neill who at one meeting mentioned to Templet there was radiation in the oilfields. The oil and gas industry’s produced water was “very toxic,” O’Neill later wrote, and being “discharged right back into” the same waterways where Louisianans drew their fish and seafood. Between growing up in Louisiana, working for Shell, and teaching environmental studies at Louisiana State University, Templet thought he knew all the oil and gas industry’s dirty secrets, but this one was new.

"It was the only environmental issue in Louisiana anyone ever sprang on me that I didn't know anything about," he says.

Templet soon found that certain officials in the Department of Environmental Quality did know of the issue, though had taken no action. "The clout of the oil and gas industry was too strong, no one wanted to go against them," he explains. The topic of oilfield radioactivity, despite all its profound ramifications and risks, was just sort of floating around among the officials of Louisiana's top environmental agency, with some folks knowing a bit, many knowing nothing, but no one having the gumption to do anything. And there the issue would have remained, except it happened to have been told to the right person.

Templet was accustomed to going against the state's big oil interests. In the 1970s he led a state coastal management program and helped develop environmental rules to protect Louisiana's coastal zone against out-of-control oil and gas development. Before Templet could craft rules to address oilfield radioactivity, he needed to understand the scale of the problem. Data was essential, and the industry did not appear to have any—at least so they said. "We ordered the oil industry to give us numbers for what is in their produced water, and it turns out no one knew," says Templet. So his staff went to work, gathering radioactivity data across as much of the industry as they could access.

Templet's investigators found the job with the most significant exposure involved cleaning oilfield pipes, and several yards were located in greater New Orleans, in a part of the city called the West Bank. As in the oilfield pipe-cleaning yards of Mississippi, dust would pile up on the ground like a radioactive snowfall. Unknowing workers might be standing in drifts inches or even feet thick, recalls Templet. "They were blowing this dust everywhere, kicking it up with their feet, workers ended up coated in this dust, and they were breathing it in too," he says.

Templet sent inspectors with Geiger counters across southern Louisiana and they found children were playing on oilfield pipes the industry had provided for free to schools and communities to build fences and playgrounds. One state official witnessed a kid sitting on a fence made from piping so radioactive they were set to receive a full year's radiation dose in an hour. "People thought this was such a great deal, getting these pipes for free from the oil industry," says Templet, "but essentially the oil companies were just getting rid of their waste."

Templet's investigators also followed around oilfield workers with Geiger counters, including one western Louisiana pipe-cleaner, tracking his movements after leaving work. They found radioactivity all over his clothes, his car, his front steps, his home carpet, and even his newborn baby. "Of course," says Templet. "The industry didn't tell the workers, and there were hundreds of these workers in Louisiana alone, perhaps thousands. They were wearing nothing protective, no lead aprons, no Tyvek suits, no respirators, not even face shields."

"And the thing is," he continues, "they do die, often years later from cancer. You would think the health agency in Louisiana would have done a study, but they didn't. That is the way the industry operates, they buy silence."

Templet had discovered another concerning pathway of environmental contamination. By the time he entered office in the late 1980s, Louisiana was discharging roughly 1.8 to 2 million barrels of oilfield brine daily into the state's coastal zone, the same rich ecosystems where the state's shrimp and oysters were caught. Templet had his top water pollution scientist, Dr Kerry St. Pé, conduct a study. St. Pé and his team placed caged oysters for about a month in several locations along the Louisiana coast, approximately several hundred feet away from outfalls where oilfield brine was being discharged. They found high radium levels in the brine itself, very high radium concentrations in the sediment near the outfalls, and elevated radium in the tissue of the oysters. If school children playing on radioactive pipes and workers bringing radioactivity home to their babies weren't bad enough, Templet now had evidence that a carcinogenic bone-seeking radioactive metal was accumulating in one of the state's premier seafood items.

His officials had turned up enough evidence to show the problems were real and posed risks to oilfield workers, the public and the environment. "I was going to do something about it," Templet says. Under his guidance, the Louisiana Department of Environmental Quality issued rules that halted the copious discharges of oilfield brine into the bayous and bays and other public waterbodies of the state's coastal zone and set regulations for radioactivity at oilfield worksites and pipe-cleaning yards. "On Sept. 20, 1989," the oil industry consultant Peter Gray noted in a 1990 paper in the *Oil & Gas Journal*. "Louisiana became the first state to regulate naturally occurring radioactive materials." Texas and Mississippi began working on rules, and the issue even received national attention.

The *New York Times* ran a front-page story on December 3,1990, headlined, "Radiation Danger Found In Oilfields Across The Nation." Another *New York Times* story, published on Christmas Eve 1990, reported radiation measured in oil and gas equipment, and natural gas itself, "exposes people to levels that are equal to and at times greater than workers receive in nuclear power plants," and lawsuits "may ultimately decide whether oil companies can be held responsible for billions of dollars in expenses associated with cleaning up and disposing radioactive wastes at thousands of oil and gas sites around the nation." The industry already had its defense. "If you don't know there's a problem," one Chevron environmental specialist is quoted as saying, "how can you be blamed?"

And the pushback was extraordinary. Templet says James Watkins, then head of the U.S. Department of Energy, personally called his boss, Governor Buddy Roemer, and insisted the regulations be halted. According to Templet, "Roemer told him to shove it." State legislators hounded Templet, requesting the rules be stripped—"I don't fix tickets," he replied. And there were more personal attacks too. Maureen O'Neill, the New Orleans Sewerage and Water Board official who had first informed Templet on oilfield radioactivity had been given a job in his administration regulating water resources. She reported harassing calls in the middle of the night and suspicious home break-ins. At one point Templet received a tip that oil industry men were going through his garbage. He rode a motorcycle to work in part, he says, because "it was a harder to plant a bomb on one." Nevertheless, Templet didn't cave.

But state rules on oilfield radioactivity were only a temporary fix. They could be changed when a more industry-friendly administration came to power, and lacked the enforcement of a federal policy. For the problem of oilfield radioactivity to truly be addressed, there would have to be nationwide rules.

On October 20, 1988, Templet wrote a letter to the Occupational Safety and Health Administration warning of serious health risks to oilfield workers and the public. "The magnitude of the problem is difficult to estimate, but it is not unrealistic to expect contamination at all oil and gas production sites and pipe handling facilities," he wrote. "There are basically no regulations governing the handling and disposal" of radioactive oilfield waste.

Because of radium-226's 1,600-year half-life, "contaminated sites will be of concern for centuries," Templet stated, and radioactivity would pose a serious health threat for any buildings later constructed over these sites. "We have very little information on the fate and effects of the materials in the aquatic and terrestrial environments and on potential movement… into food chains leading to human consumption," he continued. Templet's letter to OSHA also recommended policies be developed to train workers and research pathways of contamination. There are "very difficult questions concerning potential liabilities," he warned.

But OSHA did nothing, and they still have done nothing substantial. In fact, no federal agency has issued rules on oilfield radioactivity, and oilfield workers, the American public, and the environment continue to face an extraordinary and mounting suite of risks.

Back in the high desert country of northern New Mexico, Templet takes his lunch from the pot of gumbo on the stove. He is silent while he eats, then makes us both espressos. Out of the hot desert emerges a cool breeze. Maybe it is coming from Georgia O'Keeffe's Pedernal, maybe the Sangre de Cristo beyond, or maybe somewhere even further away. Templet disappears to an office in the back of the home. Rustling can be heard, clicks on a keyboard, and then just silence. He is gone for some time. Outside, the wind chimes tingle in the breeze, the hummingbirds drink their flowers. And the blue northern New Mexico sky blues on. When Templet eventually returns, he is carrying a small black flash drive.

"Their strategy was to keep this quiet and not let anyone know what was going on," he says. "They've known for 110 years but haven't done a thing to stop it. It's the secret of the century."

He leaves the flash drive for me on the kitchen table, and steps into the sunshine.

Acknowledgements

Thank you to all the editors, publishers, and fact-checkers who believed in this work early on, and enabled this investigation to get off the ground. Those at Longreads, DeSmog, Truthdig, and Rolling Stone. And I would like to thank the following organizations, institutions, foundations, and individuals for further support in the research and reporting of this book:

Economic Hardship Reporting Project
The 11th Hour Project
Abigail Rome
The Robert Weinberg Foundation
The McGraw Center for Business Journalism at the Craig Newmark Graduate School of Journalism at the City University of New York

This work drew on tens of thousands of documents, and conversations and correspondences with hundreds, if not thousands, of individuals. There are many others who read, and listened, and provided guidance and support in other ways. All was essential, all was appreciated. To everyone—thank you.

And to MissKarret

who I met at the play
who helped each and every day
who never gave up the way

The air is a beautiful princess...

¤ ¤ ¤

Figures

Figure 1. Maximum radium levels, and average radium levels (when available), in oilfield brine for oil and gas formations across the United States as recorded in various academic, government and industry papers.

Name of Formation or Oilfield	Maximum Radium Level (Ra-226+Ra-228) / Avg	Source
Unnamed Michigan formation	29,000 pCi/L	"Radiological Dose Assessment Related to Management of Naturally Occurring Radioactive Materials Generated by the Petroleum Industry" (Argonne National Laboratory, September 1996)
Marcellus formation, Pennsylvania	28,500 pCi/L / 9,330 pCi/L	Technologically Enhanced Naturally Occurring Radioactivity Materials (TENORM) Study Report (Pennsylvania Department of Environmental Protection, 2016).

Venango formation, Pennsylvania	25,408 pCi/L	U.S. Geological Survey (USGS) Produced Waters Geochemical Database (U.S. Geological Survey, 2014)
Antrim formation, Michigan	22,358 pCi/L / 5,416 pCi/L	Fan, W., Hayes, K.F. & Ellis, B.R. Estimating radium activity in shale gas produced brine. Environ. Sci. Technol. 52, (2018)
Texas Panhandle	10,640 pCi/L	Fisher, R.S. Naturally Occurring Radioactive Materials (NORM) in Produced Water and Scale from Texas Oil, Gas, and Geothermal Wells (Bureau of Economic Geology Univ of Texas at Austin, 1995).
Clinton formation, Ohio	9,602 pCi/L	Memo on Rad Testing Results for Conventional Brine (Ohio Department of Natural Resources, Division of Oil and Gas, 2018).
Bakken formation, North Dakota	6,490 pCi/L / 3,632 pCi/L	Almie, J. NORM Sample Analysis Results Summary (Energy & Environmental Research Center, University of North Dakota, 2014).
Helderberg Ls formation, New York	3,900 pCi/L	U.S. Geological Survey (USGS) Produced Waters Geochemical Database (U.S. Geological Survey, 2014)
Gulf Coast, US	2,828 pCi/L	Snavely, E.S. Radionuclides in Produced Water (American Petroleum Institute, 1989).
San Joaquin Basin, California	2,111 pCi/L	Stoiber, T. & Walker, B. Toxic Stew: What's in Fracking Wastewater (Environmental Working Group, 2015).

Paluxy formation, Mississippi	2,099 pCi/L	U.S. Geological Survey (USGS) Produced Waters Geochemical Database (U.S. Geological Survey, 2014)
Cherokee Platform, Oklahoma	2,020 pCi/L	B.F. Armbrust & P.K. Kuroda, On the isotopic constitution of radium (Ra-224/Ra-226 and Ra-228/Ra-226) in petroleum brines. Trans. Am. Geophys. Union 37, (1956)
Permian Basin in Texas and New Mexico	1,247 pCi/L	P. Thakur, A.L. Ward & T.M. Schaub, Occurrence and behavior of uranium and thorium series radionuclides in the Permian shale hydraulic fracturing wastes, Environmental Science and Pollution Research, Vol 29 (2022)
Denver-Julesburg Basin, Colorado	598 pCi/L	TENORM Report for the State of Colorado (Colorado Department of Public Health and Environment, 2019)
Fayetteville Shale, Arkansas	294 pCi/L	U.S. Geological Survey (USGS) Produced Waters Geochemical Database (U.S. Geological Survey, 2014)

Figure 2. Oilfield radioactivity in the human environment. Levels reported in oilfield waste from academic, government and industry papers, and also media investigations and community advocacy groups.

Location or item tested, or limit	**Levels of radium recorded (Ra-226+Ra-228)**	**Source**
Drum of oilfield waste arriving to US on cargo jet (2017)	2,095 pCi/g	Quarterly reports of Lotus LLC to Railroad Commission of Texas (RRC), files received via RRC Records Request (2nd Q 2017)
Pipe-scale from Louisiana oilfield delivered to West Texas disposal site operated by Lotus	748,430 pCi/g	Files received via Records Request from Railroad Commission of Texas
Oilfield waste being spread on pastureland in Oklahoma	Unknown	Correspondence with Oklahoma Corporation Commission
AquaSalina sample taken by Ohio Dept. of Natural Resources (ODNR) from Lowe's (2017)	1,663 pCi/L	McCracken, C. Assessment of Ra226 & Ra228 Radioactivity in AquaSalina (Ohio Department of Natural Resources, Division of Oil and Gas Management, 2017)
AquaSalina sample taken by ODNR from Hartville Hardware (2017)	2,491 pCi/L	McCracken 2017
Junex brine, used as a liquid deicer in Canada (2013)	3,892 pCi/L	Correspondence with Quebec's Ministère du Développement durable, de l'Environnement (2018)

Dirt on side of public road near main entrance of Ohio oilfield waste processing facility operated by Austin Master Services (AMS)	18.3 pCi/g	Samples by Concerned Ohio River Residents (CORR), processed at Eberline Analytical, Oak Ridge TN
Sludge on boots of worker at AMS	84.96 pCi/g	Samples by CORR, processed at Eberline Analytical, Oak Ridge TN
Contaminated soil/ sludge material at abandoned Fairmont Brine facility in Fairmont, West Virginia	5,072 pCi/g	Samples by Dr. Yuri Gorby, and Jill Hunkler of Ohio Valley Allies, processed at Eberline Analytical, Oak Ridge TN
Stream sediment at site of Blacktail Creek brine spill in Bakken oilfield, North Dakota	14.9 pCi/g – 126.6 pCi/g	Lauer, N.E., Harkness, J.S. & Vengosh A. Brine spills associated with unconventional oil development in North Dakota. Environ. Sci. Technol. 50 (2016)
Sediments sampled upstream of Blacktail Creek brine spill site	1.2 pCi/g	Lauer et al. 2016
Floodplain 4.7km (2.92 mi) downstream of Blacktail Creek brine spill site	20.8 pCi/g	Cozzarelli, I.M. et al. Geochemical and geophysical indicators of oil and gas wastewater can trace potential exposure pathways following releases to surface waters. Sci. Total Environ. 755 (2021)

Bear Den Bay brine spill site soil samples	2.9 pCi/g – 5.7 pCi/g	Lauer et al. 2016
Stream sediment at point of discharge for 3 Pennsylvania oilfield waste treatment facilities	1.5 pCi/g – 403.6 pCi/g	Lauer, N.E., Warner, N.R. & Vengosh, A. Sources of radium accumulation in stream sediments near disposal sites in Pennsylvania: implications for disposal of conventional oil and gas wastewater. Environ. Sci. Technol. 52 (2018)
Sediment upstream of discharge for 3 Pennsylvania oilfield waste treatment facilities	0.2 pCi/g – 1.1 pCi/g	Lauer et al. 2018
Sediment core from reservoir 19 km, 11.8 mi, downstream of one Pennsylvania oilfield waste treatment facility and 10km, 6.2 mi, downstream from second smaller facility	4.3 pCi/g (max concentration)	Burgos, W.D. et al. Watershed-scale impacts from surface water disposal of oil and gas wastewater in western Pennsylvania. Environ. Sci. Technol. 51 (2017)
Sediment at effluent discharge point for Pennsylvania sewage plants that received oilfield wastewater, i.e. brine (avg/max)	12.5 pCi/g / 24.5 pCi/g	Technologically Enhanced Naturally Occurring Radioactivity Materials (TENORM) Study Report (Pennsylvania Department of Environmental Protection, 2016)

Sediment at effluent discharge point for Pennsylvania oilfield wastewater treatment plants (avg/max)	104 pCi/g / 507.9 pCi/g	Pennsylvania Department of Environmental Protection TENORM Study Report, 2016
Pennsylvania dirt roads that have received or may have received oilfield brine, applied as a dust suppressant and road stabilizer (avg/max)	3.1 pCi/g / 8.8 pCi/g	Pennsylvania Department of Environmental Protection TENORM Study Report, 2016

Figure 3. Oilfield radioactivity in the human environment. Exposure and dose rates at various facilities that process oilfield waste or oil and gas products.

Item or location	Level recorded	Source
Steel drum of oilfield waste at Lotus site in West Texas	5,800 µrem/hr	May 2004 Inspection report of Lotus LLC by Railroad Commission of Texas (RRC), files received via RRC Records Request
Large "burrito" bag of waste waiting to be loaded onto rail car at AMS Ohio oilfield waste processing facility	660 µR/hr	Radiological Assessment Report (ODNR, Division of Oil and Gas Resources Management (DOGRM), Radiation Safety Section, 2/12/2019)
Green roll-off boxes at AMS Ohio oilfield waste processing facility	538 µR/hr	Inspection Report (ODNR, DOGRM, 11/8/2018)

Facility background at AMS Ohio oilfield waste processing facility	9 µR/hr	Inspection Report (ODNR, DOGRM, 11/8/2018).
Max gamma exposure recorded at Pennsylvania sewage plants that received oilfield wastewater/ avg top exposure at individual facilities/ lowest background exposure at any individual facility	257 µR/hr / 36.3 µR/hr / 5 µR/hr	Pennsylvania Department of Environmental Protection TENORM Study Report, 2016
Max gamma exposure recorded at Pennsylvania oilfield wastewater treatment plants/avg top exposure at individual facilities/ lowest background exposure at any individual facility	502 µR/hr / 24.1 µR/hr / 5 µR/hr	Pennsylvania Department of Environmental Protection TENORM Study Report, 2016
Liquids pump in a gasoline plant, maximum reading, 1 ft from pump surface	25 mR/hr	Gray, P.E. NORM contamination in the petroleum industry. J. Pet. Technol. 45 (1993)
Pump at facility that produces ethylene and polyethylene/ background at facility	40 mrem/hr / 15 µrem/hr	Canoba, A., Gnoni, G. & Truppa, W. NORM measurements in the oil and gas industry in Argentina (Autoridad Regulatoria Nuclear, 2007)
Oilfield brine equipment, avg	30–40 µR/hr (~5x background)	TENORM: Oil and Gas Production Wastes (U.S. Environmental Protection Agency, 2023)

Gas plant processing equipment, avg/max	30–70 μR/hr/ 1mR/hr	TENORM: Oil and Gas Production Wastes (U.S. Environmental Protection Agency, 2023)
Exterior of oilfield pipe with scale buildup	800 μrem/hr	Managing Naturally Occurring Radioactive Material (NORM) in the oil and gas industry (International Association of Oil & Gas Producers, 2016)
Treated oilfield wastewater sludge	6–250 μR/hr	Allard, D.J. Update on DEP's Guidance for Dealing With Radioactivity in Solid Waste (PA DEP, 2018)

Figure 4. Major US Oil & gas Fields

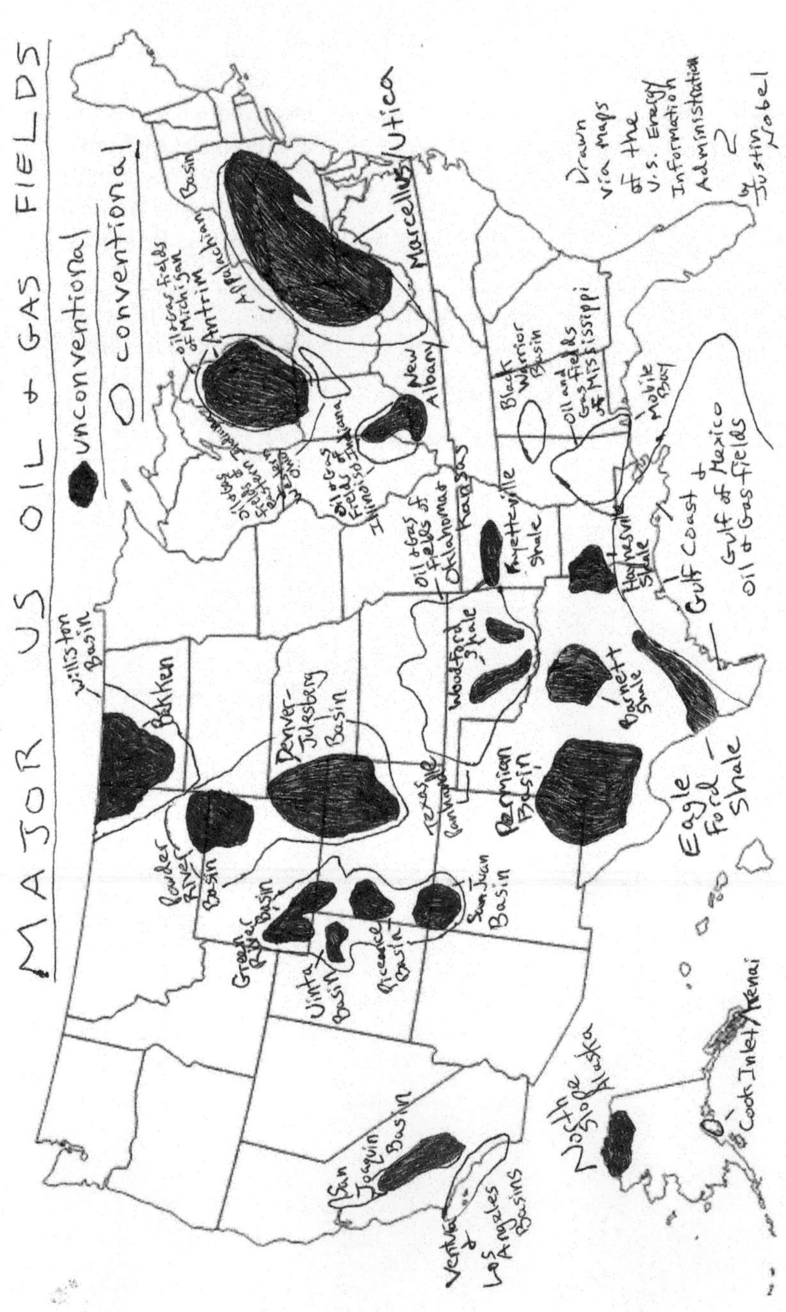

Figure 5. Uranium-238 Decay Chain

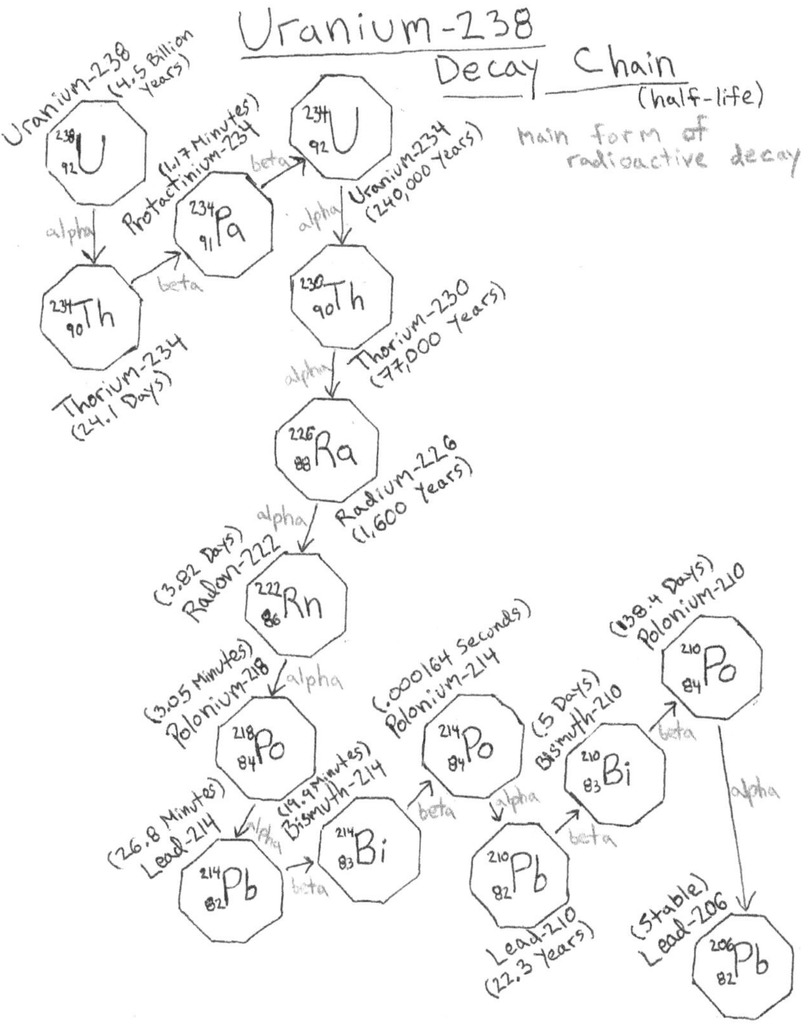

Figure 6. Thorium-232 Decay Chain

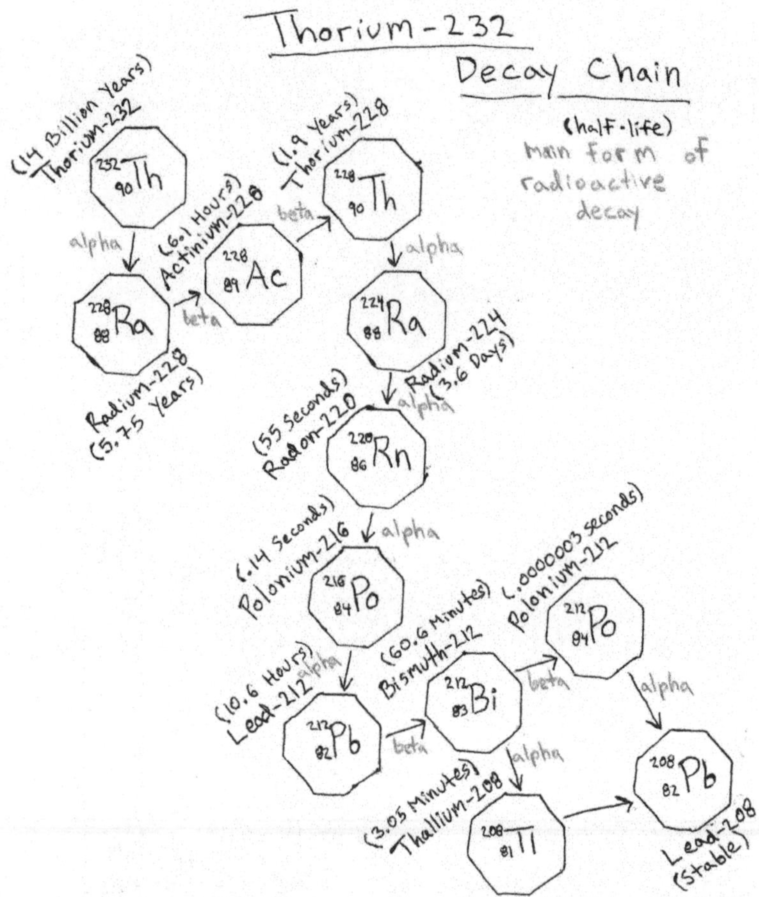

Principal Sources

page # | *part of the line or set of lines* | The Source

Author's Note

1 | ***other end of a building*** | "Acceptance and optimization of air and water systems Veolia head office - Le V" (Veolia, 2024)

1 | ***secret pile of fracking waste*** | Justin Nobel, "In West Virginia, Plan to Clean up Radioactive Fracking Waste Ends in Monster Lawsuit" DeSmog (Seattle, Washington, September 19, 2023)

1 | ***including billions of pounds of waste*** | "U.S. Produced Water Volumes and Management Practices in 2021," (Ground Water Protection Council, November 2022)

1 | ***an Ohio community organizer*** | Correspondence and conversations with Ohio community organizer Tish O'Dell, 2018-2024

1 | ***supposedly "Safe for Pets"*** | "AquaSalina Bottle Front Image" and "AquaSalina Bottle Back Image"

1 | ***had been selling it at Lowe's*** | "Interoffice Memorandum from Chuck McCracken, Manager, Radiation Safety Section to Richard J. Simmers, Chief regarding ASSESSMENT OF RA226 & RA228 RADIOACTIVITY IN AQUASALINA" (Ohio Department of Natural Resources, Division of Oil and Gas Resources Management, Radiation Safety Section, July 26, 2017)

1 | ***shoveling and scooping*** | Correspondence and conversations with oilfield waste hauler Rob Kanack, 2020-2024 ; Correspondence and conversations with brine hauler Tom McKnight, 2020-2024

2 | ***coal ash and ground up corn cobs*** | "Trip Report Division of Oil and Gas Resources Management, Petta Cambridge Facility (Chief's Order 2015-29)," (Ohio Department of Natural Resources, Division of Oil and Gas Resources Management, February 8 & 9, 2017)

2 | ***try and lower the radioactivity levels*** | "Trip Report, Austin Masters, Division of Oil and Gas Resources Management," (Ohio Department of Natural Resources, Division of Oil and Gas Resources Management, September 16, 2015) ; "Trip Report, Austin Masters, Division of Oil and Gas Resources Management," (Ohio Department of Natural Resources, Division of Oil and Gas Resources Management, April 12, 2017) ; "Trip Report, Chief's Order No. 2014-541, Division of Oil and Gas Resources Management," (Ohio Department of Natural Resources, Division of Oil and Gas Resources Management, July 5, 2017)

2 | ***sometimes in just T-shirts*** | Justin Nobel, "Radioactive Waste 'Everywhere'

at Ohio Oilfield Facility, Says Former Worker" DeSmog (Seattle, Washington, August 31, 2022) ; Justin Nobel, "'This Needs to Be Fixed': Nuclear Expert Calls Radioactivity Levels Found Outside Ohio Oilfield Waste Facility 'Excessive'" DeSmog (Seattle, Washington, April 25, 2022)

2 | ***barbecue cookouts in this absurdly contaminated*** | Conversations with Shannon Lutz, wife of deceased oilfield waste worker, 2023-2024

2 | ***sludge splattered all over*** | Conversations with oilfield waste worker David Duvall, 2022

2 | ***inhaling radioactive dust*** | A.L. Smith, "Radioactive-Scale Formation," Journal of Petroleum Technology, Volume 39, Number 06 (1987) ; Beverly Reed, Cyndhia Ramatchandirane, and Yuri Gorby, "Elevated levels of radioactivity in surface sediments near a radioactive waste processing facility in Martins Ferry, Ohio" (Concerned Ohio River Residents and Earthjustice, April 26, 2022) ; Correspondence and conversations with nuclear forensics scientist Dr. Marco Kaltofen, 2019-2024

2 | ***waste eating away their boots*** | Correspondence with oilfield waste workers Sean Guthrie and Christopher Smith, 2023-2024

2 | ***freely emitted across this nation*** | Justin Nobel, "America's Radioactive Secret" Rolling Stone (New York, New York, February 2020)

2 | ***sometimes illegally*** | "Company Owner Sentenced To More Than Two Years In Prison For Dumping Fracking Waste In Mahoning River Tributary," (United States Attorney's Office Northern District of Ohio, August 5, 2014)

2 | ***often legally*** | Nathaniel R. Warner, Cidney A. Christie, Robert B. Jackson, and Avner Vengosh, "Impacts of Shale Gas Wastewater Disposal on Water Quality in Western Pennsylvania," Environmental Science & Technology, Volume 47 (2013) ; Ian Urbina, "Regulation Lax as Gas Wells' Tainted Water Hits Rivers" New York Times (New York, New York, February 26, 2011)

2 | ***beer cans and condoms*** | Justin Nobel, "Inside West Virginia's Chernobyl: A highly radioactive oil and gas facility has become a party spot in Marion County" Truthdig (Los Angeles, California, September 18, 2023) ; Justin Nobel, "A Slow-Rolling Disaster in Fracking Country: Ex-employees at 'West Virginia's Chernobyl' speak out on lethal cancers, regulatory failure and contaminated drinking water" Truthdig (Los Angeles, California, December 7, 2023) ; "Eberline Analytical Final Report of Analysis, for Concerned OH River Residents, Water Samples" (Eberline Analytical, August 2023) ; "Eberline Analytical Final Report of Analysis, for Concerned OH River Residents, Soil Samples" (Eberline Analytical, August 2023) ; "Report from Christine Wagner, OnScene Coordinator and Cole Devine, OnScene Coordinator, at Fairmont Brine site to Jason McDougal with West Virginia Department of Environmental Protection, Jason Frame with West Virginia Department of Health and Human Resources and U.S. EPA Region III, Subject: POLREP #1, POLREP #1 & Special Bulletin, A Notice OF $250K Activation, Fairmont Brine Site, B3CL, Fairmont, WV, Latitude: 39.5082655 Longitude: 80.1254116" (U.S. EPA, September 22 2023)

2 | ***than most of the Chernobyl Exclusion Zone*** | "36 years of Chernobyl: the BfS publishes the new radioactivity maps", (Bundesamt für Strahlenschutz press release, April 20, 2022), https://www.bfs.de/SharedDocs/Pressemitteilungen/BfS/EN/2022/006.html ; "Radiation levels" (The Chernobyl Gallery), http://www.chernobylgallery.com/chernobyl-disaster/radiation-levels/

2 | ***with a former Department of Energy scientist and his Geiger Counter*** | Correspondences and conversations with former Department of Energy scientist Dr. Yuri Gorby, 2019-2024

2 | ***5,000 times general background levels*** | "The Environmental Behaviour of Radium: Revised Edition" (International Atomic Energy Agency, 2014)
2 | ***25-year-old Canadian graduate student named Eli*** | Photos of 'A Radioactive Gas From Crude Petroleum' obtained during visit to University of Toronto libraries," (University of Toronto Studies, Physical Science Series, photographed by Justin Nobel, 2019)
3 | ***second leading cause of lung cancer deaths*** | "A Citizen's Guide to Radon: The Guide to Protecting Yourself and Your Family from Radon," (EPA, 2016)
3 | ***naturally contaminates natural gas. Which means it is being emitted out of*** | Raymond H. Johnson Jr., David E. Bernhardt, Neal S. Nelson and Harry W. Calley Jr., "Assessment of Potential Radiological Health Effects from Radon in Natural Gas" (EPA Office of Radiation Programs, 1973)
An Assessment of the Lung Cancer Risk Associated with the Presence of Radon in Natural Gas Used for Cooking in Homes in New York State," (Risk Sciences International, July 4, 2012) ; Correspondence and conversations with former Amoco research scientist Dr. Bert Fisher, 2019-2024
3 | ***1982 American Petroleum Institute report concluded*** | "An Analysis of the Impact of the Regulation of 'Radionuclides' as a Hazardous Air Pollutant on the Petroleum Industry" (Committee for Environmental Biology and Community Health, Department of Medicine and Biology, American Petroleum Institute, October 19, 1982)
3 | ***was never federally regulated and remains unregulated*** | Correspondence with EPA, 2018-2023 (Enesta Jones, March 31 2022) ; Correspondence with EPA, 2018-2023 (Tricia Lynn, October 18 2018)
3 | ***legally defined their waste as nonhazardous*** | "Special Wastes," (EPA, 2023)
3 | ***despite containing toxic chemicals*** | T.S. Alomar, B.H. Hameed, M. Usman, F.A. Almomani, M.M. Ba-Abbad and M. Khraisheh, "Recent advances on the treatment of oil fields produced water by adsorption and advanced oxidation processes," Journal of Water Process Engineering, Volume 49 (2022) ; "Public Health Statement for Benzene" (Agency for Toxic Substances and Disease Registry, March 12, 2015) ; Correspondence and conversations with former USGS geologist Dr. Mark Engle, 2020-2023
3 | ***As the nuclear forensics scientist Dr. Marco Kaltofen has told me*** | Correspondence and conversations with nuclear forensics scientist Dr. Marco Kaltofen, 2019-2024
3 | ***mineral scale and sludge that accumulates*** | Alan McArthur and William Lemons, "NORM IX: Mandatory Air Monitoring of TENORM Worker Inhalation Exposure from Gas TENORM" (Pittsburgh Mineral & Environmental Technology, Inc., September 2019)
3 | ***in our 321,000-plus miles*** | "State Gas Pipelines - Breaking It Down: Understanding the Terminology" (National Conference of State Legislatures, February 22, 2011)
3 | ***can be filled with stunning levels*** | Alan McArthur and William Lemons
3 | ***an amount smaller than a grain of sand*** | Luke Harding, A Very Expensive Poison: The Assassination of Alexander Litvinenko and Putin's War With the West (New York: Vintage Books, 2017), 120-123, 181
3 | ***natural gas pipeline sludge*** | P.R. Gray, "NORM Contamination in the Petroleum Industry" Journal of Petroleum Technology, Volume 45, Number 01

(1993) ; Peter Gray, "Radioactive Materials Could Pose Problems For the Gas Industry" Oil & Gas Journal (Tulsa, Oklahoma, June 25, 1990), https://www.ogj.com/refining-processing/petrochemicals/article/17214470/radioactive-materials-could-pose-problems-for-the-gas-industry

3 | ***And yet, by US law*** | "Regulatory Determination for Oil and Gas and Geothermal Exploration, Development and Production Wastes," (EPA, July 6, 1988)

3 | ***Unlike the cosmic radiation an airline passenger*** | Correspondence and conversations with nuclear forensics scientist Dr. Marco Kaltofen, 2019-2024

4 | ***allows radioactive oilfield waste to be transported from foreign countries*** | Justin Nobel, "Where Does All The Radioactive Fracking Waste Go?" DeSmog (Seattle, Washington, April 22, 2021) ; Conversations and correspondence with former General Manager of the Texas Low-Level Radioactive Waste Disposal Authority Rick Jacobi

4 | ***live on a radioactive planet*** | Gunter Faure and Teresa M. Mensing, Introduction to Planetary Science, The Geological Perspective (Dordrecht, Netherlands: Springer, 2007) ; "Background Radiation" (U.S. Nuclear Regulatory Commission, March 9, 2021)

4 | ***concentrated in the formation below, and further concentrated by the industry's processes*** | P.R. Gray, "NORM Contamination in the Petroleum Industry" Journal of Petroleum Technology, Volume 45, Number 01 (1993) ; K.P. Smith, "An Overview of Naturally Occurring Radioactive
Materials (NORM) in the Petroleum Industry" (Argonne National Laboratory, December 1992) ; "USGS Fact Sheet: Naturally Occurring Radioactive Materials (NORM) in Produced Water and Oil-Field Equipment—An Issue for the Energy Industry" (U.S. Geological Survey, September 1999) ; R. Stephen Fisher, "Geologic and Geochemical Controls on Naturally Occurring Radioactive Materials (NORM) in Produced Water from Oil, Gas, and Geothermal Operations," Environmental Geosciences, Volume 5, Number 3 (1998)

4 | ***From day one*** | "U.S. Census Bureau History: The Oil Industry," (U.S. Census Bureau, August 2021)

4 | ***by tapping into even more radioactive formations*** | John A. Harper, "The Marcellus Shale—An Old 'New' Gas Reservoir in Pennsylvania," Pennsylvania Geology, Volume 38, Number 1 (2008)

4 | ***bringing drilling closer to communities*** | Larysa Dyrszka, Kathleen Nolan, Carmi Orenstein, Ted Schettler, Barton Schoenfeld and Sandra Steingraber, "Compendium of Scientific, Medical, and Media Findings Demonstrating Risks and Harms of Fracking and Associated Gas and Oil Infrastructure, Ninth Edition" (Concerned Health Professionals of NY, Science & Environmental Health Network and Physicians for Social Responsibility, October 2023), https://concernedhealthny.org/wp-content/uploads/2023/10/CHPNY-Fracking-Science-Compendium-9.pdf

4 | ***vastly increasing the amount of waste*** | Andrew J. Kondash, Elizabeth Albright and Avner Vengosh, "Quantity of flowback and produced waters from unconventional oil and gas exploration," Science of the Total Environment, Volume 574 (2017)

4 | ***a "one time cost of over $34 billion*** | "Railroad Commission of Texas Comments, February 28, 1979, Hazardous Waste Guidelines and Regulations Proposed by the Environmental Protection Agency, Federal Register Vol. 43, No. 243 - Mon., Dec. 18, 1978" (Reauthorization of the Resource Conservation and Recovery Act, U.S. Senate Committee on Environment and Public Works, Subcommittee on

Resource Protection, Washington, D.C., March 22, 1979)
5 | ***a multinational company out of Paris*** | Justin Nobel, "In West Virginia, Plan to Clean up Radioactive Fracking Waste Ends in Monster Lawsuit" DeSmog (Seattle, Washington, September 19, 2023)
5 | ***the guy in rural Pennsylvania who stashed fracking waste*** | Alyssa Choiniere, "Investigation reveals oil and gas drilling waste dumped at local magistrate, Dairy Queen" Herald-Standard (Uniontown, Pennsylvania, March 29, 2017)

Chapter 1
7 | ***The story begins with James Earl Renfroe*** | Correspondence and conversations with Dr. Marvin Resnikoff, nuclear physicist, 2018-2023
8 | ***"Daddy had the lawsuit with Chevron*** | Correspondence and conversations with Janice Case Britt, 2021-2023 ; Correspondence and conversations with Linda Godbold, 2021-2023
8-9 | ***"I'll drink all the oil found east of the Mississippi → freedom to lay his hand to the drill and sink wells."*** | Dudley J. Hughes, Oil in the Deep South: A History of the Oil Business in Mississippi, Alabama, and Florida, 1859-1945 (Jackson: University Press of Mississippi, 1993), vii,23-27,64-73,75-76,80,82,84,89-119
9 | ***scattered across the state like popcorn kernels*** | Correspondence with Steve Walkinshaw, veteran Mississippi driller, 2022
9 | ***oil was struck outside Yazoo City → Collier's magazine reported in 1945*** | Dudley J. Hughes, Oil in the Deep South: A History of the Oil Business in Mississippi, Alabama, and Florida, 1859-1945 (Jackson: University Press of Mississippi, 1993), 150-151,159,161-167,199-206,209-213,214-216,218-220
10 | ***much more of an extremely salty liquid,*** | Correspondence and conversations with former USGS geologist Dr. Mark Engle, 2020-2023
10 | ***throughout the industry's history drillers directed the unwanted oilfield brine*** | Wayne A. Pettyjohn, "Water pollution by oil-field brines and related industrial wastes in Ohio," Ohio Journal of Science, Vol 71, no 5 (1971)
10 | ***bayous*** | Correspondence and conversations with Dr. Paul Templet, 2018-2023
10 | ***toxic heavy metals like arsenic, lead, strontium and barium*** | Correspondence and conversations with former USGS geologist Dr. Mark Engle, 2020-2023
10-11 | ***who autopsied half a dozen* radium girls → and experienced a condition called necrosis of the jaw, or radium jaw** | Harrison S. Martland, "The Occurrence of Malignancy in Radioactive Persons," The American Journal of Cancer, Volume XV, No 4 (1931) ; Bert Coursey, "The National Bureau of Standards and the Radium Dial Painters," Journal of Research of the National Institute of Standards and Technology, Volume 126, No. 126051 (2021) ; Correspondence with Dr. Bert Coursey, radiation physicist at the National Institute of Standards and Technology, 2023
11 | ***parts of the mouth rotted so thoroughly*** | Kate Moore, The Radium Girls: The Dark Story of America's Shining Women. (Naperville, Illinois: Sourcebooks, 2017)
11 | ***Radium has many forms, or isotopes*** | Correspondence and conversations with nuclear forensics scientist Dr. Marco Kaltofen, 2019-2024
11 | ***Only an "infinitesimal amount → over long periods of time, radioactive substances."*** | Harrison S. Martland, "The Occurrence of Malignancy in

Radioactive Persons," The American Journal of Cancer, Volume XV, No 4 (1931) ; Bert Coursey, "The National Bureau of Standards and the Radium Dial Painters," Journal of Research of the National Institute of Standards and Technology, Volume 126, No. 126051 (2021)

12 | ***As oilfield brine journeys, with the oil and gas*** | "USGS Fact Sheet: Radium-226 and Radium-228 in Shallow Ground Water, Southern New Jersey" (USGS, 1998)

12 | ***certain metals, including barium, strontium and radium*** | Karen P. Smith, "An Overview of Naturally Occurring Radioactive Materials (NORM) in the Petroleum Industry" (Argonne National Laboratory, 1992)

12 | ***regularly found at a level of around 1 picocurie per gram*** | "The Environmental Behaviour of Radium: Revised Edition, Technical Reports Series no. 476" (International Atomic Energy Agency, 2014)

12 | ***below 5 picocuries per gram above the background radiation levels*** | "EPA Facts about Radium" (EPA) ; Correspondence with staff health physicist source, 2020-2024

12 | ***averages around 500 picocuries per gram*** | "TENORM: Oil and Gas Production Wastes" (EPA, 2023)

12 | ***be as high as 750,000*** | "Lotus LLC, Lotus Disposal Facility, Andrews County, Texas, Pit Permit Numbers P010928 and P010938, 2nd Quarter 2005 Report" (Files Received by Justin Nobel via Freedom of Information Act request with Railroad Commission of Texas, November 19, 2020)

12 | ***pipe-scale can grow so thick it blocks the flow*** | "EPA Diffuse Norm, Waste Characterization And Preliminary Risk Assessment," (EPA, 1991)

12 | ***A now outdated EPA report from the early 1990s*** | EPA Diffuse Norm

13 | ***"My daddy had a flatbed truck," → known as the catcher.*** | Correspondence and conversations with Janice Case Britt, 2021-2023

13 | ***Of the different jobs in a pipe-cleaning yard, catcher is the most dangerous. → and be freely piercing the catcher's body.*** | "Coleman et al v. H.C. Price Co. et al. OCCUPATIONAL EXPOSURES TO RADIOACTIVE SCALE AND SLUDGE" (Environmental Dimensions Inc & RWMA, 2013) ; Correspondence and conversations with nuclear physicist Dr. Marvin Resnikoff, 2018-2023

13-14 | ***but an eye is one of the few places in the human body → especially vulnerable to chromosome-mutating blasts of radiation.*** | H. J. Ingraham, E.D. Donnenfeld, D.H. Abramson, "Effects of Ionizing Radiation on the Conjunctiva, Cornea, and Lens. Radiotherapy of Intraocular and Orbital Tumors.," in Radiotherapy of Intraocular and Orbital Tumors, 2nd revised edition. R.H. Sagerman and W.E. Alberti (Springer, 2003) ; Correspondence with Dr. David H. Abramson, Professor of Ophthalmology, 2022-2023

14 | ***In 1987, the Society of Petroleum Engineers → the controlled area should be decontaminated."*** | A.L. Smith, "Radioactive-Scale Formation," Journal of Petroleum Technology, Vol 39, issue 6 (1987)

14-15 | ***"The pipe would be on rollers," → ate that Chevron lawyer up and down."*** | Correspondence and conversations with Janice Case Britt, 2021-2023 ; Correspondence and conversations with Linda Godbold, 2021-2023

15-18 | ***Born in New Orleans, Stuart's father was a gambler → "and their kids had frolicked in the radioactive dust."***
| Stuart Smith, Crude Justice: How I Fought Big Oil and Won, and What You Should Know About the New Environmental Attack on America (Dallas: BENBELLA Books,

2015), xi,4-19,16-17,24-25,40-41,43-45,47-48,51-52,54-55,59,65,69,74,75,79-80,84-85,90-91,93,99-102 ; Conversations and correspondence with Louisiana attorney Stuart Smith, 2020-2021 ; Correspondence and conversations with nuclear physicist Dr. Marvin Resnikoff, 2018-2023

18 | ***"God," says Linda → The children's mother was Eva Mae Renfroe, and she's still alive.*** | Janice Case Britt & Linda Godbold

18 | ***and he eventually went blind*** | Dr. Marvin Resnikoff

founded in 1818 by Samuel Jayne, who arrived | James F. Brieger, Hometown Mississippi (Town Square Books, 1997)

19 | ***founded a women's college, and owned a slave plantation. → contributed to the vibrancy of the county."*** | "Brookhaven, Mississippi: A Biographical, Genealogical and Pictorial History of Brookhaven's Fine Families" (https://brookhaven-ms.blogspot.com/2019/04/a-biographical-genealogical-and.html, 2019) ; Mary Carol Miller, Written in the Bricks: A Visual and Historical Tour of 15 Mississippi Hometowns (Quail Ridge Press, 1999)

19-20 | ***"My marster was mean an' cruel → I's free at las'. Mmmmm, mmmmm, mmmmm."*** | "Slave Narratives: A Folk History of Slavery in the United States, From Interviews with Former Slaves, 1936-1938" (Federal Writers Project, 1941)

20 | ***The Equal Justice Initiative, which maintains*** | "Equal Justice Initiative, Lynching in America" (https://lynchinginamerica.eji.org/explore, 2023)

20-21 | ***Men shot on the courthouse lawn → then hung from a tree.*** | Donna Ladd, "Buried Truth: Unresolved, Disregarded Lamar Smith Murder Haunts Lincoln County" Mississippi Free Press (Jackson, Mississippi, August 30, 2021)

21 | ***the wells are on White people's property*** | Conversations with James Crowell III, 2021-2023

21 | ***Photos of Mississippi oilfield workers → But Redmond turned his lease over to Pioneer Oil and Gas Company*** | Dudley J. Hughes, Oil in the Deep South: A History of the Oil Business in Mississippi, Alabama, and Florida, 1859-1945 (Jackson: University Press of Mississippi, 1993), 80

Chapter 2

23 | ***Clare Donohue is dressed*** | Correspondence and conversations with Clare Donohue, 2019-2023

a quantity the size of 46 sugar packets | Robin B. McFee and Jerrold B. Leikin, "Death by Polonium-210: lessons learned from the murder of former Soviet spy Alexander Litvinenko," Seminars in Diagnostic Pathology, Volume 26, Issue 1 (2009)

23 | ***When on November 1, 2006 , assassins snuck → Litvinenko's major organs failed and he was dead.*** | Luke Harding, A Very Expensive Poison: The Assassination of Alexander Litvinenko and Putin's War With the West (New York: Vintage Books, 2017) 120-123, 138-140, 167-168, 176, 181 ; John Harrison, Tim Fell, Rich Leggett, David Lloyd, Matthew Puncher and Mike Youngman, "The polonium-210 poisoning of Mr Alexander Litvinenko," Journal of Radiological Protection, Volume 37, No 1 (2017) ; Sir Robert Owen, "The Litvinenko Inquiry: Report into the death of Alexander Litvinenko" (Crown, 2016)

24 | ***earned two Nobel prizes → evaporating out of solution and contaminating lab air*** | Eve Curie, Madame Curie: A Biography (New York: Doubleday, 1937) ; "Marie Curie: Her Story in Brief," (The American Institute of Physics, 2000) ; "Five Fast Facts About Irène Joliot-Curie," (Department of Energy,

2018), https://www.energy.gov/articles/five-fast-facts-about-irene-joliot-curie ; Elizabeth Rona, "Laboratory Contamination in the Early Period of Radiation Research," Health Physics, Volume 37 (1979) ; Veronique Greenwood, "My Great-Great-Aunt Discovered Francium. And It Killed Her" The New York Times Magazine (New York, New York, December 3, 2014)

24 | ***vial of polonium shattered in her face*** | Luke Harding, A Very Expensive Poison: The Assassination of Alexander Litvinenko and Putin's War With the West (New York: Vintage Books, 2017), 183

24 | ***On December 28, 2009, Spectra Energy*** | "Spectra Energy Signs Binding Precedent Agreements for Major Pipeline Project to Deliver New Natural Gas Supplies Into New Jersey and New York Area," (Con Edison, January 14, 2010)

25 | ***gigantic units in many building basements*** | Correspondence and conversations with New York City building super, 2020-2023

25 | ***collected classic speedboats and antique maps → he ran as his personal kingdom.*** | Bryan Gruley, Joe Carroll, and Asjylyn Loder, "The Incredible Rise and Final Hours of Fracking King Aubrey McClendon: Chesapeake Energy's co-founder and CEO was a visionary who had trouble following the rules" Bloomberg Businessweek (New York, New York, March 10, 2016)

25 | ***carved into the stone of a new dormitory as gargoyles*** | Aaron Beard, "Gargoyles spook wealthy donors: University to remove figures as appreciation for $5.5 million" Associated Press (November 7, 2002).

25 | ***allegedly trying to fix oil prices*** | "Former CEO Indicted for Masterminding Conspiracy Not to Compete for Oil and Natural Gas Leases," (U.S. Department of Justice, March 1, 2016)

25 | ***fuel was "scrounged up wherever it could be found," → cooking with coal.*** | Correspondence with Andrew Alpern New York City architectural historian, 2020-2023

26 | ***200 gallons of soup, 350 to 400 pounds of beefsteak*** | "A Day With the Chef in Kitchen of a Big Hotel" The New York Times (New York, New York, February 8, 1903)

26 | ***manufactured in gasworks → thousands of miles of coal gas pipes that ran under New York City's streets*** | Jonathan Tollefson and Scott Frickel, "Cleaning Up? Gasworks, Lost and Found" Urban Omnibus (The Architectural League of New York, July 1, 2021) ; Gregory DL Morris, "First Gas Well In US Was 1825 In New York" Hart Energy (Houston, Texas, December 28, 2016) ; Correspondence with Andrew Alpern New York City architectural historian, 2020-2023

26 | ***In 1947, a pipeline network used to shuttle oil*** | Marilyn Pereboom, "An Energy Transition by War-Scale Action: Here's What That Looked Like in WWII Philadelphia" (Kleinman Center for Energy Policy, September 14, 2022)

26 | ***and into New Jersey*** | "$143,270,000 Check Ends Pipeline Sale" New York Times (New York, New York, November 15, 1947)

26 | ***A pipeline to be complete in 1951*** | Christopher J. Castaneda, "The Texas—Northeast Connection: The Rise of the Post—World War II Gas Pipeline Industry," The Houston Review, Vol. XII. No. 2 (1990)

26 | ***New York would remain on that gas for over half a century,*** | "Assessment of New York City Natural Gas Market Fundamentals and Life Cycle Fuel Emissions" New York City Mayor's Office of Long-Term Planning and Sustainability (ICF International)

27 | ***About 100 miles west of New York City → contain about 214***

trillion cubic feet of natural gas | "USGS Estimates 214 trillion Cubic Feet of Natural Gas in Appalachian Basin Formations," (U.S. Geological Survey, October 3, 2019) ; "Natural gas explained: Where our natural gas comes from," (U.S. Energy Information Administration, 2023)

27 | ***For much of the 20th century,*** | John A. Harper, "The Marcellus Shale—An Old 'New' Gas Reservoir in Pennsylvania," Pennsylvania Geology, Volume 38, Number 1 (2008)

27 | ***attempts to shatter a formation with explosives*** | "A Brief History Of Fracking" (NES Fircroft, July 31, 2022), https://www.nesfircroft.com/resources/blog/a-brief-history-of-fracking/

27 | ***The techniques of modern fracking,*** | "Shooters – A "Fracking" History" (American Oil & Gas Historical Society) ; "Galvestonian or Greek? What kind of person was George Mitchell? A quick story by the Kriticos brothers: Galveston, Texas" (Galveston Unscripted)

27 | ***first deployed to Pennsylvania*** | Emily Clough and Derek Bell, "Just fracking: a distributive environmental justice analysis of unconventional gas development in Pennsylvania, USA," Environmental Research Letters, Volume 11, Number 2 (2016)

27 | ***Explosives placed in the horizontal*** | "Animation of Hydraulic Fracturing (fracking)," (MarathonOilCorp, 2022) ; "Hydraulic Fracturing," (The American Petroleum Institute, 2014)

27 | ***Marcellus and Utica are black shales*** | E.L. Rowan, M.A. Engle, C.S. Kirby, and T.F. Kraemer, "Radium Content of Oil- and Gas-Field Produced Waters in the Northern Appalachian Basin (USA): Summary and Discussion of Data" (U.S. Geological Survey, 2011) ; John A. Harper, "The Marcellus Shale—An Old 'New' Gas Reservoir in Pennsylvania," Pennsylvania Geology, Volume 38, Number 1 (2008) ; Philip A. Meyers and Richard M. Mitterer, "Deep ocean black shales: organic geochemistry and paleocenanographic setting" Marine Geology, 70 (1986)

27 | ***country's Geological Survey, in a 1960 report for the Atomic Energy Commission,*** | Vernon E. Swanson, "Oil Yield and Uranium Content of Black Shales" (U.S. Geological Survey, 1960)

28 | ***By running a special type of Geiger → "RADIOACTIVITY = ORGANIC RICHNESS = GAS."*** | John A. Harper, "The Marcellus Shale"

28 | ***most comes from the planet itself*** | "Frequent Questions: Radiation Sources," (EPA, 2023)

28 | ***contain uranium and thorium*** | K.P. Smith. An Overview of Naturally Occurring Radioactive

Materials (NORM) in the Petroleum Industry. Argonne National Laboratory. December 1992

28 | ***continuously breathing up this radioactive gas*** | James K. Otton, "The Geology of Radon" (U.S. Geological Survey, 1992)

28 | ***"six atoms for every thumbprint-sized square"*** | "Where does Radon come from?," (HyperPhysics, Department of Physics and Astronomy, Georgia State University, 2005)

28 | ***And a home is like a big upside-down jar*** | James K. Otton, "The Geology of Radon"

28 | ***"Radon is a cancer-causing, radioactive gas," → more than half of the home*** | "A Citizen's Guide to Radon: The Guide to Protecting Yourself and Your Family from Radon," (EPA, 2016) ; "What is EPA's Action Level for Radon and What

Does it Mean?" (EPA, 2023) ; "A Citizen's Guide to Radon: What It Is And What To Do About It," (EPA, 1986) ; John H. Harley, "Radioactive Emissions and Radon," Bulletin of the New York Academy of Medicine, Volume 57, Number 10 (1981)

29 | ***In 1973, EPA analyzed the concentration → placental transfer of radioactivity*** | Raymond H. Johnson Jr., David E. Bernhardt, Neal S. Nelson and Harry W. Calley Jr., "Assessment of Potential Radiological Health Effects from Radon in Natural Gas" (EPA Office of Radiation Programs, 1973)

29 | ***linked radon to stomach cancer*** | Kyle P. Messier and Marc L. Serre, "Lung and stomach cancer associations with groundwater radon in North Carolina, USA," International Journal of Epidemiology, Volume 46, Issue 2 (2017)

29 | ***reproductive cancers in Maine*** | Hess, C. T., Weiffenbach, C. V. and Norton, S. A., "Environmental Radon and Cancer Correlations in Maine," Health Physics, Volume 45, Number 2, (1983)

29 | ***pancreatic cancer in Sweden*** | Christer Edling, Pietro Comba, Olav Axelson and Ulf Flodin, "Effects of low-dose radiation - A correlation study," Scandinavian Journal of Work, Environment & Health, Volume 8, Number 1 (1982)

29 | ***leukemia in Scotland and Canada*** | Jean-François Viel, "Radon Exposure and Leukaemia in Adulthood," International Journal of Epidemiology, Volume 22, Number 4 (1993)

29 | ***brain cancer in Denmark*** | Elvira V. Bräuner, Zorana J. Andersen, Claus E. Andersen, Camilla Pedersen, Peter Gravesen, Kaare Ulbak, Ole Hertel, Steffen Loft and Ole Raaschou-Nielsen, "Residential Radon and Brain Tumour Incidence in a Danish Cohort," PLoS One, Volume 8, Number 9, (2013)

29 | ***and Spain*** | Alberto Ruano-Ravina, Nuria Aragonés, Karl T. Kelsey, Mónica Pérez-Ríos, María Piñeiro-Lamas, Gonzalo López-Abente, and Juan M. Barros-Dios, "Residential radon exposure and brain cancer: an ecological study in a radon prone area (Galicia, Spain)," Nature, Volume 7, Number 1, (2017)

29-30 | ***1990 paper published in the respected British medical journal*** | Denis L. Henshaw, Jonathan P. Eatough, and Richard B. Richardson, "Radon as a causative factor in induction of myeloid leukaemia and other cancers," Volume 335, Number 8696 (1990)

30 | ***But a*** **Lancet** ***study published in 2000*** | Graham R Law, Eleanor V Kane, Eve Roman, Alex Smith and Ray Cartwright, "Residential radon exposure and adult acute leukaemia," The Lancet, Volume 355, Number 9218 (2000)

30 | ***"Nevertheless," writes Olav Axelson*** | Olav Axelson and Francesco Forastiere, "Radon as a Risk Factor for Extra-Pulmonary Tumours," Medical Oncology and Tumor Pharmacotherapy, Volume, 10 Number 4 (1993)

30 | ***the agency has not conducted a follow-up*** | Correspondence and conversations with EPA health physicist source

30 | ***waft up out of the earth*** | M. Wilkening, Radon in the Environment (Amsterdam: Elsevier, 1990)

30 | ***or travel with natural gas*** | P.R. Gray, "NORM Contamination in the Petroleum Industry," Journal of Petroleum Technology, Volume 45, Number 01 (1993)

30 | ***radon-222, with a half-life of 3.8 days.*** | Sam Keith, John R Doyle, Carolyn Harper, Moiz Mumtaz, Oscar Tarrago, David W Wohlers, Gary L Diamond, Mario Citra and Lynn E Barber, "Toxicological Profile for Radon" (Agency for Toxic Substances and Disease Registry, 2012 May)

30 | ***Radon-222 will decay through a long → pumps and valves, as***

a dangerous radioactive | Correspondence and conversations with nuclear forensics scientist Dr Marco Kaltofen, 2018-2023 ; P.R. Gray, "NORM Contamination in the Petroleum Industry" ; Alan McArthur and William Lemons, "Mandatory Air Monitoring of TENORM Worker Inhalation Exposure from Gas TENORM," (Pittsburgh Mineral and Environmental Technology Inc., 2019)
31 | ***to be released out a home stove and into apartments*** | "An Assessment of the Lung Cancer Risk Associated with the Presence of Radon in Natural Gas Used for Cooking in Homes in New York State," (Risk Sciences International, July 4, 2012) ; Correspondence and conversations with Clare Donohue, 2019-2023
31-32 | ***There is the scent of sugary pastries → them finally having a chance*** | Clare Donohue
32 | ***reservoirs the city relied on for water and the farmland*** | Correspondence and conversations with Eric Weltman of Food & Water Watch, 2020-2023
32 | ***The $850 million Spectra pipeline*** | Mireya Navarro, "Pipeline Plan Stirs Debate on Both Sides of Hudson" New York Times (New York, New York, October 26, 2011)
32 | ***would travel under a heron rookery*** | "New Jersey - New York Expansion Project Final Environmental Impact Statement Volume I," (Federal Energy Regulatory Commission, March 2012)
32 | ***enter Manhattan at Gansevoort Peninsula*** | "Decision and Order In the Matter of the Application of Sane Energy Project; NYH20 LLC; Food and Water Watch; United for Action; New York City Friends of Clearwater; Village Independent Democrats; Ynestra Kings; Nathaniel Johnson; Anne Heaney; Joan Beard; John Mimikos; Sherry Lane; and William 'Buck' Moorhead against the Hudson River Park Trust; Texas Eastern Transmission LP; Algonquin Gas Transmission LLC ; and Spectra Energy Corporation," (Supreme Court of the State of New York – New York County, January 16, 2013) ; Albert Amateau, "C.B. 2, Jersey City inflamed as feds accept gas pipeline" AM New York, (New York, New York, May 24, 2012)
32 | ***strip of parkland maintained by*** | Albert Amateau, "Trust board approves gas pipeline traversing park" AM NY (New York, New York, June 21, 2012)
32 | ***"We concluded," stated the Federal Energy → only five people submitted comments.*** | "New Jersey - New York Expansion Project Final Environmental Impact Statement Volume I," (Federal Energy Regulatory Commission, March 2012)
32 | ***The new pipeline" has drawn "barely a shrug*** | Mireya Navarro, "Pipeline Plan Stirs Debate on Both Sides of Hudson" New York Times (New York, New York, October 26, 2011)
32 | ***The Environmental Defense Fund promoted natural gas*** | "9,000 NYC Buildings Burning Dirty Heating Oil Identified in New Report" (Environmental Defense Fund, December 17, 2009)
32 | ***go a long way in helping the city" meet*** | "Summary of Comments/ Responses: Hudson River Park Trust's Proposed Easement in connection with the New Jersey – New York Expansion Project," (Hudson River Park Trust, May 22, 2012)
33 | ***in a book about his mayorship*** | Katherine Bagley and Maria Gallucci, Bloomberg's Hidden Legacy: Climate Change and the Future of New York City (Inside Climate News, 2013)
33 | ***Key to his policy was*** | "Converting to Natural Gas," (NYC Clean Heat) ;

"National Grid: Supporting NYC's CLEAN HEAT Program," (National Grid, February 12, 2013)
33 | *an unrepentant capitalist," Bloomberg states* | Michael Bloomberg and Carl Pope, Climate of Hope: How Cities, Businesses, and Citizens Can Save the Planet (New York: St. Martin's Press, 2017)
34 | *"I'm begging you people to stand up."* | Mireya Navarro, New York Times
34 | *"It's not just the crater: the heat radiates out* | Nick Pinto, "Will a New High-Pressure Gas Line Help New Yorkers—Or Blow Them Up?" The Village Voice (New York, New York, January 23, 2013)
34 | *Pipeline explosions do occur* | Justin Nobel, "The Hidden Risk in the Fracking Boom" Rolling Stone (New York, New York, February 20, 2019)
34 | *sometimes adorable and always flammable children* | Nick Pinto, The Village Voice
34 | *Kim Fraczek, a jewelry designer* | Correspondence and conversations with Sane Energy director Kim Fraczek, 2019-2023
34 | *informational YouTube video* | "Radon in My Apartment? The Spectra Pipeline" (Occupy the Pipeline, 2013), https://www.youtube.com/watch?v=av_opE1-Lpk
34-35 | *toxic green and walked, mostly naked* | Nick Pinto, "Naked Green People Fighting The Spectra Gas Pipeline Construction In The West Village" The Village Voice (New York, New York, October 9, 2012)
35 | *locked themselves to construction equipment → and into a squad car.* | "Spectra Pipeline Protest at Gansevoort Pier," (Sane Energy, 2012), https://www.youtube.com/watch?v=U4bgDbCLArE
35 | *Radon posed distinct threats for New York City. → at the same time to cook dinner.* | Conversations and correspondence with Dr. David Carpenter, former dean of the School of Public Health at the State University of New York at Albany, 2019-2023
35-36 | *In July 2012, a Canada-based firm → 747 lung cancers from radon could be expected* | "An Assessment of the Lung Cancer Risk Associated with the Presence of Radon in Natural Gas Used for Cooking in Homes in New York State," (Risk Sciences International, July 4, 2012) ; "What is EPA's Action Level for Radon and What Does it Mean?" (EPA, 2023) ; "Enbridge: Lambertville East Expansion Project, Resource Report 9, Air and Noise Quality," (FERC Docket No. CP18-____-000, December 2017)
36 | *under current California laws Marcellus gas* | "Proposition 65 in Plain Language," (California Office of Environmental Health Hazard Assessment, August 1, 2017)
36 | *And Con Edison* | Attempted correspondence with Con Edison media spokesperson, 2021-2023 (October 4 2021, October 13 2021, December 21 2023)
36 | *along with National Grid* | Attempted correspondence with National Grid media spokespeople, 2021-2023 (October 4 2021, October 13 2021, December 21 2023)
36 | *and the New York State Public Service Commission* | Correspondence with New York State Public Service Commission spokesperson, 2021 (October 4 2021, October 13 2021)
36 | *Dr. Marvin Resnikoff, a Vermont-based* | Correspondence and conversations with nuclear physicist Dr. Marvin Resnikoff, 2018-2023
36 | *penned a report in 2012 on radon* | Marvin Resnikoff, "Radon in Natural

Gas from Marcellus Shale" (Radioactive Waste Management Associates, 2012)
36 | ***Critics took issue with his math*** | Austin L. Mitchell, W. Michael Griffin, and Elizabeth A. Casman, "Lung Cancer Risk from Radon in Marcellus Shale Gas in Northeast U.S. Homes," Risk Analysis, Vol. 36, No. 11, (2016)
36 | ***radon values far in excess*** | Marvin Resnikoff, "Radon in Natural Gas from Marcellus Shale"
37 | ***Researchers at Carnegie Mellon University in Pittsburgh*** | Austin L. Mitchell et al
37 | ***primarily the daughters of radon*** | Raymond H. Johnson Jr., David E. Bernhardt, Neal S. Nelson and Harry W. Calley Jr., "Assessment of Potential Radiological Health Effects from Radon in Natural Gas" (EPA Office of Radiation Programs, 1973)
37 | **Dr. David Carpenter, former dean → *more hand to mouth activity than the adults do."*** | Conversations and correspondence with Dr. David Carpenter, former dean of the School of Public Health at the State University of New York at Albany, 2019-2023
37-38 | ***Department of Environmental Conservation approved the project*** | "Summary of Comments/Responses: Hudson River Park Trust's Proposed Easement in connection with the New Jersey – New York Expansion Project," (Hudson River Park Trust, May 22, 2012)
38 | ***We did everything in our power,"*** | Correspondence and conversations with Sane Energy director Kim Fraczek, 2019-2023
38 | ***and an easement was needed*** | Albert Amateau, "Trust board approves gas pipeline traversing park" AM NY (New York, New York, June 21, 2012)
38 | ***At 11am Monday morning*** | "HRPT Approves Spectra Easement," (Sane Energy files, 2012)
38 | ***June 18, 2012*** | Albert Amateau, "Trust board approves gas pipeline traversing park"
38 | ***included Pamela Frederick, an adjunct professor*** | Correspondence with Hudson River Park Trust board member Pamela Frederick, 2022
38 | ***appointee named Lawrence Goldberg, and Paul Ullman*** | Albert Amateau, "Trust board approves gas pipeline traversing park"
38 | ***a Wall Street executive and former at KeySpan Energy → 'Would you like to have a drink after this?'"*** | Ruth La Ferla, "Her Term Is Up as Well" New York Times (New York, New York, December 27, 2013) ; Katie Warren, "Inside the relationship of Mike Bloomberg and his longtime partner, Diana Taylor, who met at a business lunch 20 years ago and live in a 5-story Manhattan townhouse" Business Insider (New York City, March 4, 2020)
38 | ***Taylor had been named vice president at KeySpan*** | "KeySpan Energy Names Diana L. Taylor Vice President" Power Online (March 8, 1999), https://www.poweronline.com/doc/keyspan-energy-names-diana-l-taylor-vice-pres-0001
38-39 | ***"their interests were very much aligned."*** | Ruth La Ferla, New York Times
39 | ***they received 862 written comments → As did the local Manhattan community*** | "Summary of Comments/Responses: Hudson River Park Trust's Proposed Easement in connection with the New Jersey – New York Expansion Project," (Hudson River Park Trust, May 22, 2012)
39 | ***"alarmed that natural gas" produced by fracking "will be consumed***

| "Comments Regarding the New Jersey-New York Expansion Project: FERC Docket No. CP11-56-000," (Congress of the United States, Jerrold Nadler, 8th District of New York, October 31, 2011)
Correspondence and conversation with Daniele Gerard, 2022-2023
39 | ***sole reporter*** | "HRPT Approves Spectra Easement," (Sane Energy files, 2012)
39-40 | ***record of the meeting was produced by Daniele Gerard → journalism professor, had voted no*** | "HRPT Approves Spectra Easement," (Sane Energy files, 2012) ; Albert Amateau, "Trust board approves gas pipeline traversing park" AM NY (New York, New York, June 21, 2012)
40 | ***"ridiculous," says Gerard*** | Correspondence and conversation with Daniele Gerard, 2022-2023
40 | ***"Chair Diana Taylor realized what had happened and admonished → Spectra pipeline had been approved*** | "HRPT Approves Spectra Easement," (Sane Energy files, 2012) ; Albert Amateau, "Trust board approves gas pipeline traversing park"
40 | ***mayor's office released a report two months later*** | "Assessment of New York City Natural Gas Market Fundamentals and Life Cycle Fuel Emissions" New York City Mayor's Office of Long-Term Planning and Sustainability (ICF International, August 27, 2012)
41 | ***venue was a pizza food truck → Texas oilman had a slice*** | Files of Mayor Michael Bloomberg's speeches and press releases received via Records Request from New York City Municipal Archives
*Questions for Diana Taylor sent to a spokesperson with Citi Group, the multinational investment bank where she serves on the Board of Directors, have not received replies
**Questions to the communications team for Mike Bloomberg regarding the Spectra pipeline, the possible business interests behind his relationship with Diana Taylor, and whether her positioning on a board set to decide the easement for a natural gas pipeline when his administration had so energetically promoted natural gas represented a conflict of interest have not received replies

Chapter 3
42 | ***Inside the kitchen on the second floor → high levels being recorded in the Marcellus*** | Correspondence and conversations with Silverio Caggiano, 2018-2024
43 | ***Dr. Madalyn Blondes of the U.S. Geological Survey has examined*** | Correspondence and conversations with Dr. Madalyn Blondes of the U.S. Geological Survey, 2018-2024
43 | ***the fracking boom, Ohio legislators → decisions of import were left to the industry-friendly*** | Julie Weatherington-Rice, "ALEC and the Oil & Gas Industry v. Source Water Protection & Home Rule in Ohio: How we got to where we are and what we can do about it" (Dr. Julie Weatherington-Rice, An Ohio Fracture Flow Working Group Presentation, March 5, 2018) ; Correspondence and conversations with Ohio earth scientist Dr. Julie Weatherington-Rice, 2018-2024
44 | ***This came about*** | "Emergency Planning and Community Right-to-Know Act (EPCRA)," (EPA, 2023)
44 | ***highly toxic methyl isocyanate gas into the night*** | Edward Broughton, "The Bhopal disaster and its aftermath: a review," Environmental Health, Volume 4, Number 6 (2005)
44-45 | ***comes the fracking industry spitting → injection wells were***

multiplying | Silverio Caggiano
45 | ***oilfield brine and other toxic liquids*** | Correspondence and conversations with Peter, Marcellus/Utica brine hauler, and others, 2018-2024
45 | ***remain locked "almost indefinitely"*** | "Introduction to the Underground Injection Control Program," (EPA, Drinking Water Academy, January 2003)
45 | ***Because of its favorable regulations → Ohio has nearly more than 250*** | Justin Nobel, "America's Radioactive Secret" Rolling Stone (New York, New York, February 2020) ; Correspondence with Pennsylvania Department of Environmental Protection, 2018-2024
45 | ***Deep in the earth, radioactive elements*** | R. Stephen Fisher, "Geologic and Geochemical Controls on Naturally Occurring Radioactive Materials (NORM) in Produced Water from Oil, Gas, and Geothermal Operations," Environmental Geosciences, Volume 5, Number 3 (1998)
45-46 | ***Uranium and thorium tend to remain*** | Karen P. Smith, "An Overview of Naturally Occurring Radioactive Materials (NORM) in the Petroleum Industry" (Argonne National Laboratory, 1992)
46 | ***radium can be moderately soluble*** | Zoltan Szabo and Vincent dePaul, "Radium-226 and Radium-228 in Shallow Ground Water, Southern New Jersey" (U.S. Geological Survey, June 1998)
46 | ***more likely radium is to be displaced*** | R. Stephen Fisher, Environmental Geosciences
Correspondence with Pennsylvania Department of Environmental Protection, 2018-2024
46 |***federal exemption known as the Bentsen and Bevill*** | "Special Wastes," (EPA, 2023)
46 | ***a Texas oilfield radioactivity expert*** | Correspondence with Texas NORM expert, 2020
46 | ***Department of Transportation has never required*** | Correspondence and conversations with Department of Transportation spokesperson, 2018-2022 (Darius Kirkwood, and others)
46 | ***"heard an awful crunching, crackling, grinding noise,"*** | "Fracking brine truck overturns" The Parkersburg News and Sentinel (Parkersburg, West Virginia, September 2, 2014)
47 | ***a woman named Michele*** | Conversations and correspondence with Vienna township resident Michele, 2018-2024
47 | ***in woods behind a senior citizen mobile home*** | Dan O'Brien, "Brookfield Citizens Group Files Appeal to Stop Injection Well" The Business Journal (Youngstown, Ohio, December 7, 2018)
47 | ***the seniors protested*** | Conversations and correspondence with Brookfield community member Gloria Douglas, 2018-2019
47 | ***The activist Maria Montañez*** | Conversations and correspondences with Ohio Taíno warrior Maria Montañez
47 | ***lower radioactivity levels enough so waste can be taken to a local landfill*** | Justin Nobel, "'This Needs to Be Fixed': Nuclear Expert Calls Radioactivity Levels Found Outside Ohio Oilfield Waste Facility 'Excessive'" DeSmog (Seattle, Washington, April 25, 2022) ; Justin Nobel, "Radioactive Waste 'Everywhere' at Ohio Oilfield Facility, Says Former Worker" DeSmog (Seattle, Washington, August 31, 2022) ; "Trip Report Division of Oil and Gas Resources Management, Petta Cambridge Facility (Chief's Order 2015-29)," (Ohio Department of Natural

Resources, Division of Oil and Gas Resources Management, February 8 & 9, 2017)
47 | ***vastly more expensive*** | Melissa Belcher and Marvin Resnikoff, "Hydraulic Fracturing Radiological Concerns for Ohio, Fact Sheet Prepared for FreshWater Accountability Project Ohio" (Radioactive Waste Management Associates, June 13, 2013)
47 | ***treatment of radioactive oilfield waste, interested companies*** | "Guidelines for Application for Chief's Order," (Ohio Department of Natural Resources, Division of Oil and Gas Resources Management, December 18, 2013) ; Conversations and correspondences with director of Ohio environmental advocacy group Buckeye Environmental Network Teresa Mills
48 | ***one Ohio company operating under Chief's Order*** | "Before the Oil & Gas Commission, City of Wooster, Appeal No. 859, Appellant, -vs- Division of Oil & Gas Resources Management, Review of Chiefs Order 2014-09 (Enviro Clean Facility)" (City of Wooster Appeal No. 859, June 12, 2015)
48 | ***"Unable to evaluate — no radiation safety procedures*** | ODH Audit Report No. ODNR-14-0002, for EnviroClean Services in Wooster, Ohio, (Ohio Department of Health, Bureau of Radiation Protection, March 18, 2014) ; Correspondence with Ohio Department of Natural Resources spokespeople, 2018-2023
48 | ***"We run trucks through, analyze them, and then they go away"*** | Dan O'Brien, "Company Gets Permit to Handle Radioactive Waste" The Business Journal (Youngstown, Ohio, April 21, 2014)
49 | ***having become, "void of life."*** | "Company Owner Sentenced To More Than Two Years In Prison For Dumping Fracking Waste In Mahoning River Tributary," (United States Attorney's Office Northern District of Ohio, August 5, 2014) ; John Caniglia, "Youngstown contractor sentenced to 28 months for dumping fracking waste" Cleveland.com (Cleveland, Ohio, August 5, 2014)
49-52 | ***He believes that like cockroaches → look him in the eye, and say—hey, did I do right?"*** | Correspondence and conversations with Silverio Caggiano, 2018-2024
53 | ***Tom McKnight sits down with a burrito*** | Correspondence and conversations with Ohio brine hauler Tom McKnight, 2020-2023
53 | ***Every day across America about 3 billion gallons of brine*** | "U.S. Produced Water Volumes and Management Practices in 2021," (Ground Water Protection Council, November 2022)
53 | ***Gathering lines pipe the gas away*** | "Natural gas explained: Natural gas pipelines," (U.S. Energy Information Administration, 2023)
53 | ***Approximately 96 percent of the brine generated in America's*** | "U.S. Produced Water Volumes and Management Practices in 2021," (Ground Water Protection Council, November 2022)
53 | ***radium in Marcellus brine to average 9,330 picocuries per liter, and be as high as 28,500*** | Technologically Enhanced Naturally Occurring Radioactive Materials (TENORM) Study Report, (Pennsylvania Department of Environmental Protection, 2016)
53 | ***defining liquid waste as "radioactive,"*** | Correspondence with EPA 2020 (Angela Hackel, January 13, 2020) ; "A Regulators' Guide to the Management of Radioactive Residuals from Drinking Water Treatment Technologies," (EPA, Office of Water, July 2005)
53-54 | ***limits the Nuclear Regulatory Commission has for discharging*** |

Correspondence with David McIntyre of the Nuclear Regulatory Agency, 2020-2021 ; Correspondence and conversations with Diane D'Arrigo with Nuclear Information and Resource Service

54-56 | ***Drivers typically wear a simple blue work → cleaning off the little ducks, same deal."*** | Correspondence and conversations with Ohio brine hauler Tom McKnight, 2020-2023

57-58 | ***even bananas are naturally radioactive → damage that can lead to cancer*** | Correspondence and conversations with nuclear forensics scientist Dr. Marco Kaltofen, 2019-2024

57 | ***a long list of other radioactive isotopes*** | "Radioactive Decay: The Uranium-238 Decay Chain and The Thorium-232 Decay Chain," (EPA, 2023)

58 | ***speed of 12,4530 miles per second*** | "Alpha particles," (Australian Radiation Protection and Nuclear Safety Agency, 2023)

58-59 | ***In 2017, Tom stopped hauling brine → the warranty is bad, and they just look away."*** | Correspondence and conversations with Ohio brine hauler Tom McKnight, 2020-2023

59 | ***CS Trucking, Tom's brine hauling*** | Attempted correspondence with CS Trucking, 2019-2023

59 | ***one of Ohio's largest inland lakes*** | Seneca Lake Park: Senecaville, Ohio (Muskingum Watershed Conservancy District, 2023)

59 | ***drilled within 2,000 feet of the lake's shoreline*** | Correspondence and conversations with FracTracker Alliance analyst Ted Auch, 2018-2024

60 | ***made more than a quarter of a billion dollars*** | Correspondence with Muskingum Watershed Conservancy District attorney Jonathan Mizer, 2021

60-61 | ***A few ridges out from the lake → and her sister Jodi visited regularly*** | Correspondence and conversations with Kerri Bond, 2018-2024

61 | ***leasing company held a meeting at a Methodist church*** | Justin Nobel, "America's Radioactive Secret" Rolling Stone (New York, New York, February 2020)

61 | ***the Ohio Supreme Court, in a 4-3 decision, ruled cities*** | "Ohio Supreme Court Overrides Local Fracking Ban," (The National Trial Lawyers)

61-62 | ***on their own land, Ohioans are helpless → legally consider is the project's profitability*** | Julie Grant, "Fracking in Ohio: State law gives energy companies right to force landowners into leases" The Allegheny Front (Pittsburgh, Pennsylvania, June 28, 2019) ; Heidi Gorovitz Robertson, "Get Out From Under My Land! Hydraulic Fracturing, Forced Pooling or Unitization, and the Role of the Dissenting Landowner," The Georgetown Environmental Law Review, Volume 30 (2017) ; Correspondence and conversations with Cleveland State University law professor Heidi Gorovitz Robertson, 2021-2024

62-63 | ***an illiterate Amish farmer with seven children*** | Julie Grant, The Allegheny Front

massive drill rigs are hauled in by truck → temporarily store the highly toxic flowback | "Explore a Fracking Operation – Virtually," (FracTracker Alliance, 2023)

63 | ***July 24, 2015: Woke up*** | "Trees Dying" (Text message fracking diary of Kerri Bond, July 24, 2015)

63 | ***Sandra Colegrove*** | "Ohio EPA" (Text message fracking diary of Kerri Bond, July 30, 2015)

63 | ***Fracking begins*** | "Bond Pad" (Text message fracking diary of Kerri Bond, October 23, 2015)

Sand trucks | "Bond Pad" (Text message fracking diary of Kerri Bond, October 26, 2015)
63 | ***Noise, smell*** | "Bond Pad" (Text message fracking diary of Kerri Bond, October 30, 2015)
64 | ***Bloody noses, coughing*** | "Exposures To Industry Hazards" (Text message fracking diary of Kerri Bond, December 5, 2015)
64 | ***Everyone is scared to death*** | "Fracking The Hall Units" (Text message fracking diary of Kerri Bond, December 9, 2015)
65 | ***1926 research bulletin of the West Virginia Agricultural*** | Ludwig Schmidt and John M. Devine, "The Disposal of Oil Field Brines" (United States Bureau of Mines, Department of the Interior, June 1929) ; C.D. Howard, "occurrence of Barium in the Ohio Valley Brines and Its Relation to Stock Poisoning" (Bulletin of the West Virginia Agricultural and Forestry Experiment Station, 1926)
65 | ***in a 2012 scientific paper → health experiment on an enormous scale."*** | Michelle Bamberger and Robert E. Oswald, "Impacts of Gas Drilling on Human and Animal Health," New Solutions: A Journal of Environmental and Occupational Health Policy, Volume 22, Number 1 (2012)
66 | ***natural gas of this region*** | Natural gas explained," (US Energy Information Administration, 2022)
66 | ***every 40 to 100 miles a compressor station is needed*** | "What is a Natural Gas Compressor Station?" (Interstate Natural Gas Association of America, September 11, 2017)
"He did cattle and hay and didn't know → "he dropped dead." | Correspondence and conversations with Kerri Bond, 2018-2024
66 | ***Louisiana environmental toxicologist Wilma Subra → pathway for a unique exposure*** | Correspondence and conversations with Louisiana environmental toxicologist Wilma Subra
67 | ***Dr. Michael McCawley, at West Virginia University's*** | Correspondence and conversations with occupational and environmental health scientist Dr. Michael McCawley ; Michael Hendryx and Juhua Luo, "Natural gas pipeline compressor stations: VOC emissions and mortality rates," The Extractive Industries and Society, Volume 7, Number 3 (2020)
67 | ***In May 2016, David Lipp, a supervisor in the Ohio Department of Health's*** | "Ohio Dept Health" (Text message fracking diary of Kerri Bond, May 11, 2016)
68 | ***Kerri says Lipp told her not to worry → and smells like a dead body."*** | Kerri Bond
69 | ***for sale at any big box store,"*** | "Pioneering Plastic Recycling Through Innovation, We supply over a million pounds of recycled resin every day: Housewares" (Ultra-Poly Corporation, 2023)
69 | ***company has not answered any of my questions*** | Attempted correspondence with Ultra-Poly Corporation, 2023 (info@ultra-poly.com: March 24 2023, December 28 2023)
69 | ***9 wells*** | Correspondence and conversations with FracTracker Alliance analyst Ted Auch, 2018-2024
69-70 | ***evening is coming on → there is no place as beautiful as Ohio*** | Kerri Bond

Chapter 4

71-83 | ***I fear nothing as far as recourse. → I'm going to hit a home run*** | Correspondence and conversations with Jesse Lombardi, 2020-2024

84 | ***North Dakota experienced its first oil boom → formation's tightly-held oil and gas*** | First North Dakota Oil Well, Petroleum Pioneers," (American Oil & Gas Historical Society) ; "Beyond the Boom, Bakken Formation Geology," (Energy and Environmental Research Center, University of North Dakota, 2014) ; "A Brief History of Oil Production from the Bakken Formation in the Williston Basin," (North Dakota Department of Mineral Resources, January 2010)

84 | ***oil development exploded across the state*** | James Mason, "Bakken's maximum potential oil production rate explored" Oil & Gas Journal (Tulsa, Oklahoma, April 2 2012)

84 | ***Bakken had surpassed Alaska and North Dakota*** | James MacPherson, "North Dakota passes Alaska to become No. 2 US oil producer" Anchorage Daily News (Anchorage, Alaska, May 15, 2012)

84-85 | ***One of them was Rob Kanack → One of Rob's jobs was to clean out the filter pod*** | Correspondence with oilfield worker Rob Kanack, 2020-2024

85 | ***contain elevated levels of radium, and also radioactive lead*** | Christopher B. Harto, Karen P. Smith, Sunita Kamboj and John J. Quinn, "Radiological Dose and Risk Assessment of Landfill Disposal of Technologically Enhanced Naturally Occurring Radioactive Materials (TENORM) in North Dakota" (Argonne National Laboratory, Environmental Science Division, November 2014)

85 | ***oilfield's more highly radioactive waste*** | Jay Almlie, "NORM Sample Analysis Results Summary," (Energy & Environmental Research Center, University of North Dakota, June 12, 2014)

85 | ***produces 27 tons of dirty filter → stashed inside black*** | Lauren Donovan, "Radioactive dump site found in remote North Dakota town" Bismarck Tribune (Bismarck, North Dakota, March 11, 2014)

85 | ***city dumpsters*** | Kate Ruggles, "Filter socks are unwanted garbage" McKenzie County Farmer (Watford City, North Dakota, February 27, 2013)

85 | ***littered across the Fort Berthold*** | Lauren Donovan, "Tribe warns that children might play with illegally dumped filter socks" The Bismarck Tribune (Bismarck, North Dakota, March 5, 2013)

85 | ***illegally snuck into county landfills*** | "Radioactive North Dakota oil waste found; officials calling for action" Twin Cities Pioneer Press (St. Paul, Minnesota, February 24, 2014)

85 | ***In 2014 the state crafted rules to try and fix the problem*** | "PowerPoint: TENORM Disposal Options in North Dakota," (Dale Patrick, Radiation Control Program Manager, North Dakota Department of Health, April 2015) ; James MacPherson, "North Dakota rules target oilfield waste dumping" Associated Press (New York, New York, April 10, 2014)

85-86 | ***At Cypress Energy it was Rob's job → getting paid around $23 an hour*** | Correspondence and conversations with oilfield waste hauler Rob Kanack, 2020-2024

86 | ***In North Dakota they run radioactive solid*** | "Our Facility Locations," (Secure Energy, 2023)

86 | ***radiation monitor on a box of Master Paws kitty litter*** | Renée Jean, "Secure Energy appears set to receive its TENORM permits" Williston Herald (Williston, North Dakota, June 8, 2022)

86-88 | *Rob says he would take background → long distances to the higher-level* | Rob Kanack
87 | *International Association of Oil & Gas Producers, which considers an area* | "Managing Naturally Occurring Radioactive Material (NORM) in the oil and gas industry," (International Association of Oil & Gas Producers, March 2016)
88 | *large portal monitors that generate a reading as trucks pass through* | Correspondence and conversations with North Dakota Department of Environmental Quality Director Dave Glatt and chief radiation safety officer Dale Patrick, 2019-2020 (May 22 2019)
89 | *"I expressed...that this was % 100 not legal* | "Rob Kanack email to Secure boss complaining of violations," (Rob Kanack, August 3, 2016)
89 | *On July 24, 2016, the agency stopped by the site* | Lauren Donovan, "Alexander landfill operator found with radioactive waste" Bismarck Tribune (Bismarck, North Dakota, August 31, 2016)
89 | *in 2024 pass along to me a "Radioactive Material License"* | Correspondence with North Dakota Department of Environmental Quality, Jennifer Skjod (March 7 2024)
90 | *"I was literally so sick after that incident that I shit myself,"* | Correspondence with Bakken oilfield worker, 2020-2024
90 | *"You are supposed to shut your mouth → I will poke the beehive."* | Rob Kanack
90 | *Secure has not replied* | Attempted correspondences with Secure Energy 2022-2023
91 | *November 2021 Bill Torbett* | Conversations and correspondences with Bill Torbett, 2022-2024
91 | *in an old steel mill on the Ohio River* | Justin Nobel, "Radioactive Waste 'Everywhere' at Ohio Oilfield Facility, Says Former Worker" DeSmog (Seattle, Washington, August 31, 2022)
91 | *particularly sloppy and radioactive sludge, they take it here* | Correspondence and conversations with Peter, Marcellus/Utica brine hauler, and others, 2018-2024
91 | *to receive 120 million pounds of radioactive* | "Austin Master Services Air Permit Application, Potential to Emit," (Civil & Environmental Consultants, Inc., November 12, 2021) ; "Ohio Department of Health, License for Radioactive Material, Austin Master Services," (Ohio Department of Health, February 26, 2019) ; "Chief's Order No. 2014-541 for AMS Martins Ferry Facility," (Ohio Department of Natural Resources, Division of Oil and Gas Resources Management, November 26, 2014)
91-92 | *"That place was a hoot," → lack of concern for health and safety, Bill left.* | Conversations and correspondences with Bill Torbett, 2022-2024
92 | *down the street from the Martins Ferry high school football stadium* | Justin Nobel, "'This Needs to Be Fixed': Nuclear Expert Calls Radioactivity Levels Found Outside Ohio Oilfield Waste Facility 'Excessive'" DeSmog (Seattle, Washington, April 25, 2022) ; Beverly Reed, Cyndhia Ramatchandirane, and Yuri Gorby, "Elevated levels of radioactivity in surface sediments near a radioactive waste processing facility in Martins Ferry, Ohio" (Concerned Ohio River Residents and Earthjustice, April 26, 2022)
93 | *"the facility is now in operation...no issues to report."* | "Trip Report, Austin Masters, Division of Oil and Gas Resources Management," (Ohio Department

of Natural Resources, Division of Oil and Gas Resources Management, September 16, 2015)

93 | ***"the floors appeared to be dirty*** | "Trip Report, Austin Masters, Division of Oil and Gas Resources Management," (Ohio Department of Natural Resources, Division of Oil and Gas Resources Management, April 12, 2017)

93 | ***potential exists for radioactive and other wastes to be tracked out*** | "Trip Report, Chief's Order No. 2014-541, Division of Oil and Gas Resources Management," (Ohio Department of Natural Resources, Division of Oil and Gas Resources Management, July 5, 2017)

93 | ***waste splattered on the floor, walls*** | Justin Nobel, "Radioactive Waste 'Everywhere' at Ohio Oilfield Facility, Says Former Worker" DeSmog (Seattle, Washington, August 31, 2022) ; Justin Nobel, "'This Needs to Be Fixed': Nuclear Expert Calls Radioactivity Levels Found Outside Ohio Oilfield Waste Facility 'Excessive'" DeSmog (Seattle, Washington, April 25, 2022)

93 | ***"frac tank being removed from the facility" and waste "falling off*** | "Inspection Report, Chief's Order No. 2014-541, Division of Oil and Gas Resources Management (DOGRM)," (Ohio Department of Natural Resources, Division of Oil and Gas Resources Management, September 7, 2018)

93 | ***filter socks were being shredded*** | "Inspection Report, Chief's Order No. 2014-541, Division of Oil and Gas Resources Management (DOGRM)," (Ohio Department of Natural Resources, Division of Oil and Gas Resources Management, April 18, 2019)

93 | ***equipment called "Muffin Monster."*** | "Inspection Report, Chief's Order No. 2014-541, Division of Oil and Gas Resources Management (DOGRM)," (Ohio Department of Natural Resources, Division of Oil and Gas Resources Management, August 5, 2019)

93 | ***found some waste containers at 60 times background*** | "Inspection Report, Chief's Order No. 2014-541, Division of Oil and Gas Resources Management (DOGRM)," (Ohio Department of Natural Resources, Division of Oil and Gas Resources Management, November 8, 2018)

93 | ***73 times background "on a large 'burrito' bag*** | "Radiological Assessment Report, Radiation Protection Program Inspection, Chief's Order: 2014-541," (Ohio Department of Natural Resources, Division of Oil and Gas Resources Management, Radiation Safety Sector, February 12, 2019)

93 | ***state had issued the company no fines*** | Correspondence with the Ohio Department of Natural Resources, 2018-2023 (Stephanie O'Grady March 24 2022)

93 | ***nothing "unusual or harmful" about their operations*** | Correspondence with Austin Master Services spokesperson Christopher Martin, 2022 (March 21 2022)

93 | ***He does not reply to questions on*** | Correspondence with Austin Master Services spokesperson Christopher Martin, 2022 (Attempted correspondence July 13, 2022)

93 | ***July 2022 post from Austin Master Services*** | "Screenshot of Heavy Equipment Operator post on Indeed.com by Austin Master Services LLC, Martines Ferry, OH 43935," (Indeed.com, July 2022)

93 | ***individuals with a criminal record*** | "How Second Chance Hiring Can Address the Worker Shortage," (U.S. Chamber of Commerce, June 2, 2022)

94 | ***leaving Austin Master and headed to five different Pennsylvania landfills*** | "Client Search Details for Austin Master Services LLC, Client ID: 330813,"

(Pennsylvania Department of Environmental Protection eFacts Client Query Tool, Accessed May 19, 2022 and again January 6, 2023)

94 | ***In correspondence with Tim Orton*** | Correspondences with Energy Solutions technical officer Tim Orton, 2022-2024

94 | ***76 million pounds of oilfield waste → found those railcars to be leaking*** | "Austin Masters Shipments, Excel Spreadsheet," (Energy Solutions, March 2022)

94 | ***waste had leaked all the way across the country,"*** | Tim Orton

94-95 | ***CSX tells me they "work closely*** | Correspondence with CSX media team, April 2022

95 | ***in Salina, learn from two women at a knitting supply store*** | Conversations with staff at Yarns at 148 S Santa Fe Ave in Salina, Kansas, 2019

95 | ***a growing trail of radioactivity led right to Austin Master's*** | Correspondences and conversations with former Department of Energy scientist Dr. Yuri Gorby, 2019-2024 ; Justin Nobel, "'This Needs to Be Fixed': Nuclear Expert Calls Radioactivity Levels Found Outside Ohio Oilfield Waste Facility 'Excessive'" DeSmog (Seattle, Washington, April 25, 2022) ; Justin Nobel, "Radioactive Waste 'Everywhere' at Ohio Oilfield Facility, Says Former Worker" DeSmog (Seattle, Washington, August 31, 2022) ; Beverly Reed, Cyndhia Ramatchandirane, and Yuri Gorby, "Elevated levels of radioactivity in surface sediments near a radioactive waste processing facility in Martins Ferry, Ohio" (Concerned Ohio River Residents and Earthjustice, April 26, 2022)

95 | ***nuclear sites like uranium mills*** | "EPA Facts about Radium," (EPA)

96-97 | ***has been dealt a tough hand → lot of trucks got sent out hot*** | Correspondence and conversations with former Austin Master Services laborer David Duvall, 2022

97 | ***"While the Ohio Department of Health has been designated*** | Correspondence with the Ohio Department of Health, 2018-2023 (Alicia Shoults April 7 2021)

97 | ***"The Division does not have the authority to levy fines*** | Correspondence with the Ohio Department of Natural Resources, 2018-2023 (Stephanie O'Grady March 24 2022)

97 | ***"We went from a rural agrarian society*** | Correspondence and conversations with North Dakota Department of Environmental Quality Director Dave Glatt and chief radiation safety officer Dale Patrick, May 22 2019

97 | ***"The waste products from the oil and gas drilling operations*** | Correspondence with Nuclear Regulatory Commission spokesperson, 2021-2022 (David McIntyre, January 6 2020)

97 | ***"EPA does not regulate radioactivity in oil and gas*** | Correspondence with EPA, 2018-2023 (Enesta Jones, March 31 2022)

97 | ***There is no one federal Agency*** | Correspondence with EPA, 2018-2023 (Tricia Lynn, October 18 2018)

98 | ***"We don't track brine hauling*** | Correspondence with U.S. Department of Transportation's Pipeline and Hazardous Materials Safety Administration (PHMSA), 2018-2021 (Darius Kirkwood, October 26 2018)

98 | ***little potential for harm to workers or the public from radiation exposure*** | Correspondences with U.S. Occupational Safety and Health Administration under the U.S. Department of Labor, 2018-2023 (Michael Trupo, August 23 2018)

98 | ***In 1976, Congress passed the Resource Conservation and*** | "Summary of the Resource Conservation and Recovery Act, 42 U.S.C. §6901 et seq. (1976)," (EPA, 2023)
98 | ***legally defining oilfield waste*** | "Special Wastes," (EPA, 2023)
98 | ***David tells me, before we depart → time we get in there—it's too late."*** | Correspondence and conversations with former Austin Master Services laborer David Duvall, 2022

Chapter 5
99 | ***January 2020 I receive a call*** | Correspondence with staff health physicist source, 2020-2024
99-100 | ***Medieval miners suffered from → we now know it was radon*** | "Health Risks of Radon and Other Internally Deposited Alpha-Emitters: Beir IV, Appendix IVEpidemiological Studies of Persons Exposed to Radon Progeny" (National Research Council (US) Committee on the Biological Effects of Ionizing Radiations, National Academies Press in Washington, D.C., 1988) ; Robert K. Lewis, "A History of Radon- 1470 to 1984" (Pennsylvania Department of Environmental Protection, Bureau of Radiation Protection, Radon Division, Presented at the 2006 National Radon Meeting, 2006)
100 | ***The US story began during World War II → protect a couple oil and gas workers*** ; Correspondence with staff health physicist source, 2020-2024
100 | ***first detected in 1904, by a 25-year-old Canadian*** | "Photos of 'A Radioactive Gas From Crude Petroleum' obtained during visit to University of Toronto libraries," (University of Toronto Studies, Physical Science Series, photographed by Justin Nobel, 2019)
100-102 | ***But "there is night and day differences → just keep digging*** | Correspondence with staff health physicist source, 2020-2024

Chapter 6
105 | ***Killdeer Mountains, Tah-kah-o-kuty*** | Ed Murphy, "North Dakotas Mountains" North Dakota Horizons Magazine (Bismarck, North Dakota, Summer 2006)
105 | ***Missouri River, Ouemessourita*** | "The Missouri River," (Spirit of Nebraska, April 21, 2022)
105 | ***"One does not sell the earth," said Crazy Horse*** | Dee Brown, Bury My Heart at Wounded Knee (New York, New York: Holt Paperbacks, 2007)
105 | ***Homestead Act enabled White settlers to claim "unappropriated*** | "Transcript of the Homestead Act,"(U.S. National Archives, 2022)
105-106 | ***Roughly 10 percent of the United States → tracts of land now belonging to the reservations*** | David Edlefsen, "How the West was Claimed: The Homestead Act and the General Allotment Act," (Prepared for Western Political Science Association Conference, San Francisco, California, March 31, 2018) ; "Dawes Act (1887)," (U.S. National Archives, 2022)
106 | ***1911 US government poster advertised*** | "Indian land for sale : get a home of your own, easy payments. Perfect title. Possession within thirty days. Fine lands in the West," (U.S. Library of Congress, 2024)
106 | ***"Are you a stockholder?"*** | Dominic Schaff, "The History of the North Dakota Oil Industry," (A Thesis Submitted to the Faculty of the Graduate School of the University of North Dakota in partial fulfillment of the requirements for the

Degree of Master of Arts, Grand Forks, North Dakota, 1962)
106 | ***America's oil boom started in the east*** | "U.S. Census Bureau History: The Oil Industry," (U.S. Census Bureau, August 2021)
106 | ***Edwin Drake famously struck "black gold"*** | "Development of the Pennsylvania Oil Industry," (American Chemical Society, 2024)
106 | ***Spindletop, in 1901*** | "History of Oil Discoveries in Texas," (Texas Almanac)
106 | ***Glenn Pool, 1905*** | Bobby D. Weaver, "Glenn Pool Field," (The Encyclopedia of Oklahoma History and Culture, Oklahoma Historical Society)
106 | ***at Stapleton, 1915*** | "Kansas Oil Boom," (American Oil & Gas Historical Society)
106 | ***natural gas was discovered in North Dakota in 1892*** | Renée Jean, "More than a century of history for oil and gas" Williston Herald (Williston, North Dakota, April 14, 2021)
106-107 | ***On a summer day in 1925 a man stops → pay off mortgages and all other debts*** | Dominic Schaff, "The History of the North Dakota Oil Industry" ; "NPL Founder Dies in Crash, Colorful N.D. Farm Revolt Figures Gone," St. Cloud Times (St. Cloud, Minnesota, November 9, 1959)
107 | ***on April 4, 1951, true oil was discovered*** | "First North Dakota Oil Well," (American Oil & Gas Historical Society, March 31, 2014)
107 | ***Within two months, nearly 30 million acres were leased*** | "This Week in Petroleum History, April 3 to April 9, April 4, 1951 – First North Dakota Oil Well taps Williston Basin," (American Oil & Gas Historical Society, 2023)
107 | ***oil was discovered on the Henry O. Bakken farm → in 1907 located land in North Dakota*** | "Famous Bakken formation named for North Dakota homesteaders" Mitchell Republic (Mitchell, South Dakota, December 2, 2012)
107-108 | ***blows over the fields of BJ and Wes Lindvig → flares are visible even by day*** | Correspondence and conversations with BJ and Wes Lindvig, 2019-2024
108 | ***is simply burned off*** | "Natural gas explained," (U.S. Energy Information Administration, 2022) ; Ala Eddine Aoun, Hui Pu, Youcef Khetib and Mohamed Cherif Ben Ameur, "Natural gas flaring status in the Bakken shale play and potential remedial solutions," Fuel, Volume 342, Number 127807 (2023) ; "Natural gas venting and flaring in North Dakota and Texas increased in 2019," (U.S. Energy Information Administration, 2020)
108 | ***health physicist source from the DC sports bar had told*** | Correspondence and conversations with federal agency staff health physicist, 2020-2024
108 | ***I ask the North Dakota Department of Environmental Quality*** | Correspondence with North Dakota Department of Environmental Quality, Jennifer Skjod (March 7 2024)
109 | ***unit that separates oil from brine*** | "heater treater," (Schlumberger Energy Glossary, 2024)
109 | ***known to buildup radioactive sludge and scale*** | "EPA Diffuse Norm, Waste Characterization And Preliminary Risk Assessment," (EPA, 1991)
109 | ***Many have been made of fiberglass-based materials*** | Amy Dalrymple, "Fine ordered for 2014 Fort Berthold pipeline spill" Bismarck Tribune (Bismarck, North Dakota, February 2, 2018)
109 | ***leak hundreds of thousands of gallons into the landscape*** | Avner Vengosh, "Salting the Earth: The Environmental Impact of Oil and Gas Wastewater

Spills" Environmental Health Perspectives, Volume 124, Number 12 (2016)
109 | ***Bakken oilfield brine is among the nation's more most radium-rich*** | Justin Nobel, "Highest Recorded Radium Readings in various US Oil & Gas Plays" (unpublished work, 2023)
109 | ***examined 20 Bakken samples*** | Jay Almlie, "NORM Sample Analysis Results Summary," (Energy & Environmental Research Center, University of North Dakota, June 12, 2014) ; Correspondence with Energy & Environmental Research Center Engineer Jay Almlie, 2019-2021 (November 27, 2019)
109 | ***11.8 million gallons of brine spilled in North Dakota*** | Deborah Sontag and Robert Gebeloff, "The Downside of the Boom" New York Times (New York, New York, November 22, 2014) ; Jordan Wirfs-Brock, "Wastewater Spills In North Dakota: What The Data Tell Us – insideenergy.org," (Dakota Resource Council, February 3, 2015)
109 | ***nearly 90 percent of the state is farm*** | "North Dakota Department of Agriculture," (North Dakota Department of Agriculture, 2022)
I learn firsthand when I tour Daryl and Christine Peterson's 2,500 acres | Correspondence and conversations with Daryl and Christine Peterson, 2019-2024
110 | ***When spills happen, there is often little or no fine*** | Deborah Sontag and Robert Gebeloff, "The Downside of the Boom" New York Times (New York, New York, November 22, 2014)
110 | ***listed as 10 gallons, but was actually*** | Justin Nobel, "Did North Dakota Regulators Hide an Oil and Gas Industry Spill Larger Than Exxon Valdez?" DeSmog (Seattle, Washington, August 19, 2019)
110 | ***"moderately or extremely contaminated with brine."*** | Tara L. Chesley-Preston, James L. Coleman, Robert A. Gleason, Seth S. Haines, Karen E. Jenni, Timothy L. Nieman, Zell E. Peterman, Max Post van der Burg, Todd M. Preston, Bruce D. Smith, Brian A. Tangen, and Joanna N. Thamke, "Brine Contamination to Aquatic Resources from Oil and Gas Development in the Williston Basin, United States" (U.S. Geological Survey, 2014)
110 | ***contaminated private wells and also the city of Poplar's*** | "Delineation of Brine Contamination in and near the East Poplar Oil Field, Fort Peck Indian Reservation, Northeastern Montana," (Wyoming-Montana Water Science Center, U.S. Geological Survey, May 1, 2018)
110 | ***North Dakota's brine makes it to injection wells*** | "U.S. Produced Water Volumes and Management Practices in 2021," (Ground Water Protection Council, November 2022)
110 | ***report by the environmental group Earthworks*** | Melissa Troutman, "Still Wasting Away: The failure to safely manage oil and gas waste continues" (Earthworks, May 2019) ; "Aquifer Exemptions in the Underground Injection Control Program" (EPA, August 2, 2023)
110 | ***swath of North Dakota's Dakota aquifer*** | Kyle Ferrar, "What Are Aquifer Exemptions? Permitted Exemptions from the Safe Drinking Water Act" (FracTracker Alliance, October 26, 2017)
110 | ***which is larger than Portugal*** | "Aquifers of North Dakota" (North Dakota Department of Environmental Quality, October 2021)
111 | ***stuck with the lease your parents → creates a cognitive dissonance,"*** | Correspondence and conversations with Dakota Resource Council executive director Scott Skokos, 2019-2024
111-112 | ***BJ has short hair and black glasses → as he explains it, "you***

want to keep something." | Correspondence and conversations with BJ and Wes Lindvig, 2019-2024
112 | ***tour guide Sakakawea*** | Paul A. Johnsgard, "Journals of the Lewis & Clark Expedition" (University of Nebraska Press Center for Great Plains Studies, 2003) ; "Lewis & Clark National Historic Trail, Sacagawea" (U.S. National Park Service, 2023)
112 | ***German prince, Maximilian of Wied → "After we ate, our host lit a pipe"*** | Prince Maximilian of Wied, Travels in North America, 1832-1834: A Concise Edition of the Journals of Prince Maximilian of Wied (Norman, Oklahoma: University of Oklahoma Press, 2017), cover flap, index, 235, 239, 243, 244, 272, 316, 325-335
113 | ***smallpox epidemic wiped out*** | "North Dakota: People Living on the Land, Small Pox Epidemic" (North Dakota state government)
113 | ***Fort Laramie Treaty of 1851 granted → 12-million-acre territory had become less*** | "North Dakota Studies: Mandan, Hidatsa, Sahnish" (North Dakota state government, State Historical Society of North Dakota)
113-114 | ***had rebounded by the early 1900s → formed behind the dam was named Lake Sakakawea*** | Marilyn Cross Hudson, "We're not here to sell our land: The Mandan, Hidatsa, and Arikara people and the Flood Control Act of 1944" Points West Magazine (Cody, Wyoming, Winter 2005)
114 | ***still recall as the Great Flood*** | Natasha Rausch "How smallpox brought the Mandan, Hidatsa and Arikara tribes together" Grand Forks Herald, (Grand Forks, North Dakota, November 28, 2019)
114 | ***the people of the Three Affiliated Tribes still occupy*** | "MHA Nation: The Mandan, Hidatsa and Arikara Nation" (Mandan, Hidatsa & Arikara Nation, 2018)
114 | ***in the middle of a major oil boom*** | Deborah Sontag and Brent McDonald, "In North Dakota, a Tale of Oil, Corruption and Death" New York Times (New York, New York, December 28, 2014)
114-116 | ***The couple runs Fort Berthold's → endangered butterfly called the Dakota skipper*** | Correspondence and conversations with Lisa and Walter DeVille, 2019-2024
116 | ***fails to even show Fort Berthold Indian Reservation*** | "Sacagawea Pipeline System Map, Paradigm Energy Partners, LLC" (Screenshot of description on https://paradigmmidstream.com/news/openseason, October 15, 2021) ; "The Sacagawea Pipeline Project, Paradigm Energy Partners, LLC" (Screenshot of description on https://paradigmmidstream.com/news/openseason, October 15, 2021)
116 | ***"they helped create a dream for our babies"*** | Blair Emerson, "'A dream for our babies': New Head Start facility opens in Mandaree" Bismarck Tribune (Bismarck, North Dakota, July 18, 2019)
116-117 | ***policy he called, "sovereignty by the barrel" → image as an honest oil broker was tainted*** | Deborah Sontag and Brent McDonald, "In North Dakota, a Tale of Oil, Corruption and Death" New York Times (New York, New York, December 28, 2014)
116 | ***yacht called Island Girl*** | David Rooks, "Mandan, Hidatsa and Arikara Dreams on Dry Dock for Now" Indian Country Today (Phoenix, Arizona, June 27, 2016)
117 | ***"Our own tribal government is not seeing → oilfield brine has been***

regularly dumped | Correspondence and conversations with Lisa and Walter DeVille, 2019-2024

117 | ***According to a lengthy newspaper investigation*** | Deborah Sontag and Brent McDonald, New York Times

118 | ***to July 8, 2014, a million gallons of oilfield brine leaked*** | Amy Dalrymple, "Fine ordered for 2014 Fort Berthold pipeline spill" Bismarck Tribune (Bismarck, North Dakota, February 2, 2018)

118 | ***provides drinking water to the reservation*** | "Local leader investigates million-gallon Bear Den Bay Spill" (Dakota Resource Council press release, August 20, 2014)

118 | ***spill laid a path across the landscape → pay EPA a fine for the spill of $49,000*** | Amy Dalrymple, "Fine ordered for 2014 Fort Berthold pipeline spill" Bismarck Tribune (Bismarck, North Dakota, February 2, 2018) ; "Cleanup area extends nearly 2 miles after N.D. spill" Associated Press (New York, New York, July 10, 2014)

118 | ***has jurisdiction on the reservation, but the North Dakota Department*** | "Development of oil and gas infrastructure on the Fort Berthold Indian Reservation, North Dakota (FBIR)" (North Dakota Industrial Commission, March 9, 2020) ; Correspondence with North Dakota Department of Environmental Quality, Jennifer Skjod (March 7 2024)

118 | ***"more development, more drilling, more jobs."*** | "Chairman Fox and Governor Burgum Sign Tax Compact" (Chairman Fox's website, Chairmanfox.com, March 14, 2019)

118 | ***But he has not responded to my questions*** | Attempted correspondence with Chairman Mark Fox, 2022-2024 (March 10 2022, January 20, 2024)

119 | ***"which supplies the reservation its drinking water."*** | "Local leader investigates million-gallon Bear Den Bay Spill" (Dakota Resource Council press release, August 20, 2014)

119 | ***not been able to obtain test results*** | Deborah Sontag and Brent McDonald, New York Times

119 | ***Crestwood, for their part, has not replied*** | Attempted correspondence with Crestwood Equity Partners, 2022-2024 (July 25 2022, January 20, 2024)

119-120 | ***July 2015, a year after the spill → long-term ecological and possible human health impacts"*** | Nancy E. Lauer, Jennifer S. Harkness, and Avner Vengosh, "Brine Spills Associated with Unconventional Oil Development in North Dakota," Environmental Science & Technology, Volume 50, Number 10 (2016) ; "Avner Vengosh, Duke Nicholas School of the Environment" (Duke Nicholas School of the Environment, 2024) ; Justin Nobel, "America's Radioactive Secret" Rolling Stone (New York, New York, February 2020)

120 | ***"This," she says, "is a radioactive spill."*** | Lisa and Walter DeVille

120 | ***when I mentioned it to Dave Glatt → "a biased view."*** | Correspondence and conversations with North Dakota Department of Health officials Dale Patrick and Dave Glatt, 2019 ; Correspondence with North Dakota Department of Environmental Quality, Jennifer Skjod (March 7 2024)

121 | ***In 2021, a team of scientists → could be subject to a similar situation*** | Isabelle M. Cozzarelli, Douglas B. Kent, Martin Briggs, Mark A. Engle, Adam Benthem, Katherine J. Skalak, Adam C. Mumford, Jeanne Jaeschke, Aïda Farag, John W. Lane Jr and Denise M. Akob, "Geochemical and geophysical indicators of oil and gas wastewater can trace potential exposure pathways following

releases to surface waters," Science of the Total Environment, Volume 755 (2021)
121 | ***"Now," Lisa jokes, "you've got the brine in you."*** | Lisa and Walter DeVille

Chapter 7
122 | ***"It's not like it's just boohoo poor James → some of them stepped up, and some spoke out."*** | Correspondence and conversations with James Brugh, 2020-2024
132 | ***Marathon Oil has not replied to my questions*** | Attempted correspondence with Marathon Oil, 2022-2023 (July 25, 2022, April 19, 2023)

Chapter 8
134-136 | ***Sister Elizabeth has devoted herself → a Geiger counter she is carrying in her purse*** | Correspondence and conversations with Sister Elizabeth Riebschlaeger, 2019-2024
136 | ***burned off into the atmosphere*** | Amanda Drane "Flyover event spies Eagle Ford flares in South Texas" Houston Chronicle (Houston, Texas, July 27, 2023)
136 | ***development here didn't begin until 2008*** | Robert W. Gilmer and Raúl Hernandez and Keith R. Phillips, "Oil Boom in Eagle Ford Shale Brings New Wealth to South Texas," Federal Reserve bank of Dallas (Dallas, Texas, Second Quarter 2012)
136 | ***Sister Elizabeth grew up in Cuero → Moczygemba, Bartkowiak, Korzekwa*** | Correspondence and conversations with Sister Elizabeth Riebschlaeger, 2019-2024
137-138 | ***Amanda chaperones Sister Elizabeth by a bull → unfortunately, I will take it."*** | Correspondence and conversations with Amanda Baumann, 2019-2024
138 | ***environmental toxicologist Wilma Subra*** | Sara Sneath, "Residents learn risks of possible facilities" Victoria Advocate (Victoria, Texas, March 14, 2014)
138 | ***"I'll be candid, I don't like the site," → probably be wrecks on the highway."*** | Sergio Chapa, "SA-based company begins construction on controversial landfill" San Antonio Business Journal (San Antonio, Texas, October 12, 2018)
138 | ***It accepts used drilling muds, drill cuttings*** | "Final Order Granting the Application of Pyote Reclamation Systems, LLC, Pursuant to Statewide Rule 8 for a Permit to Maintain and Operate a Commercial Stationary Treatment and Disposal Faiclity, Hohn Road Facility, Dewitt County, Texas" (Permit Application for Hohn Road Faiclity, Railroad Commission of Texas, May 4, 2016)
138 | ***other oil and gas waste that has been deemed nonhazardous*** | "Hohn Road Facility" (Waste Management, 2024)
139 | ***once did chuck over a dead skunk*** | Conversations and correspondence with Paul Baumann Jr., 2019-2024
139 | ***"if any portion of the material passes through and drops from the filter"*** | "Method 9095B, Paint Filter Liquids Test" (EPA, November 2004)
139 | ***wet waste goes to a receiving pit*** | "Transferred/Amended permit for Petro Waste Environmental LP, Hohn Road Facility" (Railroad Commission of Texas, May 3, 2016)
140 | ***"I call it Neanderthal engineering" → sleep for about four hours*** | Sister Elizabeth Riebschlaeger ; Conversations and correspondence with Paul Baumann Jr., 2019-2024
140 | ***application to build the landfill*** | Sergio Chapa, "SA-based company

begins construction on controversial landfill" San Antonio Business Journal (San Antonio, Texas, October 12, 2018)
141 | *Documents I receive under a record's request to the Railroad Commission* | PetroWaste Environmental Quarterly Report to Railroad Commission of Texas (PetroWaste Environmental, April 28, 2022) ; PetroWaste Environmental Quarterly Report to Railroad Commission of Texas (PetroWaste Environmental, November 23, 2021) ; PetroWaste Environmental Quarterly Report to Railroad Commission of Texas (PetroWaste Environmental, July 28, 2022)
141 | *Tank bottoms can contain radium and radioactive lead* | "TENORM: Oil and Gas Production Wastes" (EPA, 2024) ; "Transferred/Amended permit for Petro Waste Environmental LP, Hohn Road Facility" (Railroad Commission of Texas, May 3, 2016)
141 | *of which there are 25* | Correspondence with spokespeople of the Railroad Commission of Texas, 2018-2024 (R.J. Desilva, April 27, 2022)
141 | *be "scanned for the presence of NORM"* | "Transferred/Amended permit"
141 | *Railroad Commission says landfills do not have to submit documents* | Correspondence with Open Records office spokesperson of the Railroad Commission of Texas, May 17, 2022
141 | *George Wommack, a young businessman from Midland Texas* | "George J. Wommack, CEO, Petro Waste Environmental LP, San Antonio" (Hart Energy)
142 | *Wommack told Hart Energy* | George J. Wommack, Hart Energy
142 | *photo from 2017 shows Wommack at the ribbon-cutting* | Sergio Chapa, "SA-based oil and gas waste company poised to become Permian Basin's largest" San Antonio Business Journal (San Antonio, Texas, December 8, 2017)
142 | *"I think the best advice I'd give to anyone* | George J. Wommack, Hart Energy
142 | *He sold Petro Waste to Waste Management* | "Waste Management Energy Services Acquires Petro Waste Environmental from Tailwater Capital to Expand Service to the Oil and Gas Industry" (Waste Management press release, March 11, 2019)
142 | *figure in the hundreds of millions* | "2020 Waste Management Annual Report" (Waste Management, 2020)
142 | *"We are very proud of the platform"* | (Waste Management press release, 2019)
143 | *operates 267 landfills across the United States* | "WM, About, North America's Leading Solid Waste Services Provider" (Waste Management, 2024)
143 | *traces its origins to a Dutch immigrant named Harm Huizenga* | "Our Story, Always Working For A Sustainable Tomorrow" (Waste Management, 2024)
143 | *often independently owned, poorly designed, and weakly regulated* | Correspondence and conversations with former oilfield waste landfill engineer, 2020-2023
143 | *nation was facing a crisis* | "EPA Activities, Under the Resource Conservation and Recovery Act, Fiscal Year 1978, Annual Report to the President and the Congress Discal Year 1978" (EPA, March 1979)
143 | *Solid Waste Disposal Act of 1965 had* | "Legislative History of RCRA" (EPA, 2022)
143 | *"Disposal... has gone largely uncontrolled"* | "New Law to Control

Hazardous Wastes, End Open Dumping, Promote Conservation of Resources" (EPA press release, December 13, 1976)
143 | ***The new rules required things like → and expanded their waste empire*** | Correspondence and conversations with former oilfield waste landfill engineer, 2020-2023
144 | ***with more than $1 billion in sales*** | "Our Story, Always Working For A Sustainable Tomorrow" (Waste Management, 2024)
144 | ***oil spill debris is not classified as hazardous waste*** | Jay Reeves, "Dirty disposal of oil cleanup material" NBC News (New York, New York, June 24, 2010) ; "Frequent Questions About Hazardous Waste Identification " (EPA, 2023)
144 | ***"the oil spill along the Gulf Coast → spills "have a limited time span."*** | "Waste Management 2010 Annual Report" (Waste Management, 2010)
144 | ***in an August 2013 press release*** | Nicole Wrona, "Waste Management expands into $30B fracking sector" WasteDive (Washington D.C., August 21, 2013)
145 | ***"unlock hydrocarbons from shale rock formations"*** | "Waste Management 2012 Annual Report" (Waste Management, 2012)
145 | ***industry waste conference called WasteExpo → represented a $20 to 30 billion market*** | Mark Schleifstein "Shale fracking proves $30 billion-a-year boon to waste disposal industry" New Orleans Times-Picayune (New Orleans, Louisiana, May 21, 2013)
145 | ***R360 Environmental Solutions for approximately $1.3 billion*** | Allan Gerlat, "Waste Connections to Buy Oil Field Waste Company for $1.3 Billion"
145 | ***America's second largest waste disposal company*** | Sky Ariella, "The 10 Largest Waste Management Companies In The United States" (Zippia, the Career Expert, April 27, 2023)
145 | ***Republic to establish "a significant platform"*** | Nicole Wrona, "Republic Services strikes $485M oil and gas deal with Tervita Corp" WasteDive (December 19, 2014) ; "Republic Services to Acquire Tervita Corporation's U.S.-Based Operations" (Republic press release, December 19, 2014)
145 | ***Republic's website has called on the oil and gas industry*** | "Republic Services, Energy Services" and "Republic Services, Exploration and Production Services" (Republic website information, accessed 2021 and 2022)
146 | ***Waste Management has put out an Oil & Gas Brochure*** | "Waste Services for the Oil & Gas Industry" (Waste Management web page, 2024)
146 | ***paid $4.6 billion for Advanced Disposal*** | "Waste Management Completes $4.6 Billion Acquisition of Advanced Disposal" (Waste Management press release, October 30, 2020)
146 | ***Waste Management president Jim Fish stated in 2021*** | "Waste Management Announces First Quarter Earnings" (Waste Management press release, April 27, 2021)
146 | ***partner in a boutique hotel in Zihuatanejo*** | "George Wommack's LinkedIn page" (My screenshots of George Wommack's LinkedIn page, April 20, 2022)
146 | ***"Virtual Sustainability Investor Day"*** | "WM Hosts 2023 Virtual Sustainability Investor Day" (Waste Management press release, April 5, 2023)
147 | ***largest shareholder in Republic*** | Sean Martin "Republic Services Workers on Strike Call On Gates, the Company's Principal Shareholder, to Provide Living Wages and Affordable Health Care" Teamster.org (September 25, 2019) ; Christopher Helman, "How Bill Gates-Backed Republic Services Turns Trash Into

Big Cash" Forbes (Jersey City, New Jersey, July 27, 2022)
147 | ***more than 35 million shares invested in Waste Management*** | "Waste Management Top Shareholders" YahooFinance (As of September 29, 2023) ; John Edwards "This Is What Bill Gates' Portfolio Looks Like" Investopedia (December 22, 2020)
147 | ***universities and together manage $22 trillion*** | Farhad Manjoo "What BlackRock, Vanguard and State Street Are Doing to the Economy" New York Times (New York, New York, May 12, 2022)
147 | ***analyst Steven Cress asks*** | Steven Cress, "Bill Gates Is Betting On Waste Management, And Here's Why" Forbes (Jersey City, New Jersey, March 12, 2018)
147 | ***chasing down dump trucks*** | Correspondence and conversations with Bill Hughes, 2018-2019
148 | ***leachate showed "clear increasing trends."*** | Marc Glass and Kendra Hatcher, "Comments on Proposed Changes to the West Virginia Solid Waste Management Rule 33CSR1" (Downstream Strategies, prepared for Wetzel County Solid Waste Authority, July 28, 2014)
148 | ***Locals refer to Arden as Mount Trashmore*** | Kristen Locy and Justin Nobel, "If Only I Would've Known: Oil & Gas Whistleblowers Speak Out About Exposure to Radioactivity on Fracking Jobs" Public Herald (Pittsburgh, Pennsylvania, December 14, 2020)
148-149 | ***meet Dr. Julie Weatherington-Rice → most of earth's crude oil and natural gas*** | Correspondences and conversations with Ohio geologist Dr. Julie Weatherington-Rice, 2018-2024 ; Gunter Faure and Teresa M. Mensing, "Introduction to Planetary Science: The Geological Perspective" (Dordrecht, The Netherlands: Springer, 2007)
149 | ***Over millions of year oil and gas → thorium-232 and uranium-238*** | Correspondence and conversations with Ohio earth scientist Dr. Julie Weatherington-Rice, 2018-2024 ; Correspondence and conversations with federal staff health physicist source, 2020-2024 ; Correspondence and conversations with former U.S. Geological Survey geochemist Dr. Mark Engle
149 | ***"will be radioactive until the sun burns out"*** | Dr. Julie Weatherington-Rice
149-150 | ***unknown amount of radioactive waste unaccounted for."*** | Conversations and correspondence with former Commissioner of Agriculture Sarah Vogel, 2019-2024
150 | ***stop the waste stream you can actually stop the industry*** | Correspondence and conversations with Dakota Resource Council executive director Scott Skokos, 2019-2024
150 | ***looking to come up with money to test the urine*** | Correspondence and conversations with North Dakota journalist Darrell Dorgan, 2019-2024
150 | ***he wrote in a 2014 op-ed in the* Grand Forks Herald** | Darrell Dorgan, "N.D. as 'Superfund' site: It can happen here" Grand Forks Herald, "Grand Forks, North Dakota, April 20, 2014)
150 | ***a North Dakota environmental attorney named Fintan Dooley*** | Correspondence and conversations with Fintan Dooley, 2019-2024
150 | ***has received more than 687,000 tons of oilfield waste*** | Correspondence with Montana Department of Environmental Protection, 2022 (spokesperson Kevin Stone)
150 | ***too radioactive for North Dakota's own oilfield waste landfills*** |

Ed Kemmick "Montanans Ask Why State Bears Brunt of Bakken Waste, While North Dakota Reaps Riches," Missoula Current (Missoula, Montana, June 22, 2018)
150 | ***Seth tells us that from 2013 to 2016*** | Correspondence with Montana rancher Seth Newton, 2019-2024
150 | ***A 2019 hydrology report*** | "2018 Annual Groundwater Sampling Report Oaks Disposal Services Site, Dawson County, Montana, License # 528" (Hydrometrics, Inc, February 28, 2019)
151 | ***"to promote additional evaporation."*** | Correspondence with Montana Department of Environmental Protection, 2022 (spokesperson Kevin Stone)
151 | ***dead cattle that spurs people to action"*** | Seth Newton
151 | ***a grassroots conservation group established in 1972*** | Correspondence with Caitlin Cromwell and Dustin Ogdin of Northern Plains Resource Council, 2019-2024
151 | ***group of "conservative investors"*** | "Altus Capital Partners home page" (Altus Capital Partners, 2024)
151 | ***"lower middle market niche manufacturing businesses"*** | "Altus Capital Partners investing brochure" (Altus Capital Partners, 2020)
151 | ***Altus issued a press release touting*** | "Altus Capital Partners II, L.P. Acquires MAX Environmental Technologies, Inc." (Altus Capital Partners press release, February 7, 2017)
152 | ***67,340 tons of oilfield waste*** | "Pennsylvania Waste Map" (PSE, Physicians, Scientists, and Engineers for Healthy Energy), https://www.psehealthyenergy.org/pa-waste-map/
152 | ***I am joined by several scientists*** | Conversations and correspondence with Stacey Magda, community organizer with Mountain Watershed Association, 2019-2024
152-153 | ***We meet Tina Marie → examine the agency's inspection reports*** | Conversations and correspondence with Yukon Pennsylvania resident Tina Marie, 2019-2024
152 | ***also accepts hazardous waste*** | Altus Capital Partners II, L.P. Acquires MAX Environmental Technologies, Inc." (Altus Capital Partners press release, February 7, 2017)
153 | ***presently a manager at MAX, in charge of*** | "Carl Spadaro, Environmental General Manager at MAX Environmental Technologies, Inc." (Carl Spadaro LinkedIn page, January 2024)
153-160 | ***January 9, 1985: "Mismanagement of hazardous waste" → October 23, 2023: "NPDES - Failure*** | "MAX ENV TECH/YUKON FAC, Address: 233 MAX LN, YUKON, PA, 15698-1003, South Huntingdon Township, Westmoreland County, Pennsylvania Department of Environmental Protection eFacts Facility Search Details" (Pennsylvania Department of Environmental Protection, Accessed 2022)
Brian Kennedy and Bradley Miller, "NEIC Civil Investigation Report MAX Environmental Technologies, Inc., 233 MAX Lane, Yukon, Pennsylvania, 15698" (EPA, March 20-24, 2023)
160 | ***a scathing report on landfill practices*** | Brian Kennedy and Bradley Miller, "NEIC Civil Investigation Report MAX Environmental Technologies, Inc., 233 MAX Lane, Yukon, Pennsylvania, 15698" (EPA, March 20-24, 2023)
160 | ***Yukon is one of at least 30 landfills across Pennsylvania*** | Emma Lichtwardt and Joshua Boaz Pribanic, "Mountains of Radioactive Fracking Waste &

the One in Joe Biden's Hometown Is Under Criminal Investigation" Public Herald (Pittsburgh, Pennsylvania, June 1, 2021)
160 | ***One concern is that leachate from these landfills*** | Lauren M. Badertscher, Memphis J. Hill, Tetiana Cantlay, John F. Stolz and Daniel J. Bain Ecological Indicators, "Elevated sediment radionuclide concentrations downstream of facilities treating leachate from landfills accepting oil and gas waste," Ecological Indicators Volume 154 (2023) ; Conversations with Dr. John Stolz, director of the Center for Environmental Research and Education at Duquesne University, 2019-2024
160 | **Public Herald, *a Pittsburgh-based nonprofit*** | Conversations and correspondences with Public Herald co-founder Joshua Pribanic, 2019-2024
160 | ***investigated the topic and published a series of exposes*** | Emma Lichtwardt and Joshua Boaz Pribanic, "Mountains of Radioactive Fracking Waste & the One in Joe Biden's Hometown Is Under Criminal Investigation" Public Herald (Pittsburgh, Pennsylvania, June 1, 2021)
160-162 | ***meet with then superintendent Guy Kruppa → Radium is not required testing*** | Conversations and correspondence with Belle Vernon sewage plant superintendent Guy Kruppa, 2019-2020 ; Justin Nobel, "America's Radioactive Secret" Rolling Stone (New York, New York, February 2020)
161 | ***One of the key processes in a modern sewage*** | "How Wastewater Treatment Works...The Basics" (EPA, May 1998)
161 | ***the sewage plant has permits that control*** | "Commonwealth of Pennsylvania, Department of Environmental Protection, Consent Order and Agreement between Westmoreland Sanitary Landfill, LLC, and Rostraver Township, Solid Waste Management Act, Air Pollution Control Act" (Pennsylvania Department of Environmental Protection, February 13, 2020)
162 | ***Pennsylvania Department of Environmental Protection tells me*** | Justin Nobel, "America's Radioactive Secret" Rolling Stone (New York, New York, February 2020) ; Correspondence with Pennsylvania Department of Environmental Protection, 2018-2024 (Lauren Fraley, June 27, 2019)
162 | ***tests the leachate and reports elevated radium*** | "Copy of Belle Vernon Leachate Data from Dr. John Stolz, Excel Document" (Dr. John Stolz, April 11, 2019)
162 | ***co-publishes a scientific paper in the journal*** | Lauren M. Badertscher, Memphis J. Hill, Tetiana Cantlay, John F. Stolz and Daniel J. Bain Ecological Indicators, "Elevated sediment radionuclide concentrations downstream of facilities treating leachate from landfills accepting oil and gas waste," Ecological Indicators Volume 154 (2023)
162 | ***Pennsylvania Department of Environmental Protection also tell me*** | Correspondence with Pennsylvania Department of Environmental Protection, 2018-2024 (Lauren Fraley, June 27, 2019)
162 | ***Westmoreland Sanitary Landfill doesn't answer*** | Attempted correspondence with Westmoreland Sanitary Landfill, 2019-2024 (December 5, 2019, January 25, 2024)
162 | ***letter sent to one Belle Vernon area local from a whistle-blowing truck driver*** | "Whistle Blower Letter to Rostraver Township Resident" (August 2019)
163 | ***"What this place basically is" → asshole of the fracking industry*** | Guy Kruppa ; Justin Nobel, "America's Radioactive Secret"
163 | ***In May 2019, a county judge*** | Justin Nobel, "America's Radioactive

Secret"

163 | *I file questions to George Wommack* | Attempted correspondence of George Wommack via Headwall Investment's general contact form (https://headwallinvestments.com, April 18, 2022 and their general email query info@headwallinvestments.com January 21, 2024)

163 | *Buckhorn Waste Services, which runs Oaks Disposal* | Attempted correspondence with Buckhorn Waste Services, 2022-2024

163-164 |*Altus Capital Partners has not replied* | Attempted correspondence with Altus Capital, 2022-2024 (rscampoli@marketcompr.com: June 8 2022 ; rscampoli@marketcompr.com,
tgroh@altuscapitalpartners.com: January 25 2024)

164 | *MAX Environmental has not replied* | Attempted correspondence with Carl Spadaro at MAX Environmental, 2022-2024 (June 7, 2022 and January 25, 2024)

164 | *Republic tells me* | Correspondence with Republic Services, 2024 (media@republicservices.com January 26 and January 31 2024) ; Attempted correspondence with Republic Services, 2022-2024 (June 6, 2022 and January 25,2024)

164 | *Waste Management has not replied* | Attempted correspondence with Waste Management, 2022-2024 (June 6, 2022 and January 25,2024)

164 | *Bill & Melinda Gates Foundation has not replied* | Attempted correspondence with the Bill and Melinda Gates Foundation, 2022-2024 (media@gatesfoundation.org, June 7, 2022, January 25, 2024)

Chapter 9

165-167 | *introduced to an Oklahoma engineer → you don't examine it—it doesn't exist."* | Correspondences and conversations with Oklahoma engineer, 2019-2024

166 | *"Distribution of Radioactivity in Ancient Sediments"* | Roland F. Beers and Clark Goodman, "Distribution of Radioactivity in Ancient Sediments," Bulletin of the Geological Society of America, Volume 55 (1944)

169-170 | *Patricia Billingsley, who for many years oversaw → no toxicologists on staff"* | Correspondence with former manager of the Oklahoma Corporation Commission's Brownsfield Program Patricia Billingsley, 2020-2024

170 | *A 1940 photo in one of Billingsley's presentations* | Madeline Dillner and Patricia Billingsley, "Known Locations of Groundwater Contamination Across the State" (Presentation made for Oklahoma Clean Lakes and Watersheds conference in Stillwater, OK, April 2-3, 2014)

170 | *Another one of her images shows a smoking* |Madeline Dillner and Patricia Billingsley, "Applying for EPA Brownfields Grants" (Oklahoma Corporation Commission)

170 | *295,000 domestic wells, and more than 300 cities and towns* | Patricia Billingsley and Madeline Dillner, "Using Oil and Gas Data to Find Groundwater Supplies" (Oklahoma Corporation Commission, presentation for IPEC 2014: Waste Management & Pollution Prevention, 2014)

170 | *sent out to sample → exceeded limits in 30 percent* | Madeline Dillner and Patricia Billingsley, "Known Locations of Groundwater Contamination Across the State" (Presentation made for Oklahoma Clean Lakes and Watersheds conference in Stillwater, OK, April 2-3, 2014)

171 | *the 1927 work of Tcherepennikov* | W.A. Kolb and M. Wojcik, "Enhanced radioactivity due to natural oil and gas production and related radiological problems" Science of the Total Environment, Volume 45 (1985)

171 | ***the agency "does not have any."*** | Correspondence with Oklahoma Corporation Commission, 2019-2021 (Sarah Terry-Cobo, December 13, 2019)

171 | ***presentation entitled "Old Oilfield vs. New Homes"*** | Patricia Billingsley, "Old Oilfield vs. New Homes, Case Study - Site history" (Oklahoma Corporation Commission, May 25, 2012)

171 | ***"We did not look at radioactive isotopes*** | Correspondence with former manager of the Oklahoma Corporation Commission's Brownsfield Program Patricia Billingsley, 2020-2024

172 | ***Continental Oil and Transportation Company, now part of ConocoPhillips*** | "Blocker v. ConocoPhillips Co., United States District Court for the Western District of Oklahoma case text" (Blocker v. ConocoPhillips Co., United States District Court for the Western District of Oklahoma, May 6, 2019) ; "Expert Report of Daniel Tormey, Ph.D., P.G., James Blocker et al., v. ConocoPhillips Company, Case No. 5:17-cv-00248-D, United States District Court for the Western District of Oklahoma" (Expert Report of Dr. Daniel Tormey, March 19, 2018)

172 | ***per standards of the time was stored in unlined pits*** | Expert Report of Daniel Tormey

172 | ***waste leaked into the surrounding soils*** | Patricia Billingsley, Old Oilfield vs. New Homes

172 | ***wrote Dr. Daniel Tormey, a California → same resulting conditions present*** | "Expert Report of Daniel Tormey, Ph.D., P.G., James Blocker et al., v. ConocoPhillips Company, Case No. 5:17-cv-00248-D, United States District Court for the Western District of Oklahoma" (Expert Report of Dr. Daniel Tormey, March 19, 2018)

172 | ***in a 2016 lawsuit brought by Clifford Farms residents*** | Nuria Martinez-Keel, "ConocoPhillips settles contamination lawsuit with OKC homeowners" The Oklahoman (Oklahoma City, May 23, 2019)

172-174 | ***connect by phone with Dr. Bert Fisher → Fisher kept the six-page memo*** | Correspondence and conversations with former Amoco research scientist Dr. Bert Fisher, 2020-2024

173 | ***Fisher wrote in a six-page memo sent on July 1, 1993*** | Bert Fisher, "NORM: Recommendations Regarding Health Physics Issues Surrounding Gas Production in Western Kansas" (Memorandum to Amoco Production Company officials, July 1, 1993)

174 | ***According to one note, Terry Adamson*** | Bert Fisher, "NORM: Recommendations Regarding Health Physics Issues Surrounding Gas Production in Western Kansas" (Memorandum to Amoco Production Company officials, July 1, 1993)

174 | ***I ask spokespeople there when Amoco*** | Attempted correspondence with BP spokespeople, 2022-2024 (uspress@bp.com, July 18, 2022, and January 26, 2024)

174 | ***His handwritten notes remain legible*** | Bert Fisher, NORM: Recommendations

174 | ***"It would be interesting to do a study"*** | Correspondence and conversations with former Amoco research scientist Dr. Bert Fisher, 2020-2024

174-175 | ***"EPA does not track*** | Correspondence with EPA, 2018-2024, (Enesta Jones, September 21, 2020)

175 | ***U.S. Department of Agriculture "does not have*** | Correspondence with U.S. Department of Agriculture, 2020 (Sue King, September 8, 2020)
175 | ***"We believe it is a fairly common practice*** | Correspondence with Department of Energy, 2020 (Matthew Davis in the Office of Fossil Fuels, September 21, 2020)
175-176 | ***I learn about the practice of land-spreading in Oklahoma → surveys the site from the window of his Rubicon*** | Correspondence and conversations with former Waste Analytics analyst Jeff Tyson and Waste Analytics president Blake Scott, 2020-2024
176 | ***the company's engineering report*** | "Project Engineering Report for Heartland Environmental Resources, LLC, filed Feb 6 2017 with Court Clerk's Office of the Corporation Commission of Oklahoma" (Project Engineering Report for Heartland Environmental Resources, February 6, 2017) ; Attempted contact with Heartland Environmental Resources not possible as the company is permanently closed
176 | ***rebranding their toxic waste as something beneficial → simply need to get rid of it*** | Correspondence and conversations with former Waste Analytics analyst Jeff Tyson and Waste Analytics president Blake Scott, 2020-2024
177 | ***an October 2013 letter from Waurika's city manager to Polk*** | "City of Waurika letter to Polk Operating, from City of Waurika Office of City Manager" (City of Waurika, October 1, 2013)
177 | ***Polk's product was also requested by Brad Scott*** | "Letter from Waurika rancher Brad Scott to Oklahoma Corporation Commission" (Brad Scott Ranch, August 29, 2013)
177 | ***five school board members wrote a letter to the Oklahoma Corporation Commission*** | "Letter from Ryan High School Athletic Director, Superintendent, and Five School Board Members to the Oklahoma Corporation Commission Re: Oil or Drill Cuttings Use By County Commissioner" (Letter from Ryan High School Athletic Director, Superintendent, and Five School Board Members to the Oklahoma Corporation Commission, April 26, 2010)
177-178 | ***I know this seems simplistic → dust billowing up behind the bus*** | Jeff Tyson & Blake Scott
179 | ***Form 1014W with the Oklahoma Corporation Commission*** | "Form 1014W, Application For Oil or Drill Cuttings Use By County Commissioners" (Oklahoma Corporation Commission, 2020)
180 | ***Continental has not replied*** | Attempted correspondence with Continental Resources, 2022-2024 (Kristin Thomas, August 1, 2022, and January 27, 2024, and February 5, 2024)
180 | ***Title 165, Chapter 10, Section 165:10-7-19*** | "Okla. Admin. Code § 165:10-7-19, Section 165:10-7-19 - Land application of water-based fluids from earthen pits, tanks and pipeline construction" (Casetext.com, current through January 16, 2024)
181 | ***"Please don't misunderstand what I am about to say"*** | Correspondence and conversations with Waste Analytics president Blake Scott, 2020-2024
182 | ***One of the companies approved to apply drilling waste*** | "Application for Land Application for Continental Resources at Cunningham 3 & 4 Pad, Oklahoma Corporation Commission " (Oklahoma Corporation Commission Application for Land Application, March 11, 2020)
182-184 | ***"This is what I can tell you," says Danny → "We have a RCRA exemption"*** | Phone conversation with Morris Farms President Danny Morris, May

10 2021

183 | ***nine years after state rules on the practice were written*** | Bob Vandewater, "Soil-Farming Guidelines Approved" The Oklahoman (Oklahoma City, Oklahoma, October 17, 1986)

184 | ***In 1966, British researchers published an article*** | B.F. Sansom and R.J. Garner, "The Metabolism of Radium in Dairy Cows," Biochemical Journal, Volume 99 (1966)

184 | ***A 1978 research article published by Charles Garten Jr.*** | Charles T. Garten Jr., "A review of parameter values used to assess the transport of plutonium, uranium, and thorium in terrestrial food chains," Environmental Research, Volume 17, Number 3 (1978)

184 | ***fuel for reactors and nuclear weapons is concentrated*** | "Conventional Uranium Mills" (U.S. Nuclear Regulatory Commission, 2021)

184 | ***The U.S. Geological Survey, in a 2011 report*** | E.L. Rowan, M.A. Engle, C.S. Kirby, and T.F. Kraemer, "Radium Content of Oil- and Gas-Field Produced Waters in the Northern Appalachian Basin (USA): Summary and Discussion of Data" (U.S. Geological Survey, 2011)

185 | ***significant research on human radioactivity exposure*** | R.E. Rowland, "Radium in Humans: A Review of U.S. Studies" (Argonne National Laboratory, September 1994)

185 | ***in 1983 published a paper → These contaminated plants are eaten by cows*** | Donald R. Rayno, "Estimated Dose to Man from Uranium Milling Via the Beef/Milk Food-Chain Pathway," The Science of the Total Environment, Volume 31 (1983)

185 | ***In one 2012 paper, Slovenian researchers examined a dairy farm → new data quantifying the transfer of natural radionuclides to milk*** | Marko Štrok and Borut Smodiš, "Transfer of natural radionuclides from hay and silage to cow's milk in the vicinity of a former uranium mine," Journal of Environmental Radioactivity, Volume 110 (2012)

185 | ***equivalent of four chest X-rays*** | "Doses in Our Daily Lives" (U.S. Nuclear Regulatory Commission, 2022)

185 | ***In 2017, another set of Slovenian researchers*** | Miha Trdin and Ljudmila Benedik, "Uranium, polonium and thorium in infant formulas (powder milk) and assessment of a cumulative ingestion dose," Journal of Food Composition and Analysis, Volume 64 (2017)

185 | ***Texas*** | Kay Ledbetter, "Increased oil and gas drilling demands more land-applied fluid disposal" (Texas A & M press release, July 5, 2013)

185-186 | ***not been thoroughly examined by US academic researchers*** | Chad Penn and Hailin Zhang, "An Introduction to the Land Application of Drilling Mud in Oklahoma" (Oklahoma State University press release, February 2017)

186 | ***2013 article on the practice of land-spreading by researchers at Texas A&M*** | Chad Penn & Hailin Zhang

186 | ***speak to one of the co-authors by phone → "solely with the potential of salts and nutrients associated with these materials."*** | Mark L. McFarland, Sam E. Feagley and Tony L. Provin, "Land Application of Drilling Fluids: Landowner Considerations" Texas A & M AgriLife Extension (Texas A & M, July 2013) ; Correspondence and conversation with soil chemist Dr. Tony Provin, 2019-2024 (conversation on August 8, 2019)

186-187 | ***I ask the Oklahoma Department of Agriculture, Food*** |

Attempted Correspondence with Oklahoma Department of Agriculture, Food Safety Division, 2021-2024 (https://ag.ok.gov/contact-us/, May 17, 2021 and Kirsten.Hollansworth@ag.ok.gov January 28, 2024)

187 | *One 2017 paper of Oklahoma State University's agricultural extension* | Chad Penn & Hailin Zhang

187 | *a paper in 1996 that assessed radiation doses* | K.P. Smith, D.L. Blunt, G.P. Williams, and C.L. Tebes, "Radiological Dose Assessment Related to Management of Naturally Occurring Radioactive Materials Generated by the Petroleum Industry" (Environmental Assessment Division, Argonne National Laboratory, U.S. Department of Energy, September 1996)

187 | *have not answered any of my questions on oilfield radioactivity* | Attempted correspondence with various Argonne National Laboratory officials, 2018-2024 (August 17 2018 Argonne researcher Karen P. Smith ; August 8 2022 Chief communications officer Leslie Krohn and general media contact media@anl.gov ; January 29 2024 Chief communications officer Leslie Krohn and general media contact media@anl.gov)

187 | *According to Oklahoma Ag in the Classroom* | "Agricultural Facts, Dairy" (Oklahoma Ag in the Classroom)

187 | *Oklahoma has the fourth highest cancer death rate* | "Cancer Mortality by State" (Centers for Disease Control and Prevention, National Center for Health Statistics, February 28, 2022)

187-188 | *questions of whether the Oklahoma Corporation Commission has enabled* | Correspondence and attempted correspondence with Oklahoma Corporation Commission, 2019-2024

188 | *answers indeed may be waiting, in the bodies and bones* | R.E. Rowland, "Radium in Humans: A Review of U.S. Studies" (Argonne National Laboratory, September 1994)

188 | *paper published in the journal Energy Economics* | Nicholas Apergis, Ghulam Mustafa and Sayantan Ghosh Dastidar, "An analysis of the impact of unconventional oil and gas activities on public health: New evidence across Oklahoma counties," Energy Economics, Volume 97 (2021)

188 | *No state or local newspaper published the findings* | Conversation with University of Texas at El Paso economist Dr. Nicholas Apergis, 2021 (April 9, 2021)

Chapter 10

189 | *used to encounter an interesting billboard* | "AquaSalina highway sign" (Photo from Ohio resident, 2018)

189 | *based in the Cleveland suburb of Brecksville* | Joe Pagonakis, "Ohio plans to stop using controversial road deicer AquaSalina" News 5 Cleveland (Cleveland, Ohio, October 5, 2021) ;
"Nature's Own Source, LLC website homepage" (Nature's Own Source, 2024)

189 | *along the Pennsylvania Turnpike* | Conversations with Jay Walerstein, Vice President at Road Solutions, Inc, September 27 2018 and October 12/16 2018 ; Attempted correspondence with Pennsylvania Turnpike Commission, October 16 2018 and February 4 2019 and June 29 2021

189 | *1.56 million gallons was applied by the Ohio Department* | Correspondence with Ohio Department of Transportation, 2021 (Press secretary Matt Bruning, July 6 2021)

189 | ***tells me it's "400 million year old ancient seawater*** | Correspondence with Nature's Own Source President Dave Mansberry, November 13 2019
189 | ***He told regional news station WKRC*** | Justin Nobel, "America's Radioactive Secret" Rolling Stone (New York, New York, February 2020)
190 | ***says it is "Safe for Environment & Pets"*** | "AquaSalina Bottle Front Image" and "AquaSalina Bottle Back Image" from Ohio resident
190 | ***issued Duck Creek Energy a Chief's Order*** | "Investigation of the effect on Radium-226 and Radium-228 concentrations in conventional production brine by the AquaSalina production processes at the Duck Creek, Inc. Mogadore and Cleveland facilities" (Ohio Department of Natural Resources, August 9, 2019)
190 | ***on June 2, 2017, an official with the Ohio Department of Natural Resources entered a Lowe's*** | "Interoffice Memorandum from Chuck McCracken, Manager, Radiation Safety Section to Richard J. Simmers, Chief regarding ASSESSMENT OF RA226 & RA228 RADIOACTIVITY IN AQUASALINA" (Ohio Department of Natural Resources, Division of Oil and Gas Resources Management, Radiation Safety Section, July 26, 2017)
190 | ***Samples were drawn from the jugs*** | Interoffice Memorandum from Chuck McCracken, Manager, Radiation Safety Section to Richard J. Simmers, Chief regarding ASSESSMENT OF RA226 & RA228 RADIOACTIVITY IN AQUASALINA" (Ohio Department of Natural Resources, Division of Oil and Gas Resources Management, Radiation Safety Section, July 26, 2017)
190 | ***Nuclear Regulatory Commission discharge limit: 60*** | Correspondence with David McIntyre of the Nuclear Regulatory Agency, 2020-2021 ; Correspondence and conversations with Diane D'Arrigo, Radioactive Waste Project Director with the Nuclear Information and Resource Service, 2020-2024 ; "Radium-226 limits" (U.S. Nuclear Regulatory Commission, 2024)
190 | ***Level at which EPA defines a liquid waste as "radioactive": 60*** | Correspondence with EPA 2020 (Angela Hackel, January 13, 2020)
190 | ***AquaSalina sample from Lowe's: 1,059*** | Interoffice Memorandum from Chuck McCracken, Manager, Radiation Safety Section to Richard J. Simmers, Chief regarding ASSESSMENT OF RA226 & RA228 RADIOACTIVITY IN AQUASALINA" (Ohio Department of Natural Resources, Division of Oil and Gas Resources Management, Radiation Safety Section, July 26, 2017)
190 | ***AquaSalina sample from Hartville Hardware: 1,158*** | Interoffice Memorandum from Chuck McCracken
190 | ***Nuclear Regulatory Commission discharge limit: 60*** | Correspondence with David McIntyre of the Nuclear Regulatory Agency, 2020-2021 ; Correspondence and conversations with Diane D'Arrigo, Radioactive Waste Project Director with the Nuclear Information and Resource Service, 2020-2024 ; "Radium-228 limits" (U.S. Nuclear Regulatory Commission, 2024)
190 | ***Level at which EPA defines a liquid waste as "radioactive": 60*** | Correspondence with EPA 2020 (Angela Hackel, January 13, 2020)
190 | ***AquaSalina sample from Lowe's: 604*** | Interoffice Memorandum from Chuck McCracken
190 | ***AquaSalina sample from Hartville Hardware: 1,333*** | Interoffice Memorandum from Chuck McCracken
191 | ***EPA Safe Drinking Water Act limit: 5*** | "Radionuclides Rule" (EPA, November 7, 2023)
191 | ***Level at which EPA defines a liquid waste as "radioactive": 60*** | "A

Regulators' Guide to the Management of Radioactive Residuals from Drinking Water Treatment Technologies," (EPA, Office of Water, July 2005)
191 | ***AquaSalina sample from Lowe's: 1,663*** | Interoffice Memorandum from Chuck McCracken
191 | ***AquaSalina sample from Hartville Hardware: 2,491*** | Interoffice Memorandum from Chuck McCracken
191 | ***"If I had a beaker of that on my desk*** | Correspondence with former Department of Energy scientist Dr. Yuri Gorby, 2019-2024
191 | ***"Every time you put this solution onto your front steps*** | Justin Nobel, "America's Radioactive Secret" Rolling Stone (New York, New York, February 2020) ; Correspondences and conversations with Duke University geochemist Dr. Avner Vengosh, 2018-2023
191 | ***Spunky dies of doggy bone cancer*** | Correspondence with former Youngstown Ohio Battalion Fire Chief Silverio Caggiano, 2018-2024
191 | ***In 2018, and again in 2019 and 2023, I ask Lowe's*** | Attempted correspondence with Lowe's, 2018-2023 (October 15 2018 PublicRelations@lowes.com ; February 4 2019 Publicrelations@lowes.com and Maureen Wallace Manager of Corporate Communications & Public Relations ; April 24 2023 PublicRelations@lowes.com)
192 | ***Jay Wells, a Pacific Northwest Snowfighers representative tells me*** | Correspondence with Pacific Northwest Snowfighters, 2018-2023 (Jay Wells, October 11 2018)
192 | ***Qualified Products List, as of September 2023*** | "Clear Roads Qualified Product List" (Clear Roads, September 15, 2023)
192 | ***When I ask Pacific Northwest Snowfighters in 2023*** | Correspondence with Pacific Northwest Snowfighters, 2018-2023 (Patti Caswell, April 25 2023)
192 | ***Much of the nation's salt supply for road salts*** | "Hydrologic Environment of the Silurian Salt Deposits in Parts of Michigan, Ohio, and New York" (U.S. Geological Survey, 1978)
193 | ***posted on his blog,* Deiceman Dave** | Dave Budd "Do you get what your paying for?" (Post on Deiceman Dave blog, July 26, 2016)
193 | ***the U.S. Department of Transportation says, "we don't*** | Correspondence with U.S. Department of Transportation's Pipeline and Hazardous Materials Safety Administration (PHMSA), 2018-2021 (Darius Kirkwood, October 26 2018)
193 | ***his agency is yet to respond*** | Attempted correspondence with the U.S. Department of Transportation 2021 (PressOffice@dot.gov November 17 2021, November 23 2021, November 26 2021)
193 | ***Neither is the Nuclear Regulatory Commission or EPA*** | Correspondence with Nuclear Regulatory Commission spokesperson, 2021-2022 (David McIntyre, January 6 2020) ; Correspondence with EPA, 2018-2024
193 | ***From 2001 to 2013*** | Correspondence with Quebec's Ministère du Développement durable, de l'Environnement et de la Lutte contre les changements climatiques 2018 (Daniel Messier, September 19, 2018)
194 | ***they sold the product "to municipalities throughout*** | "An Efficient Dust-Controller and De-Icing Product" (Descriptions on Junex website, Accessed 2018-2019)
194 | ***I learn from Dr. Yusuf Mehta*** | Conversation with Dr. Yusuf Mehta, October 12 2018

194 | ***in 2012 co-authored a 212-page*** | Kauser Jahan and Yusuf Mehta, "Task Assignment No. C-06-07, Potential for Natural Brine for Anti-Icing and De-Icing, Final Report" (NYS Department of Transportation, September 2012)
194 | ***spokesperson Joseph Morrissey tells me*** | Correspondence with New York State Department of Transportation spokesperson Joseph Morrissey 2018 (October 19, 2018)
194 | ***Quebec government spokesperson Daniel Messier says*** | Correspondence with Quebec's Ministère du Développement durable, de l'Environnement et de la Lutte contre les changements climatiques 2018 (Daniel Messier, September 19, 2018)
194 | ***"did not send too much to the US."*** | Conversation with New Cude vice president Matthew Lavoie, September 24 2018, later fact-checking attempted via phone and email in February 2019
194 | ***neither Quebecois or Canadian environmental agencies have been able to inform me*** | Daniel Messier 2018 ; Correspondence with Environment Canada 2018 (ec.media.ec@canada.ca and Catherine Burge, September 17 2018)
195 | ***has tested Seneca Mineral LS25*** | Correspondence and conversations with Penn State environmental engineer Dr. Bill Burgos, 2019-2024
195 | ***When in 2018 I press owner Sherm Shollenberger*** | Correspondence with Sherm Shollenberger October 18 2018, and attempted follow-up fact-checking correspondence February 4 and 5 2019
195 | ***follow-up email solicited a reply*** | Attempted correspondence with Sherm Shollenberger February 5 2019, Response from Michael Thomas with MacDonald, Illig, Jones & Britton February 5 2019
195 | ***co-authored by Burgos was published in the journal* Environmental Science & Technology** | T. L. Tasker, W. D. Burgos, P. Piotrowski, L. Castillo-Meza, T. A. Blewett, K. B. Ganow, A. Stallworth, P. L. M. Delompre,´ G. G. Goss, L. B. Fowler, J. P. Vanden Heuvel, F. Dorman and N. R. Warner, "Environmental and Human Health Impacts of Spreading Oil and Gas Wastewater on Road," Environmental Science & Technology, Volume 52 (2018)
195 | ***Burgos and his colleagues revealed*** | Tasker et al
195-196 | ***one September afternoon I find Burgos → "inhalation pathway not even yet considered"*** | Correspondence and conversations with Penn State environmental engineer Dr. Bill Burgos, 2019-2024
196 | ***little to no more effective than rainwater*** | Dr. Bill Burgos ; James Farnan, Andrew Eck, Andrew Kearney, Frank L. Dorman, Hassan Ismail, Eric Chase, Xiaofeng Liu, Nathaniel R. Warner and William D. Burgos, "Oil and gas produced waters fail to meet beneficial reuse recommendations for use as dust suppressants," Science of the Total Environment, Volume 919 (2024)
196 | ***complete lack of data indicating the practice is effective*** | Bryce F. Payne Jr., "Oil and Gas Well Brines for Dust Control on Unpaved Roads – Part 1: Ineffectiveness" European Scientific Journal, Volume 14 (2018)
196 | ***Department of Environmental Protection attached radiation detectors*** | "Technologically Enhanced Naturally Occurring Radioactive Materials (TENORM) Study Report" (Prepared by Perma-Fix Environmental Services Inc for the Pennsylvania Department of Environmental Protection, May 2016)
197 | ***more than 95 percent was spread in rural townships*** | Dr. Bill Burgos ; T. L. Tasker, W. D. Burgos, P. Piotrowski, L. Castillo-Meza, T. A. Blewett, K. B. Ganow, A. Stallworth, P. L. M. Delompre,´ G. G. Goss, L. B. Fowler, J. P. Vanden

Heuvel, F. Dorman and N. R. Warner, "Environmental and Human Health Impacts of Spreading Oil and Gas Wastewater on Road," Environmental Science & Technology, Volume 52 (2018)

197 | ***Siri Lawson lives with her husband → maple syrup sold at a local farmer's market*** | Correspondence and conversations with northwest Pennsylvania resident Siri Lawson, 2018-2024 ; Justin Nobel, "America's Radioactive Secret" Rolling Stone (New York, New York, February 2020)

197 | ***"chisels were needed to remove the toxic caked muck."*** | Siri Lawson, "A First-Hand Account Of How Repeated, Unlimited Road Dumping Of Oil & Gas Drilling Wastewater Is Tearing Apart Dirt Roads And Creating Multiple Environmental Hazards" PA Environment Digest Blog (Harrisburg, Pennsylvania, November 16, 2021)

198-200 | ***Blair Miller, happens to be → "We deal with the Bass Island, the Medina*** | Conversations and correspondence with Blair and Sabrena Miller, 2019-2024

199 | ***never get out of the vac truck business*** | Judy Kneiszel, "Rednecks & Racing" Pumper Magazine (Eagle River, Wisconsin, February 2010)

200 | ***U.S. Geological Survey National Produced Waters Geochemical Database*** | "U.S. Geological Survey National Produced Waters Geochemical Database v2.3" (U.S. Geological Survey, May 17 2019)

200 | ***in the range of 1,800 picocuries per liter*** | "U.S. Geological Survey National Produced Waters Geochemical Database, version 3.0" (U.S. Geological Survey, 2024)

200-201 | ***a crew of local farmers arrive → need to be able to sleep*** | Blair and Sabrena Miller

202 | ***freshly laced with brine*** | Siri Lawson

202 | ***The activist couple has collected*** | Correspondence and conversations with Michigan environmental activists LuAnne Kozma and Ellis Boal, 2019-2024

202 | ***reads a 1936 article in the* St. Louis Leader** | "Oil Well Brine is of Value on Gratiot Roads" St. Louis Leader (St. Louis, Michigan, June 25, 1936)

202 | ***first reports of contamination surfaced*** | Jeffrey E. Herrold, "The Use of Oil Field Brine on Michigan Roadways" (Geological Survey Division, Michigan Department of Natural Resources, January 27, 1984)

202 | ***A 1953 paper of the Michigan Geological Survey*** | W.L. Daoust, "Salts of the Earth: Brine Disposal is Oilmen's Headache" Michigan Conservation (A magazine of the Michigan Geological Survey Division, January-February 1953)

202 | ***conducted a study in August 1984 → to increase the amount of cancer*** | "State of Michigan, Before the Natural Resources Commission, In the matter of Supervisor of Wells Special Order 1-85, Brief on Appeal, Testimony of Michael C. McDaniel, Assistant Attorney General, Attorney for Department of Natural Resources" (Michigan Natural Resources Commission, December 4, 1985)

203 | ***issued Special Order 1-85 → end the practice altogether*** | "State of Michigan, The Circuit Court for the County of Ingham: Presque Isle, Et al vs Natural Resources Commission and the Supervisor of Wells" (Circuit Court for the County of Ingham, State of Michigan Court Filing, December 18, 1985)

203 | ***Supervisor's Order 1-85 is not a hasty*** | "State of Michigan, Before the Natural Resources Commission, In the matter of Supervisor of Wells Special Order 1-85, Brief on Appeal, Testimony of Michael C. McDaniel, Assistant Attorney General, Attorney for Department of Natural Resources" (Michigan Natural Resources

Commission, December 4, 1985)
203 | ***group of 24 county road commissions did not see it → as it has been for 30 years."*** | "State of Michigan, The Circuit Court for the County of Ingham: Presque Isle, Et al vs Natural Resources Commission and the Supervisor of Wells" (Circuit Court for the County of Ingham, State of Michigan Court Filing, December 18, 1985)
203 | ***The practice could continue, says the 1986 ruling*** | "Letter from R. Thomas Segall, Assistant Supervisor of Wells Michigan Geological Survey Division to ALL Oil and Gas Producers Re: Supervisor's Order 1-85: Spreading of Oil Field Brine on Michigan Roadways" (Michigan Department of Natural Resources, September 25, 1986)
203-204 | ***And the practice of brine-spreading continues in Michigan*** | Correspondence with Michigan Department of Environmental Quality Geologist Specialist Ray Vugrinovich, 2018-2019 ; "Groundwater Discharge General Permit GW1550000" (Michigan Department of Environmental Quality Water Resources, April 1, 2015)
204 | ***Michigan not testing the oilfield brine applied to public roads for radium*** | "Groundwater Discharge Permit, General Permit No. GW1550000" (State of Michigan, Department of Environment, Great Lakes, and Energy, April 1, 2020)
204 | ***among the highest levels of radium*** | K.P. Smith, D.L. Blunt, G.P. Williams, and C.L. Tebes, "Radiological Dose Assessment Related to Management of Naturally Occurring Radioactive Materials Generated by the Petroleum Industry" (Environmental Assessment Division, Argonne National Laboratory, U.S. Department of Energy, September 1996)
204 | ***"No agency at the State level compiles statistics"*** | Correspondence with Michigan Department of Environmental Quality Geologist Specialist Ray Vugrinovich, 2018-2019
204 | ***the case of Karla and Bryan Black*** | "Toxic Oil and Gas Wastes Dumped in Platte River Estuary: BTEX chemicals found, three tanker trucks dumped" (Ban Michigan Fracking, July 11, 2013)
204 | ***54 barrels of fracking waste was spread on camp*** | "Update: Northern Michigan Frack Flowback Disaster–where the frack wastes were dumped" (Ban Michigran Fracking, January 14, 2013)
204-205 | ***Ellis wrote in 2013 to Hal Fitch*** | "Email from Ellis Boal to Hall Fitch Re: radium 226, 228" (Ellis Boal, April 22, 2013)
205 | ***this waste to be about 40 times*** | "Email from Ellis Boal to Hall Fitch Re: radium 226, 228" (Ellis Boal, April 22, 2013) ; "Lab Results for Project Excelsior Brine, Pace Project No. 3081274" (Pace Analytical , November 28, 2012)
205 | ***In October 2018, at EPA headquarters*** | Reporting trip, October 2018
205 | ***EPA is yet to issue a final decision*** | "Final Report: Oil and Gas Extraction Wastewater Management" (EPA, June 2023)
205 | ***have already passed or attempted bills that would make it easier*** | Correspondence and conversations with investigative journalist and researcher Melissa Troutman, 2018-2024
205 | ***Pennsylvania legislators have pursued a bill*** | Correspondence and conversations with northwest Pennsylvania resident Siri Lawson, 2018-2024
205 | ***Representative Bob Young has pushed a bill*** | "H. B. No. 282, As Introduced by Representatives Young, B., Jones, 134th General Assembly, Regular Session, 2021-2022" (Proposed Bill of Ohio State Legislature, 2021-2022)

205 | ***Young, in a statement he made about the bill*** | "Statement of Representative Bob Young, House District 36, House of Representatives, The General Assembly of The State of Ohio" (Bob Young, 2021)
206 | *In **August 2021, the Ohio Department of Transportation decided to stop purchasing*** | Beth Harvilla, "Ohio plans to discontinue use of controversial road deicer AquaSalina" The Columbus Dispatch (Columbus Ohio, August 31 2021)
206 | ***In 2022, the Ohio Department of Health analyzed*** | "Brine Radiation Analysis for Radium Concentrations: Radiation Dose Assessment of Residential Brine Application" (Ohio Department of Health, Bureau of Environmental Health and Radiation Protection, September 30 2022)
206 | ***set up trainings, and are working with a network of local activists*** | Correspondence and conversations with Silverio Caggiano, 2018-2024 ; Conversations and correspondences with director of Ohio environmental advocacy group Buckeye Environmental Network Teresa Mills

Chapter 11
207 | ***here that the Oklahoma attorney Randy Miller*** | Correspondence and conversations with Oklahoma attorney Randy Miller, 2020-2024
207 | ***lawsuit he filed in 2021 in the District Court of Major County*** | "Kliewer Lawsuit: Kliewer et al vs Harold Hamm, in the District Court of Major County, State of Oklahoma" (District Court of Major County, State of Oklahoma, January 22 2021)
208 | ***gave a talk at the University of Tulsa*** | William R. Keffer, J. Randall Miller, and J. Berton Fisher, "The Fracks of Life of Life: Plus ça change, plus c'est la même chos" (PowerPoint presentation)
208 | ***"The logical question," says Miller*** | Correspondence and conversations with Oklahoma attorney Randy Miller, 2020-2024
208 | ***state has more than 10,000*** | "All Oklahoma UIC Wells" (Oklahoma Corporation Commission, January 22, 2024)
208 | ***injects approximately 200 million gallons*** | "U.S. Produced Water Volumes and Management Practices in 2021," (Ground Water Protection Council, November 2022)
208 | ***legendary Oklahoma oilman*** | "Harold G. Hamm: Executive Chairman" (Continental Resources webpage for Harold Hamm, 2023)
208 | ***helped establish the Harold Hamm School*** | "Harold Hamm, Horatio Alger Award Recipient, Class of 2016" (Horatio Alger Association of Distinguished Americans, Inc, 2024)
209 | ***into the Oklahoma Hall of Fame*** | "Hamm, Harold: 2011" (Oklahoma Hall of Fame, 2011)
210 | ***Ronald and Donald Schweitzer. They are twins*** | "Eight wells shut down, but more saltwater continues to spew out near Kingfisher" KFOR News 4 Oklahoma (Oklahoma City, Oklahoma, November 20, 2019)
210 | ***"It's the worst thing that ever happened"*** | "Property owners speak out about Kingfisher saltwater purge" Oklahoma News 4 (Oklahoma City, Oklahoma, 2020)
210 | ***the flow of waste was about 15 gallons a minute*** | Reporting trip, August 2020
210 | ***injection wells were the source*** | "Eight wells shut down, but more saltwater continues to spew out near Kingfisher" KFOR News 4 Oklahoma (Oklahoma

City, Oklahoma, November 20, 2019)
211 | ***"It never stops," says Donald*** | Reporting trip, August 2020
211 | ***Hiersche will tell the local news*** | Karl Torp, "Lawsuit Filed Over Saltwater Purge In Kingfisher County" News 9 Oklahoma (March 11, 2021)
211 | ***Files he obtained from the Oklahoma Corporation Commission*** | Correspondence with Oklahoma attorney Justin Hiersche, 2020-2021 ; "Daily Purge Volumes Excel Spreadsheet, received from attorney Justin Hiersche" (Excel Spreadsheet received from attorney Justin Hiersche, May 3, 2021)
211 | ***everything is fine now*** | Conversations with Donald Schweitzer, 2020-2024
211 | ***each barrel of out-of-state waste injected, Ohio receives twenty cents*** | Correspondence with Ohio Department of Natural Resources, 2018-2024 (Andy Chow, June 6 2023)
212 | ***"I am writing concerning injection wells → this type of argument is somewhat flawed"*** | "Letter from Donald C. Poole, General Manager of Tupper Plains-Chester Water District to Ohio Department of Natural Resources regarding Brine Disposal by Way Of Injection Wells in Ohio" (Tupper Plains-Chester Water District in Reedsville, Ohio, July 24, 2015)
212 | ***state replied to Tupper Plains-Chester with a letter*** | "Letter from Ohio Department of Natural Resources Division of Oil and Gas Resources Management Richard J. Simmers to Donald Poole, General Manager of Tupper Plains-Chester Water District regarding Brine Disposal by Way Of Injection Wells in Ohio" (Ohio Department of Natural Resources, August 4, 2015)
212 | ***In 2018 I meet an Ohio brine hauler → if I get sick, I want to be able to prove this"*** | Conversations and correspondences with Peter, oil and gas industry brine hauler, 2018-2024
214 | ***Testing revealed that radium-226*** | "Excel File with Radium Levels in Peter Brine Hauler's Samples Tested by Labs of Dr Daniel Bain and Dr John Stolz" (2019)
214 | ***considered "radioactive" by EPA*** | Correspondence with EPA 2020 (Angela Hackel, January 13, 2020)
215 | ***One local woman who has helped → she was booed by her classmates*** | Correspondence and conversations with Torch CAN DO co-founder Felica Mettler, 2017-2024
215-218 | ***emerges in 2019 from two men who operate → still is any justice left*** | Correspondence and conversations with Bob and Bob, conventional gas well owners in southeastern Ohio, 2020-2024
219 | ***The agency found signatures of fracking waste → "allowing wastewater to migrate"*** | Naing Aye and Roland Blauer, "Washington County Produced Water Investigation Prepared for Ohio Department of Natural Resources Division of Oil & Gas Management by Resource Services International (RSI)" (Ohio Department of Natural Resources, June 2020) ; Nicholas J. Lohr and Jack L. Vasalani, "Final Assessment Report, Redbird #4: Washington County, Ohio, Prepared for Ohio Department of Natural Resources by Groundwater & Environmental Services, Inc. (GES)" (Ohio Department of Natural Resources, Division of Oil and Gas Resources Management, June 2021)
219 | ***"flared up and mushroomed instantaneously"*** | "Cuyahoga River Fire" (Ohio History Central, 2021) ; Laura Johnston, "The original Cleveland Fire Department report from the June 22, 1969, Cuyahoga River fire" Cleveland.com (Cleveland, Ohio, June 17, 2019)

219 | ***in 1972 Congress signed*** | "Discover the History of the Clean Water Act" (EPA, 2023)
219 | ***discharge of pollutants into the navigable waters*** | "Text of the Federal Water Pollution Control Act" (EPA, 2002)
219-220 | ***Underground Injection Control program, formally established by EPA in 1980*** | "Introduction to the Underground Injection Control Program" (EPA, January 2003)
220 | ***new home for liquid industrial waste would be underground*** | Robert W. Stallman, "Subsurface Waste Storage—the Earth Scientist's Dilemma," Underground Waste Management and Environmental Implications: Proceedings of the Symposium held December 6-9, 1971, in Houston Texas and sponsored jointly by the United States Geological Survey and The American Association of Petroleum Geologists, edited by T.D. Cook (Tulsa, Oklahoma: The American Association of Petroleum Geologists, 1972)
220 | ***In 1950, there were four industrial waste injection wells*** | "Introduction to the Underground Injection Control Program" (EPA, January 2003)
220 | ***EPA figures indicate there are 181,431*** | "Underground Injection Control Program fact sheet" (EPA, April 2020)
220 | ***"Injection," states an EPA website, "proved*** | "General Information About Injection Wells" (EPA, 2023)
220 | ***down an eight to twelve-inch-wide hole*** | "Introduction to the Underground Injection Control Program" (EPA, January 2003) ; "Injection Wells: A Guide to Their Use, Operation, and Regulation: Injection Wells" (Groundwater Protection Council, 2022)
220 | ***referred to as the injection zone*** | "General Information About Injection Wells" (EPA, 2023)
220-221 | ***Injection wells are defined by a set of ideas*** | Correspondence and conversations with Oklahoma attorney Randy Miller, 2019-2024 ; A. Gene Collins and M.E. Crocker, "Protocol for Laboratory Research on Degradation, Interaction, and Fate of Wastes Disposed by Deep Well-Injection" (NIPER program of U.S. Department of Energy and EPA, December 1987)
221 | ***But this all comes with extraordinary risks.*** | A. Gene Collins and M.E. Crocker, "Protocol for Laboratory Research on Degradation, Interaction, and Fate of Wastes Disposed by Deep Well-Injection" (National Institute for Petroleum and Energy Research program of U.S. Department of Energy and EPA, February 29, 1988)
221 | ***This includes waste pickle liquor from iron and steel production, incinerator scrubber water*** | Heather Simpson and Stephen Lester, "Deep Well Injection an Explosive Issue" (Center for Health, Environment & Justice, May 26, 2009)
221 | ***Oilfield waste goes down Class II wells. Fluids used in*** | "Introduction to the Underground Injection Control Program" (EPA, January 2003)
222 | ***1996 paper on injection well regulations published by the Texas environmental*** | Earle A. Herbert, "The Regulation of Deep-Well Injection: A Changing Environment Beneath the Surface," Pace Environmental Law Review, Volume 14, Number 1 (1996)
222 | ***This technique was called waterflooding and generated*** | James T. Smith and William M. Cobb, "Waterflooding," (Petroleum Recovery Research Center, New Mexico Tech, December 17, 1997)

222 | ***led to significant groundwater contamination*** | "City of Hawkins, Wood County, Texas: Investigation of Ground-Water Contamination" (Texas Water Commission, August 1962) ; Correspondence and conversations with Oklahoma attorney Randy Miller, 2020-2024

222 | ***fracking spread across the nation*** | Vivian R. Underhill and Lourdes Vera, "Opinion: The Halliburton Loophole" The Denver Post (Denver, Colorado, April 11 2023) ; "A Brief History Of Fracking" (NES Fircroft, July 31, 2022)

222-223 | ***makes each fracked well an injection well → modern fracking would have been impossible*** | Vivian R. Underhill and Lourdes Vera, "Opinion: The Halliburton Loophole" The Denver Post (Denver, Colorado, April 11 2023)

223 | ***including billions of gallons of chemically slickened fracking flowback*** | Andrew J. Kondash, Elizabeth Albright and Avner Vengosh, "Quantity of flowback and produced waters from unconventional oil and gas exploration," Science of the Total Environment, Volume 574 (2017)

223 | ***96 percent of that will be disposed of down an injection well*** | "U.S. Produced Water Volumes and Management Practices in 2021," (Ground Water Protection Council, November 2022)

223 | ***danger of subsequent contamination," reads a 1929 report*** | Ludwig Schmidt and John M. Devine, "The disposal of oil-field brines" (U.S. Department of the Interior, Bureau of Mines, 1929)

223 | ***Research Lab in Ada, Oklahoma extensively researched*** | "Robert S. Kerr, Environmental Research Laboratory" (Office of Research and Development, EPA, November 1987)

223 | ***one of the lab's reports on*** **Injection of Hazardous Wastes into Deep Wells** | Arden Strycker and A. Gene Collins, "Project Summary, State-of-the-Art Report: Injection of Hazardous Wastes into Deep Wells" (Robert S. Kerr Environmental Research Laboratory, U.S. EPA, July 1987)

224 | ***collaboration between researchers at EPA and the Department of Energy*** | A. Gene Collins and M.E. Crocker, "Protocol for Laboratory Research on Degradation, Interaction, and Fate of Wastes Disposed by Deep Well-Injection" (National Institute for Petroleum and Energy Research program of U.S. Department of Energy and EPA, December 1987)

224 | ***warned that injection was a short-term fix → change to such technology would be required"*** | Earle A. Herbert, "The Regulation of Deep-Well Injection: A Changing Environment Beneath the Surface," Pace Environmental Law Review, Volume 14, Number 1 (1996)

225 | ***Dr. Bill Alley, Director of Science and Technology at the National Groundwater*** | Correspondence and conversations with former chief of the Office of Groundwater with the U.S. Geological Survey Dr. Bill Alley, 2020 (June 22 2020)

225 | ***1971 talk by Stanley Greenfield*** | Stanley Greenfield, "EPA—The Environmental Watchman," in Underground Waste Management and Environmental Implications: Proceedings of the Symposium held December 6-9, 1971, in Houston Texas and sponsored jointly by the United States Geological Survey and The American Association of Petroleum Geologists, edited by T.D. Cook (Tulsa, Oklahoma: The American Association of Petroleum Geologists, 1972)

225 | ***I find an old bound blue book with gold writing that contains*** | Underground Waste Management and Environmental Implications: Proceedings of the Symposium held December 6-9, 1971, in Houston Texas and sponsored jointly by the United States Geological Survey and The American Association of Petroleum

Geologists, edited by T.D. Cook (Tulsa, Oklahoma: The American Association of Petroleum Geologists, 1972)

226 | ***Henri Swolfs explains that injecting chemical-filled waste*** | Henri S. Swolfs, "Chemical Effects of Pore Fluids on Rock Properties," In Underground Waste Management and Environmental Implications: Proceedings of the Symposium held December 6-9, 1971, in Houston Texas and sponsored jointly by the United States Geological Survey and The American Association of Petroleum Geologists, edited by T.D. Cook (Tulsa, Oklahoma: The American Association of Petroleum Geologists, 1972)

226 | ***Tsuneo Tamura*** | Tsuneo Tamura, "Sorption Phenomena Significant in Radioactive-Waste Disposal," Underground Waste Management and Environmental Implications: Proceedings of the Symposium

226 | ***"My message to you is not a cheerful one," Frank Trelease*** | Frank J. Trelease, "Liability for Harm from Underground Waste Disposal," Underground Waste Management and Environmental Implications: Proceedings of the Symposium 1972

226 | ***Robert Stallman, a Colorado research hydrologist*** | Robert W. Stallman, "Subsurface Waste Storage—the Earth Scientist's Dilemma," Underground Waste Management and Environmental Implications: Proceedings of the Symposium 1972

227 | ***understood the lack of science behind the practice of injection as well as John Ferris*** | John G. Ferris, "Response of Hydrologic Systems to Waste Storage," Underground Waste Management and Environmental Implications: Proceedings of the Symposium 1972

227 | ***"Where will the waste reside 100 years from now?" asks Orlo Childs*** | Orlo E. Childs, "Summary," Underground Waste Management and Environmental Implications: Proceedings of the Symposium 1972

227 | ***would have reached Jupiter*** | "U.S. Produced Water Volumes and Management Practices in 2021," (Ground Water Protection Council, November 2022) and personal calculations.

228 | ***issues a letter to a company called DeepRock Disposal Solutions*** | "Order by the Chief, Order No. 2023-02, from Ohio Department of Natural Resources, Division of Oil and Gas Resources Management to Deeprock Disposal Solutions LLC" (Ohio Department of Natural Resources, Division of Oil and Gas Resources Management, January 9, 2023)

228 | ***her worst fears have been realized. Here too waste is leaking*** | "Order by the Chief, Order No. 2023-139, from Ohio Department of Natural Resources, Division of Oil and Gas Resources Management to K & H Partners LLC" (Ohio Department of Natural Resources, Division of Oil and Gas Resources Management, June 26, 2023)

228 | ***In August 2023, I learn of yet another problematic Ohio injection well*** | "Order by the Chief, Order No. 2023-94, from Ohio Department of Natural Resources, Division of Oil and Gas Resources Management to Reliable Enterprises Ohio, Inc." (Ohio Department of Natural Resources, Division of Oil and Gas Resources Management, May 1, 2023)

228 | ***Randy Miller takes a long, deep breath*** | Correspondence and conversations with Oklahoma attorney Randy Miller, 2020-2024

229 | ***Continental has not replied to my questions*** | Attempted correspondence with Continental Resources, 2022-2024 (Continental Senior Executive in Public

Relations Kristin.Thomas@clr.com August 1 2022, January 27 2024, February 5 2024)
229 | ***efforts to run questions by Harold Hamm have been unsuccessful*** | Attempted correspondence with Harold Hamm via Council for a Secure America, 2023-2024 (Council for a Secure America Contact Page https://councilforsecureamerica.org/contact-us/ May 10 2023 and February 5 2023)
229 | ***we have ruined our groundwater."*** | Oklahoma attorney Randy Miller

Chapter 12
231 | ***Until about four years ago, one could find him perennially hard at work*** | Correspondence and conversations with Lee Fuller, 2020-2023
231 | ***Egypt and Syria attacked Israel*** | "Energy Crisis (1970s)" (History.com, August 30 2010) ;
"Oil Embargo, 1973–1974" (Office of the Historian, State Department of the United States of America)
232 | ***American oil production was in decline in the early 1970s*** | "Petroleum & Other Liquids, U.S. Field Production of Crude Oil" (U.S. Energy Information Administration, 2024)
232 | ***"We must recognize," Nixon said*** | "Foreign Relations of the United States, 1969–1976, Volume XXXVI, Energy Crisis, 1969–1974" (Office of the Historian, State Department of the United States of America)
232 | ***"midnight dumpers" were making a mockery of the nation's landfill system*** | "Hearings on the Reauthorization of the Resource Conservation and Recovery Act, Thursday, March 22, 1979, U.S. Senate, Committee on Environment and Public Works, Subcommittee on Resource Protection, Washington, D.C." (Hearing Transcripts Obtained via HeinOnline, 2020)
232 | ***Bentsen's grandfather had arrived from Denmark to*** | "Bentsen, Lloyd Millard, Sr. (1894–1989)" (Texas State Historical Association, August 1, 1995)
233 | ***By the time Lloyd Bentsen was born*** | "Bentsen, Lloyd Millard, Jr. (1921–2006)" (Texas State Historical Association, 2024)
233 | ***eventually came to command a B-24 bomber squadron*** | "Hall of Fame, Lloyd M. Bentsen, Jr." (Lone Star Flight Museum, Houston Texas, 2024)
233 | ***In 1948, at the age of 27, Bentsen was elected*** | David E. Rosenbaum, "Lloyd Bentsen Dies at 85; Senator Ran With Dukakis" New York Times (New York, New York, May 24, 2006) ; "Bentsen, Lloyd Millard, Jr. (1921–2006)" (Texas State Historical Association, 2024)
233 | ***profile of Bentsen that ran as a 1974 cover story for* Texas Monthly** | Al Reinert, "The Unveiling of Lloyd Bentsen" Texas Monthly (Austin, Texas, December 1974)
233 | ***"Throughout his career," the New York Times wrote*** | David E. Rosenbaum, "Lloyd Bentsen Dies at 85; Senator Ran With Dukakis" New York Times (New York, New York, May 24, 2006)
234 | ***a practice that is as yet largely unregulated," stated one EPA report to Congress*** | "EPA Activities: Under the Resource Conservation and Recovery Act of 1976, Annual Report to the President and the Congress Fiscal Year 1978" (US EPA, March 1979)
234 | ***90 percent of the nation's hazardous waste was being improperly*** | "Proposed Rules, Environmental Protection Agency, 40 CFR Part 250, Hazardous Waste Guidelines and Regulations" (U.S. Federal Register, Volume 43, Number 243,

Monday December 18, 1978)
234 | *passed by Congress on September 30, 1976* | "Resource Conservation and Recovery Act Timeline: Milestones in RCRA History" (US EPA, 2023)
234 | *noted Harvard educators who examined the process* | Marc K. Landy, Marc J. Roberts and Stephen R. Thomas, The Environmental Protection Agency: Asking the Wrong Questions, From Nixon to Clinton (Oxford, England: Oxford University Press, 1994)
234 | *On December 18, 1978, EPA finally published their proposed rules* | "Proposed Rules, Environmental Protection Agency, 40 CFR Part 250, Hazardous Waste Guidelines and Regulations" (U.S. Federal Register, Volume 43, Number 243, Monday December 18, 1978), https://www.epa.gov/sites/default/files/2016-03/documents/43fr58946.pdf
235 | *the air had a faint, choking smell," one government official reported* | Eckardt C. Beck, "The Love Canal Tragedy" (U.S. EPA, EPA Journal, January 1979)
235 | *Trucks loading hazardous waste would have to be appropriately marked* | "Resource Conservation and Recovery Act Timeline: Milestones in RCRA History" (US EPA, 2023) ; "Summary of the Resource Conservation and Recovery Act, 42 U.S.C. §6901 et seq. (1976)" (US EPA, 2023) ; "EPA's Hazardous Waste Regulations Effective November 19, 1980" (US EPA press release, November 19 1980) ; "Learn the Basics of Hazardous Waste" (US EPA, 2023), https://www.epa.gov/hw/learn-basics-hazardous-waste ; "How to Comply with Federal Hazardous Materials Regulations" (Federal Motor Carrier Safety Administration, 2022) ; "National Hazardous Materials Route Registry - By State" (Federal Motor Carrier Safety Administration, 2023)
235 | *important question remained—what waste would actually be defined as hazardous?* | Marc K. Landy, Marc J. Roberts and Stephen R. Thomas, The Environmental Protection Agency: Asking the Wrong Questions, From Nixon to Clinton (Oxford, England: Oxford University Press, 1994)
235-236 | *EPA provided two definitions → expanded to include* | "Proposed Rules, Environmental Protection Agency, 40 CFR Part 250, Hazardous Waste Guidelines and Regulations" (U.S. Federal Register, Volume 43, Number 243, Monday December 18, 1978)
236 | *I have asked EPA for more details* | Correspondence with EPA 2023 (Enesta Jones and Melissa Sullivan May 10 2023 and May 16 2023 ; Cathy Milbourn May 16 2023)
236 | *much of it is sufficiently radioactive* | Justin Nobel, "Highest Recorded Radium Readings in various US Oil & Gas Plays From Historic Reports and Documents" (unpublished work, 2023)
236 | *radioactivity threshold above which EPA considered a waste to be "hazardous"* | "Proposed Rules, Environmental Protection Agency, 40 CFR Part 250, Hazardous Waste Guidelines and Regulations" (U.S. Federal Register, Volume 43, Number 243, Monday December 18, 1978), https://www.epa.gov/sites/default/files/2016-03/documents/43fr58946.pdf
236 | *Radium in brine of the Marcellus* | Technologically Enhanced Naturally Occurring Radioactive Materials (TENORM) Study Report, (Pennsylvania Dept of Environmental Protection, 2016)
236 | *Radium levels in the Antrim formation* | Justin Nobel, "Highest Recorded Radium Readings in various US Oil & Gas Plays From Historic Reports and Documents" (unpublished work, 2023)

236-237 | ***EPA's website shows radium levels*** | "TENORM: Oil and Gas Production Wastes" (EPA, 2024)
237 | ***610,420 picocuries*** | "Lotus LLC, Lotus Disposal Facility, Andrews County, Texas, Pit Permit Numbers P010928 and P010938, 2nd Quarter 2005 Report" (Files Received by Justin Nobel via Freedom of Information Act request with Railroad Commission of Texas, November 19, 2020) ; Justin Nobel, "Where Does All The Radioactive Fracking Waste Go?" DeSmog (Seattle, Washington, April 22, 2021)
237 | ***Lee Fuller believed certain industries were at a disadvantage → Something would have to be done*** | Correspondence and conversations with Lee Fuller, 2020-2023
237 | ***members of the Senate Committee on Environment and Public Works met to discuss*** | "Hearings on the Reauthorization of the Resource Conservation and Recovery Act, Thursday, March 22, 1979, U.S. Senate, Committee on Environment and Public Works, Subcommittee on Resource Protection, Washington, D.C." (Hearing Transcripts Obtained via HeinOnline, 2020)
238 | ***Throughout the two-day hearing → "be expensive and, in many cases, of little value"*** | Hearings on the Reauthorization of the Resource Conservation and Recovery Act 1979
239 | ***could not be trusted to do exactly what the oil and gas industry wanted*** | Lee Fuller
239 | ***"run as high as $10.8 billion per year."*** | Hearings on the Reauthorization of the Resource Conservation and Recovery Act 1979
240 | ***It exempted "drilling fluids, produced waters, and other wastes*** | "Wastes - Non-Hazardous Waste - Industrial Waste: Special Wastes" (U.S. EPA, 2016)
240 | ***EPA clarified which particular oil and gas wastes were exempt → under US law declared to be nonhazardous*** | "Environmental Protection Agency, FRL-3403-9, 53 FR 25447, July 6, 1988, Regulatory Determination for Oil and Gas and Geothermal Exploration, Development and Production Wastes" (U.S. EPA, July 6, 1988)
240 | ***highly radioactive and containing shocking amounts of polonium*** | Alan McArthur and William Lemons, "NORM IX: Mandatory Air Monitoring of TENORM Worker Inhalation Exposure from Gas TENORM" (Pittsburgh Mineral & Environmental Technology, Inc., September 2019) ; Conversations and correspondence with Wayne State Univ. radon progeny expert Dr. Wayne Baskaran, 2020-2023
240 | ***adopted by the Senate's Committee on Environment and Public Works on May 15, 1979*** | "Legislative History for S.1156 - Solid Waste Disposal Act Amendments of 1980 96th Congress (1979-1980)" (Congress.gov, Accessed 2024)
240 | ***signed into law on October 21, 1980*** | Hearings on the Reauthorization of the Resource Conservation and Recovery Act 1979
241 | ***Written into the Solid Waste Disposal Act Amendments*** | "Wording of the Solid Waste Disposal Act of 1980, Public Law 96–482—Oct. 21, 1980" (Public Law of the United States, October 21, 1980)
241-242 | ***Carla Greathouse was born in the San Luis Valley → spent two days sitting on the floor of this closet*** | Correspondence and conversations with Carla Greathouse, 2021-2024
242-243 | ***Carla found that in West Virginia → contaminated the Ogallala*** | "Report to Congress, Management of Wastes from the Exploration,

Development, and Production of Crude Oil, Natural Gas, and Geothermal Energy, Volume 1 of 3, Oil and Gas" (U.S. EPA, December 1987) ; "Report to Congress, Management of Wastes from the Exploration, Development, and Production of Crude Oil, Natural Gas, and Geothermal Energy, Volume 3 of 3, Appendices, A-Summary of State Oil and Gas Regulations, B-Glossary of Terms Volume 1, C-Damage Case Summaries" (U.S. EPA, December 1987)

243 | ***"In February 1987 I landed in Fairbanks, Alaska*** | Correspondence and conversations with Carla Greathouse, 2021-2024

244 | ***underlain by permafrost up to 2,500 feet thick*** | "Report to Congress, Management of Wastes from the Exploration, Development, and Production of Crude Oil, Natural Gas, and Geothermal Energy, Volume 1 of 3, Oil and Gas" (U.S. EPA, December 1987) ; "Report to Congress, Management of Wastes from the Exploration, Development, and Production of Crude Oil, Natural Gas, and Geothermal Energy, Volume 3 of 3, Appendices, A-Summary of State Oil and Gas Regulations, B-Glossary of Terms Volume 1, C-Damage Case Summaries" (U.S. EPA, December 1987)

244 | ***most industrialized place in North America I have ever seen."*** | Carla Greathouse

245 | ***leached into a caribou calving*** | Report to Congress Management of Wastes Volume 1&3

245 | ***early 1980s, North Slope Salvage*** | Report to Congress Management of Wastes Volume 1&3

245-247 | ***Kenai, Alaska's other main producing region → conclusions to her nearly 900-page report were, as Carla puts it, "politically altered."*** | Carla Greathouse

247 | ***Labelling oilfield waste hazardous would "cause*** | "Regulatory Determination for Oil and Gas and Geothermal Exploration, Development and Production Wastes," (EPA, July 6, 1988)

248 | ***US Senate staffers called on her for decades*** | Carla Greathouse

248 | ***find that during the 1960s and 1970s a variety of Texas government agencies*** | "Environmental aspects of produced-water salt releases in onshore and coastal petroleum-producing areas of the conterminous U.S. – a bibliography" (U.S. Geological Survey, 2006)

248-249 | ***the Red River → called Lake Texoma*** | Donald K. Leifeste, James F. Blakey, and Leon S. Hughes, "Reconnaissance of the Chemical Quality of Surface Waters of the Red River Basin, Texas" (U.S. Geological Survey and the Texas Water Development Board, May 1971)

249 | ***Canadian River downstream from Amarillo*** | H.L. Kunze and J.N. Lee, "Reconnaissance of the Chemical Quality of Surface Waters of the Canadian River Basin, Texas" (U.S. Geological Survey and the Texas Water Development Board, December 1968)

249 | ***Lake Fork Creek, Hubbard Creek, Socagee Creek*** | L.S. Hughes and D.K. Leifeste, "Reconnaissance of the Chemical Quality of Surface Waters of the Sabine River Basin Texas and Louisiana" (Texas Water Commission, May 1964)

249 | ***City of Hawkins → drilling mud when pumped*** | S.C. Burnitt, "City of Hawkins, Wood County, Texas: Investigation of Ground-Water Contamination" (Texas Water Commission, August 1962)

249 | ***Clear Fork of the Brazos River → proposed Breckenridge Reservoir*** | Jack Rawson, "Study and Interpretation of Chemical Quality of Surface Waters in the Brazos River Basin, Texas" (U.S. Geological Survey and the Texas

Water Development Board, July 1967)
249 | ***Lake J.B. Thomas on the Colorado River*** | R.L. Crouch and S.C. Burnitt, "Investigation of Ground-Water Contamination in the Vealmoor Oil Field, Howard and Borden Counties, Texas" (Texas Water Commission, January 1965)
249 | ***Mission River at Refugio → Copano Bay*** | J.F. Blakey and H.L. Kunze, "Reconnaissance of the Chemical Quality of Surface Waters of the Coastal Basins of Texas" (U.S. Geological Survey and the Texas Water Development Board, June 1971)
249-250 | ***Colorado River all the way to Austin → and Scurry Counties*** | Donald K. Leifeste and Myra W. Lansford, "Reconnaissance of the Chemical Quality of Surface Waters of the Colorado River Basin" (U.S. Geological Survey and the Texas Water Development Board, March 1968)
250 | ***Frio and Atascosa Rivers, the Nueces River*** | H.L. Kunze, "Reconnaissance of the Chemical Quality of Surface Waters of the Nueces River Basin, Texas" (U.S. Geological Survey and the Texas Water Development Board, September 1971)
250 | ***Pecos River between Orla and Girvin*** | H.B. Mendieta, "Reconnaissance of the Chemical Quality of Surface Waters of the Rio Grande Basin, Texas" (U.S. Geological Survey and the Texas Water Development Board, March 1974)
250 | ***lower reach of Plum Creek, the San Marcos and Guadalupe Rivers*** | Jack Rawson, "Reconnaissance of the Chemical Quality of Surface Waters of the Guadalupe River Basin, Texas" (U.S. Geological Survey and Texas Water Development Board, December 1968)
250 | ***Elm Creek and Cibolo Creek near Falls City*** | Jack Rawson, "Reconnaissance of the Chemical Quality of Surface Waters of the San Antonio River Basin, Texas" (U.S. Geological Survey and the Texas Water Development Board, April 1969)
250 | ***Henderson Oilfield of Rusk County on the property of N.R. Dorsey and R.P. Yandle*** | S.C. Burnitt, "Henderson Oil Field Area, Rusk County, Texas, Investigation of Ground-Water Contamination" (Texas Water Commission, October 1962)
250 | ***Ogallala one of America's most important → additional large areas of contamination will be revealed*** | S.C. Burnitt and J.B. Adams, "Effects of Surface Disposal of Oil-Field Brine on the Quality and Development of Ground Water in the Ogallala Formation High Plains of Texas" (Texas Water Commission, for presentation at a Public Hearing Held by the Texas Water Pollution Control Board on September 25, 1963, in Austin, Texas, September 25 1963)
250 | ***Crab and Cedar Creeks in Navarro County → Chambers and Richland Creeks*** | F.L. Osborne Jr. and V.M. Shamburger Jr., "Brine Production and Disposal on the Lower Watershed of Chambers and Richland Creeks, Navarro County, Texas" (Texas Board of Water Engineers, March 1960)
250 | ***wells used for watering livestock across → the chemical character of the water"*** | Richard D. Preston, "Occurrence and Quality of Ground Water in Shackelford County, Texas" (Texas Water Development Board, October 1969)
250 | ***Lake Grand and Gonzales Creek → salt-impregnated soil and salt deposits*** | David C. Bayha, "Occurrence and Quality of Ground Water in Stephens County, Texas" (Texas Water Commission, September 1964)
250-251 | ***in the Juliana and West Jud Oilfields of Haskell and Stonewall Counties*** | Robert L. Crouch, "Investigation of Ground-Water Contamination in the Juliana and West Jud Oil Fields, Haskell and Stonewall Counties, Texas" (Texas

Water Commission, March 1964)
251 | ***domestic consumptions and livestock in Baylor County*** | Richard D. Preston, "Occurrence and Quality of Ground Water in Baylor County, Texas" (Texas Department of Water Resources, July 1978)
251 | ***Cypress Creek and Buffalo Bayou subbasins in the San Jacinto River Basin*** | Leon S. Hughes and Jack Rawson, "Reconnaissance of the Chemical Quality of Surface Waters of the San Jacinto River Basin, Texas" (U.S. Geological Survey and the Texas Water Development Board, January 1966)
251 | ***on the Edwards Plateau and in Reagan County*** | Loyd E. Walker, "Occurrence, Availability, And Chemical Quality of Ground Water in the Edwards Plateau Region of Texas" (Texas Department of Water Resources, July 1979)
251 | ***soil damage and vegetative kill → Throckmorton County*** | Richard O. Preston, "Occurrence and Quality of Ground Water in Throckmorton County, Texas" (Texas Water Development Board, April 1970)
251 | ***groundwater contamination in Archer County and numerous vegetative kill areas*** | Donald E. Morris, "Occurrence and Quality of Ground Water in Archer County, Texas" (Texas Water Development Board in cooperation with the Texas Water Pollution Control Board, July 1967)
251 | ***also surface vegetation kills several acres in size in Young County*** | Donald E. Morris, "Occurrence and Quality of Ground Water in Young County, Texas" (Texas Water Commission in cooperation with the Texas Water Pollution Control Board, December 1964)
251 | ***shallow ground waters throughout the drainage system of the Brazos River*** | R.T. Littleton, "Contamination of Surface and Ground Water in Southeast Young County, Texas" (Texas Board of Water Engineers, 1956) ; Texas Water Development Board site where it shows this paper is from 1956 https://www.twdb.texas.gov/publications/reports/historic_groundwater_reports/index.asp
251 | ***vegetative kill areas and water wells in Montague County*** | David C. Bayha, "Occurrence and Quality of Ground Water in Montague County, Texas" (Texas Water Development Board in cooperation with the Texas Water Pollution Control Board, August 1967)
252 | ***Coleman County → destruction of a pecan orchard*** | Loyd E. Walker, "Occurrence and Quantity of Ground Water in Coleman County, Texas" (Texas Water Development Board, Sept 1967)
252 | ***Little Cypress Creek → Omaha in Franklin County*** | Donald K. Leifeste, "Reconnaissance of the Chemical Quality of Surface Waters of the Sulphur River and Cypress Creek Basins, Texas" (U.S. Geological Survey in cooperation with the Texas Water Development Board, December 1968)
252 | ***in Jones County contaminated water wells and groundwater*** | Robert D. Price, "Occurrence, Quality, and Availability of Ground Water in Jones County, Texas" (Texas Department of Water Resources, April 1978)
252 | ***All this information had been available*** | "Environmental aspects of produced-water salt releases in onshore and coastal petroleum-producing areas of the conterminous U.S. – a bibliography" (U.S. Geological Survey, 2006) ; "City of Hawkins, Wood County, Texas: Investigation of Ground-Water Contamination" (Texas Water Commission, August 1962)
253 | ***Lotus LLC is situated off a dusty road 19 miles west*** | Justin Nobel, "Where Does All The Radioactive Fracking Waste Go?" DeSmog (Seattle, Washington, April 22, 2021)

253 | ***financed by Facebook that powers the oil giant Shell's fracking operations*** | Justin Nobel, "This Massive Facebook Solar Project Will Power Shell's Fracking Operations in Texas" DeSmog (Seattle, Washington, October 21, 2020)
253 | ***have all sent radioactive oilfield waste here*** | Justin Nobel, "Where Does All The Radioactive Fracking Waste Go?" DeSmog (Seattle, Washington, April 22, 2021) ; "Lotus LLC, Lotus Disposal Facility, Andrews County, Texas, Pit Permit Numbers P010928 and P010938, All Records from Facilities Opening through 2020" (Files Received by Justin Nobel via Records Request with Railroad Commission of Texas, November 19, 2020)
253 | ***have been deemed by the Department of Energy*** | J.A. Veil, K.P. Smith, D. Tomasko, D. Elcock, D. Blunt and G.P. Williams, "Disposal of NORM-contaminated oil field wastes in Salt Caverns" (Argonne National Lab, U.S. Department of Energy, August 28 1998) ; John A. Veil, Karen P. Smith, David Tomasko, Deborah Elcock, Deborah L. Blunt, and Gustavious P. Williams," Disposal of NORM-Contaminated Oil Field Wastes in Salt Caverns" (Argonne National Laboratory for Office of Fossil Energy, National Petroleum Technology Office, U.S. Department of Energy, August 1998)
253 | ***one million barrels worth of oilfield waste*** | Justin Nobel, "Where Does All The Radioactive Fracking Waste Go?" DeSmog (Seattle, Washington, April 22, 2021) ; Correspondence and conversations with Lotus official James Dillingham, 2021
254 | ***spend a year researching Lotus and discover a 2000 letter*** | Justin Nobel, "Where Does All The Radioactive Fracking Waste Go?" DeSmog (Seattle, Washington, April 22, 2021) ; "Lotus LLC, Lotus Disposal Facility, Andrews County, Texas, Pit Permit Numbers P010928 and P010938, All Records from Facilities Opening through 2020" (Files Received by Justin Nobel via Freedom of Information Act request with Railroad Commission of Texas, November 19, 2020)
254 | ***James Dillingham, Lotus's Global Director of Sales and Operations, insists the operation*** | Correspondence and conversations with Lotus official James Dillingham, 2021
254 | ***Railroad Commission will not directly answer my questions*** | Correspondence with Railroad Commission spokesperson 2021 (R. J. Desilva, April 1 2021)
254-255 | ***On October 12, 2016, Lotus asked EPA → meet the...definition of radioactive waste."*** | Justin Nobel, "Where Does All The Radioactive Fracking Waste Go?" DeSmog (Seattle, Washington, April 22, 2021) ; "Lotus LLC, Lotus Disposal Facility, Andrews County, Texas, Pit Permit Numbers P010928 and P010938, All Records from Facilities Opening through 2020" (Files Received by Justin Nobel via Freedom of Information Act request with Railroad Commission of Texas, November 19, 2020)
255 | ***Lotus's first international shipment → aboard a Singapore Airlines cargo jet*** | Correspondence and conversations with Lotus official James Dillingham, 2021 ; Justin Nobel, "Where Does All The Radioactive Fracking Waste Go?" DeSmog (Seattle, Washington, April 22, 2021) ; "Lotus LLC, Lotus Disposal Facility, Andrews County, Texas, Pit Permit Numbers P010928 and P010938, All Records from Facilities Opening through 2020" (Files Received by Justin Nobel via Freedom of Information Act request with Railroad Commission of Texas, November 19, 2020)
255 | ***containing radium at concentrations of 2,095 picocuries per gram***

| Justin Nobel, "Where Does All The Radioactive Fracking Waste Go?" DeSmog (Seattle, Washington, April 22, 2021) ; "Lotus LLC, Lotus Disposal Facility, Andrews County, Texas, Pit Permit Numbers P010928 and P010938, All Records from Facilities Opening through 2020" (Files Received by Justin Nobel via Freedom of Information Act request with Railroad Commission of Texas, November 19, 2020)
presence in oilfields on every continent → help countries develop local solutions." | Correspondence and conversations with Lotus official James Dillingham, 2021 ; Justin Nobel, "Where Does All The Radioactive Fracking Waste Go?" DeSmog (Seattle, Washington, April 22, 2021)
255 | *"EPA has no records," they say* | Correspondence with U.S. EPA, August 9 2019 (Maggie Sauerhage) ; Correspondence and conversations with Rick Jacobi, former General Manager of the Texas Low-Level Radioactive Waste Disposal Authority, 2021

Chapter 13
256 | *the remains of a 300-million-year-old set of shallow seas* | Joseph R. Dancy, "From the Drake Well to the Santa Rita #1: The History of the U.S. Permian Basin: A Miracle of Technological Innovation" Oil and Gas, Natural Resources, and Energy Journal, Volume 3, Number 5 (2018)
256 | *"An open, empty land," reads one West Texas history* | Claude W. Brown, "Mr. McCamey" – The Life of a Texas Oilman (Fort Worth, Texas: Eakin Press, 1995)
256 | *"working in dust, eating in dust, sleeping in dust."* | Jerry L. Doyle, "McCamey: The Boom Town 1925-1933" (Southwest Texas State University, 1974) [Documents Reviewed While At the McCamey Museums - Mendoza Trail Museum and the Adrian House, in McCamey, Texas, August 2020]
256 | *Humble Oil Company, which eventually* | Bill Modisett, "M.L. Baker No. 1 well gave McCamey a town and a name for it" Midland Reporter-Telegram (Midland, Texas, August 22, 2009)
257 | *"it was not unusual to see a Cadillac parked in front of a tent"* | Jerry L. Doyle, "McCamey: The Boom Town 1925-1933" (Southwest Texas State University, 1974)
257 | *"Drilling was an art as much as a science," reads one book* | Claude W. Brown, "Mr. McCamey" – The Life of a Texas Oilman (Fort Worth, Texas: Eakin Press, 1995)
257 | *There are photographs in the museum in McCamey of the wide → "Man of the Year"* | Upton County Historical Commission, "Pictorial History of Upton County" (Fort Worth, Texas: NorTex Press, 1994) ; "1925 – 1975 50th Anniversary History Retrospective," Compiled by Some Interested Citizens of McCamey [Documents Reviewed While At the McCamey Museums]
258-267 | *Sir, my name is Linda Cordes Fox → looking in the right places. We are the harm* | Conversations and correspondence with Linda Cordes Fox and Derek Fox, 2020-2023
266 | *young boy in the photo has the same deformity as Derek. Mr. Jairo Yumbo* | Steven Donzieger, "Don't Let Big Oil Open A New Front In Its War On Environmental Defenders (Commentary)" Mongabay (Menlo Park, California, August 11, 2020)

Chapter 14

268-269 | ***American Petroleum Institute generated an incredible report → are they going to do with that?*** | "An Analysis of the Impact of the Regulation of 'Radionuclides' as a Hazardous Air Pollutant on the Petroleum Industry" (Committee for Environmental Biology and Community Health, Department of Medicine and Biology, American Petroleum Institute, October 19, 1982)
269 | ***sometimes referred to as the longer-lived daughters of radon*** | Correspondence and conversations with nuclear forensics scientist Dr. Marco Kaltofen, 2019-2024
269 | ***Yale University had nearly a quarter of a billion dollars*** | Lorenzo Arvanitis, "Filing reveals University's fossil fuel investment" Yale Daily News (New Haven, Connecticut, December 4, 2018)
269 | ***building known as* Le V** | "Acceptance and optimization of air and water systems Veolia head office - Le V" (Veolia, 2024)
269 | ***Clearwater was built to process 600 trucks*** | Justin Nobel, "In West Virginia, Plan to Clean up Radioactive Fracking Waste Ends in Monster Lawsuit" DeSmog (Seattle, Washington, September 19, 2023)
269 | ***best project like this in the world.*** | Charles Young, "Antero Resources leads environmental progress with Clearwater Facility in Doddridge County, WV" WV News (April 13, 2019)
270 | ***Taste of the Marcellus"*** | "9 15 15 -- Antero Resources Speaks AT DC Commission Meeting" (Minute 18:00 of YouTube Video, September 15, 2015), https://www.youtube.com/watch?v=9YEUttsfaqQ ; Justin Nobel, "In West Virginia, Plan to Clean up Radioactive Fracking Waste Ends in Monster Lawsuit" DeSmog (Seattle, Washington, September 19, 2023)
270 | ***"This plant, if it works, it would be great," stated the retired industrial electrician*** | "9 15 15 -- Antero Resources Speaks AT DC Commission Meeting" (Minute 34:30 to Minute 37:00 of YouTube Video, September 15, 2015), https://www.youtube.com/watch?v=9YEUttsfaqQ
270 | ***"We don't want another Chernobyl."*** | "9 15 15 -- Antero Resources Speaks AT DC Commission Meeting" (Minute 38:00 of YouTube Video, September 15, 2015)
270 | ***The balmy April morning in 2019 I visited Clearwater*** | Correspondence with Ohio environmental organizer Felicia Mettler, 2017-2024
270 | ***Peter suggested flying through a drone*** | Conversations and correspondences with Peter, oil and gas industry brine hauler, 2018-2024
270 | ***September 2019 had been idled*** | Justin Nobel, "In West Virginia, Plan to Clean up Radioactive Fracking Waste Ends in Monster Lawsuit" DeSmog (Seattle, Washington, September 19, 2023)
270 | ***ran the question by the Vermont-based nuclear physicist*** | Correspondence and conversations with nuclear physicist Dr. Marvin Resnikoff, 2018-2023
271 | ***can be filtered treated with certain types of membranes," says Burgos*** | Correspondence and conversations with Penn State environmental engineer Dr. Bill Burgos, 2019-2024
271 | ***When I ask Carrie Griffiths*** | Correspondence and conversations with Carrie Griffiths, executive vice president and chief communications officer for Veolia North America, 2023
271 | ***Antero has not replied to any of my questions*** | Attempted correspondence with Antero Resources, 2019-2023 (August 22, 2019 Alvyn Schopp

and owner-relations@anteroresources.com, November 13, 2019 ; March 10, 2023; July 20, 2023

271 | ***I ask the West Virginia Department of Environmental Protection*** | Correspondence with West Virginia Department of Environmental Protection spokesperson Casey Korbini, 2019 (May 5 2019)

271 | ***On March 13, 2020, Antero filed a lawsuit against Veolia*** | "District Court, City and County of Denver, Colorado, Antero Treatment LLC, a Delaware limited liability company, v. Veolia Water Technologies, Inc., a Delaware corporation, and Veolia Water Norther America Operating Servies, LLC, a Delaware limited liability company: COMPLAINT" Files Obtained February 2 2023 Via Public Request From The District Court (District Court, City and County of Denver, Colorado, March 13 2020)

272 | ***nothing to do with a drop in natural gas prices*** | "District Court, City and County of Denver, Colorado, Antero Treatment LLC, a Delaware limited liability company, v. Veolia Water Technologies, Inc., a Delaware corporation, and Veolia Water Norther America Operating Servies, LLC, a Delaware limited liability company: COMPLAINT" Files Obtained February 2 2023 Via Public Request From The District Court (District Court, City and County of Denver, Colorado, March 13 2020)

272 | ***denies that it committed fraud"*** | Correspondence and conversations with Carrie Griffiths, executive vice president and chief communications officer for Veolia North America, 2023

272 | ***When I ask Griffiths in 2023 how radium was removed*** | Carrie Griffiths

272 | ***reviewing project permits*** | "Antero Treatment LLC, Antero Clearwater Facility, NSR Permit Class II Administrative Update Application to R13-3260C, West Virginia Department of Environmental Protection Division of Air Quality, Doddridge County, West Virginia" (Kleinfelder, April 9 2018)

272 | ***"The sludge was transported to several disposal sites*** | Carrie Griffiths ; Justin Nobel, "In West Virginia, Plan to Clean up Radioactive Fracking Waste Ends in Monster Lawsuit" DeSmog (Seattle, Washington, September 19, 2023)

272 | ***Department of Environmental Protection has not responded*** | Correspondence and attempted correspondence with West Virginia Department of Environmental Protection, 2021-2023 (June 22 2021, July 27 2021, November 15 2021, and March 17 2023, Terry Fletcher)

272 | ***In early 2024 I hear from Nick Fischer, who had stumbled across my reporting*** | Correspondence and conversations with former Clearwater worker Nick Fischer, 2024

273 | ***nowhere does the complaint specifically mention the people and communities of West Virginia*** | District Court, COMPLAINT

273 | ***taking this enormous aspect of their operations and making it vanish,"*** | Correspondence with President of the Center for International Environmental Law Carroll Muffet, 2023

273 | ***emergency management official*** | Justin Nobel, "Fire at Oil and Gas Waste Site Raises Safety Concerns Around Possible Radioactive Accidents" DeSmog (Seattle, Washington, February 18, 2021)

273-274 | ***In June 2023, I am back in West Virginia → at around 2 milliroentgens per hour*** | Justin Nobel, "Inside West Virginia's Chernobyl: A highly radioactive oil and gas facility has become a party spot in Marion County"

Truthdig (Los Angeles, California, September 18, 2023) ; Correspondences and conversations with former Department of Energy scientist Dr. Yuri Gorby, 2019-2024
274 | *EPA later finds levels as high as 3 milliroentgens per hour* | "Report from Christine Wagner, OnScene Coordinator and Cole Devine, OnScene Coordinator, at Fairmont Brine site to Jason McDougal with West Virginia Department of Environmental Protection, Jason Frame with West Virginia Department of Health and Human Resources and U.S. EPA Region III, Subject: POLREP #1, POLREP #1 & Special Bulletin, A Notice OF $250K Activation, Fairmont Brine Site, B3CL, Fairmont, WV, Latitude: 39.5082655 Longitude: 80.1254116" (U.S. EPA, September 22 2023)
274 | *covered in graffiti → "Oh my god, did they go swimming?"* | Justin Nobel, "Inside West Virginia's Chernobyl: A highly radioactive oil and gas facility has become a party spot in Marion County" Truthdig (Los Angeles, California, September 18, 2023) ; Justin Nobel, "A Slow-Rolling Disaster in Fracking Country: Ex-employees at 'West Virginia's Chernobyl' speak out on lethal cancers, regulatory failure and contaminated drinking water" Truthdig (Los Angeles, California, December 7, 2023)
274 | *5,000 times general background levels* | "Eberline Analytical Final Report of Analysis, for Concerned OH River Residents, Soil Samples" (Eberline Analytical, August 2023)
274 | *contaminated with radioactivity than over 99 percent of the present-day Chernobyl Exclusion Zone* | "36 years of Chernobyl: the BfS publishes the new radioactivity maps", (Bundesamt für Strahlenschutz press release, April 20, 2022), https://www.bfs.de/SharedDocs/Pressemitteilungen/BfS/EN/2022/006.html ; "Radiation levels" (The Chernobyl Gallery), http://www.chernobylgallery.com/chernobyl-disaster/radiation-levels/
274 | *Jill calls me. A former Fairmont Brine worker* | Conversations and correspondences with former Fairmont Brine worker Sean Guthrie, 2023 ; Justin Nobel, "A Slow-Rolling Disaster in Fracking Country: Ex-employees at 'West Virginia's Chernobyl' speak out on lethal cancers, regulatory failure and contaminated drinking water" Truthdig (Los Angeles, California, December 7, 2023)
274-277 | *In September 2023, Jill calls me → In a second incident, Guthrie says, he was asked to dump fluids from a set of frack tanks into the parking lot* | Conversations and correspondences with former Fairmont Brine worker Sean Guthrie, 2023 ; Justin Nobel, "A Slow-Rolling Disaster in Fracking Country: Ex-employees at 'West Virginia's Chernobyl' speak out on lethal cancers, regulatory failure and contaminated drinking water" Truthdig (Los Angeles, California, December 7, 2023)
277 | *Moniot has not replied to specific questions* | Correspondence with Venture Engineering President and CEO Dave Moniot, 2023
277 | *connects me, at the end of 2023, to Shannon Lutz → I look back I am like, Oh my god."* | Correspondence and conversations with Shannon Lutz, 2023-2024
278 | *connect with the University of Pittsburgh geochemist, Dr. Daniel Bain* | Correspondence and conversations with University of Pittsburgh geochemist Dr. Daniel Bain, 2021-2024
278 | *conclude oilfield workers don't receive enough exposure to cause cancers* | Technologically Enhanced Naturally Occurring Radioactive Materials (TENORM) Study Report, (Pennsylvania Department of Environmental Protection,

2016) ; K.P. Smith, D.L. Blunt, G.P. Williams, and C.L. Tebes, "Radiological Dose Assessment Related to Management of Naturally Occurring Radioactive Materials Generated by the Petroleum Industry" (Environmental Assessment Division, Argonne National Laboratory, U.S. Department of Energy, September 1996)

279 | ***In 2020, researchers at Harvard's School of Public Health published*** | Longxiang Li, Annelise J. Blomberg, John D. Spengler, Brent A. Coull, Joel D. Schwartz and Petros Koutrakis, "Unconventional oil and gas development and ambient particle radioactivity," Nature Communications, Volume 11, Number 1 (2020)

279 | ***Petros Koutrakis told a British newspaper*** | Damian Carrington, "Airborne radioactivity increases downwind of fracking, study finds" The Guardian (London, England, October 13, 2020)

279 | ***he says it is "a reasonable" theory.*** | Correspondence and conversations with Harvard School of Public Health researcher Dr. Longxiang Li, 2020

279 | ***named Alan McArthur gave a presentation*** | Alan McArthur and William Lemons, "NORM IX: Mandatory Air Monitoring of TENORM Worker Inhalation Exposure from Gas TENORM" (Pittsburgh Mineral & Environmental Technology, Inc., September 2019) ; "TENORM in Unconventional Oil & Gas Production Workshop, sponsored by the National Council on Radiation Protection and Measurements" (National Council on Radiation Protection and Measurements, February 1, 2016)

279 | ***McArthur was born on Lamlash*** | Correspondence and conversations with oil and gas industry consultant Alan McArthur, 2021

280 | ***In his 2019 presentation, McArthur explained*** | Alan McArthur and William Lemons, "NORM IX: Mandatory Air Monitoring of TENORM Worker Inhalation Exposure from Gas TENORM" (Pittsburgh Mineral & Environmental Technology, Inc., September 2019)

280 | ***extraordinary level of 1.2 million picocuries per*** | Alan McArthur and William Lemons

280 | ***two million times general background levels*** | F. Carvalho, S. Fernandes, S. Fesenko, E. Holm, B. Howard, P. Martin, M. Phaneuf, D. Porcelli, G. Pröhl and J. Twining, "The Environmental Behaviour of Polonium" (International Atomic Energy Agency, 2017) ; Correspondence and conversations with Wayne State University radon and radon progeny expert Dr. Mark Baskaran, 2020-2023

280 | ***even though the lethal dose swallowed was just 26.5 micrograms*** | Luke Harding, A Very Expensive Poison: The Assassination of Alexander Litvinenko and Putin's War With the West (New York: Vintage Books, 2017), 181

280 | ***indicates that 218 pounds of sludge scraped from the filters of a natural gas pipeline*** | Alan McArthur and William Lemons ; (The dose that killed Litvinenko was 4.4 GBq, or 1.189188 x 10E11 pCi, and since McArthur found 1.2 microCuries/gram of polonium 210 in the filter in a natural gas pipeline, or 1,200,00 picocuries/gram we set up a simple equation to learn that it would take 99,099 grams of pipeline filter sludge to get that much polonium-210, which is 218.47 pounds)

280-281 | ***the United States has at least 321,000 miles*** | "State Gas Pipelines - Breaking It Down: Understanding the Terminology" (National Conference of State Legislatures, February 22, 2011)

281 | ***No government agency, including the two main ones*** | Correspondence with Federal Energy Regulatory Commission spokesperson, 2019-2022 (MediaDL@ferc.gov March 30 2022) ; Correspondence with U.S. Department of Transportation's

Pipeline and Hazardous Materials Safety Administration (PHMSA), 2018-2021 (Darius Kirkwood, April 6 2022)

281 | ***It's a "GREAT QUESTION," he tells me*** | Correspondence and conversations with oil and gas industry consultant Alan McArthur, 2021

281 | ***Cleaning out this toxic radioactive waste → piggers clean off the radioactive waste*** | Correspondence and conversations with nuclear forensics scientist Dr. Marco Kaltofen, 2019-2024

281-282 | ***"We set up this big tarp containment → injected into the salt cavern operated by Lotus*** | Correspondence and conversations with former Texas oilfield worker, 2019-2020

282 | ***Pigging waste, no matter how much deadly polonium it contains*** | "Environmental Protection Agency, FRL-3403-9, 53 FR 25447, July 6, 1988, Regulatory Determination for Oil and Gas and Geothermal Exploration, Development and Production Wastes" (U.S. EPA, July 6, 1988)

282 | ***Alan McArthur, in his 2019 presentation, warned that the inhalation*** | Alan McArthur and William Lemons, "NORM IX: Mandatory Air Monitoring of TENORM Worker Inhalation Exposure from Gas TENORM" (Pittsburgh Mineral & Environmental Technology, Inc., September 2019)

282 | ***Canadian graduate student Eli Franklin Burton first discovered in 1904*** | "Photos of 'A Radioactive Gas From Crude Petroleum' obtained during visit to University of Toronto libraries," (University of Toronto Studies, Physical Science Series, photographed by Justin Nobel, 2019)

282 | ***follows in oil pipelines, oil tanker trucks and railway*** | P.R. Gray, "NORM Contamination in the Petroleum Industry" Journal of Petroleum Technology, Volume 45, Number 01 (1993) ; Alan McArthur and William Lemons

282 | ***does not appear to be much research on*** | Nada Farhan Kadhim, Omer Haythem Adnan, Ali Abdulwahab Ridha, "Studying the Radioactivity of Local and Imported Cars Oil in Baghdad Using High Purity Germanium Detector," Nuclear Science, Volume 2, Number 2 (2017)

282 | ***long before reaching the neighborhood gas station*** | P.R. Gray, "NORM Contamination in the Petroleum Industry" Journal of Petroleum Technology, Volume 45, Number 01 (1993) ; Correspondence and conversations with nuclear forensics scientist Dr. Marco Kaltofen, 2019-2024

282 | ***Radioactive emissions, however, would be expected at oil refineries*** | M. Behbehani, S. Uddin and M. Baskaran, "210Po concentration in different size fractions of aerosol likely contribution from industrial sources," Journal of Environmental Radioactivity, Volume 222 (2020) ; Correspondence and conversations with Wayne State University radon expert Dr. Mark Baskaran, 2020-2023

282 | ***There are 129 in the United States*** | "Frequently Asked Questions: When was the last refinery built in the United States?" (U.S. Energy Information Administration, 2023)

283 | ***Their findings indicate radioactivity levels are two to three times higher*** | Conversations and correspondence with Colorado atmospheric scientist Dr. Detlev Helmig, 2020-2024

283 | ***radioactivity would be expected to be released at locations along the pipeline system*** | Alan McArthur and William Lemons, "NORM IX: Mandatory Air Monitoring of TENORM Worker Inhalation Exposure from Gas TENORM" (Pittsburgh Mineral & Environmental Technology, Inc., September 2019)

; P.R. Gray, "NORM Contamination in the Petroleum Industry" Journal of Petroleum Technology, Volume 45, Number 01 (1993) ; A. Canoba, G. Gnoni, W. Truppa, "NORM measurements in the oil and gas industry in Argentina" (Autoridad Regulatoria Nuclear, 2006) ; "Fact Sheet: Pump and Compressor Stations" (U.S. Department of Transportation, Pipeline & Hazardous Materials Safety Administration, 2018)
283 | *A plastics plant may seem like an unlikely place to look for radioactivity* | P.R. Gray, "NORM Contamination in the Petroleum Industry" Journal of Petroleum Technology, Volume 45, Number 01 (1993) ; A. Canoba, G. Gnoni, W. Truppa, "NORM measurements in the oil and gas industry in Argentina" (Autoridad Regulatoria Nuclear, 2006)
283 | *due to radon's boiling point being closer to the boiling points of propane and ethane* | P.R. Gray, "NORM Contamination in the Petroleum Industry"
284 | *National Energy Board issued a safety advisory that warned* | "Safety Advisory NEB SA94-1: Potential for Elevated Radiation Levels In Propane" (National Energy Board, April 1994)
284 | *I ask the National Energy Board's current iteration* | Correspondence and attempted correspondence with Canada Energy Regulator, 2023-2024 (July 12 2023 and February 17 info@cer-rec.gc.ca), (Lisa Lebel, February 22 2024)
284 | *much of the world's plastics are made* | "Ethane Cracker Plants: What Are They?" (The Climate Reality Project, October 23 2018)
284 | *coating the inside of pumps and valves* | Correspondence and conversations with nuclear forensics scientist Dr. Marco Kaltofen. 2019-2024
284 | *a pump in a plastics plant of 40 millirems per hour* | A. Canoba, G. Gnoni, W. Truppa, "NORM measurements in the oil and gas industry in Argentina" (Autoridad Regulatoria Nuclear, 2006)
284 | *radiation levels lingering in the basement of the hospital at Chernobyl* |
"Radiation levels" (The Chernobyl Gallery), http://www.chernobylgallery.com/chernobyl-disaster/radiation-levels/
284 | *will annually produce 3.5 billion pounds of plastics* | "Shell begins operations at polymers plant in Pennsylvania" (Shell press release, November 15, 2022)
284 | *the plant was exceeding pollution limits* | Katarina Sabados, Kenzi Abou-Sabe and Hannah Rappleye, "Months after residents sound the alarm, Pennsylvania 'cracks' down on Shell plant" NBC News (New York, New York, May 25, 2023)
284 | *Clean Air Council filed a lawsuit* | Michael Rubinkam, "Environmental groups sue Shell over air quality at massive new Pennsylvania petrochemical plantnvironmental groups sue Shell over air quality at massive new Pennsylvania petrochemical plant" AP News (New York, New York, May 11 2023)
284 | *Shell also doesn't answer my question* | Correspondence with Shell spokesperson Curtis Smith 2019-2020 ; Attempted correspondence with Shell Polymers Monaca February 17 2024
284-285 | *one expert I speak to says they wouldn't expect much* | Correspondence and conversations with nuclear forensics scientist Dr. Marco Kaltofen, 2019-2024
285 | *Dennis Schum began working for a company called → I was the man," says Dennis* |

Correspondence and conversations with former John Crane worker Dennis Schum, 2019-2024

285-286 | ***The Oklahoma industry consultant, Peter Gray → to prevent inhalation of radioactive dust."*** | P.R. Gray, "NORM Contamination in the Petroleum Industry" Journal of Petroleum Technology, Volume 45, Number 01 (1993) ; Peter Gray, "Radioactive Materials Could Pose Problems For the Gas Industry" Oil & Gas Journal (Tulsa, Oklahoma, June 25, 1990)

286-287 | ***roughly 25-feet-long by 15-feet-wide → finding a good lawyer willing to take his case*** | Correspondence and conversations with former John Crane worker Dennis Schum, 2019-2024

286 | ***John Crane merged with Smiths*** | "100 Years of Company History" (John Crane, 2024)

286 | ***storied British company founded in 1851*** | "Smiths Group celebrates 100 years on London Stock Exchange" (Smiths, July 21 2014)

286-287 | ***leaders in climate*** | "Sustainable Sulzer: Sustainability Report, 2022" (Sulzer, 2022)

287 | ***180 facilities worldwide*** | "Sulzer: Sustainably successful since 1834" (Sulzer, 2024)

287 | ***report on oilfield radioactivity bearing the logo of John Crane and Smiths*** | "Naturally Occurring Radioactive Material (NORM)" (John Crane/Smiths)

287 | ***Neither John Crane*** | Attempted correspondence with John Crane, 2021-2024 (info@johncrane.com September 13 2021 and February 17 2024)

287 | ***Smiths,*** | Attempted correspondence with Smiths, 2021-2024 (facilities.enquiries@smiths.com September 13 2021 and February 17 2024)

287 | ***or Sulzer have replied to any of my questions*** | Attempted correspondence with Sulzer, 2021-2024 (Via their web contact form September 13 2021 and February 17 2024)

288 | ***built a booming business around oilfield radioactivity*** | Stuart Smith, Crude Justice: How I Fought Big Oil and Won, and What You Should Know About the New Environmental Attack on America (Dallas: BENBELLA Books, 2015)

288 | ***not just workers directly connected to the waste → derrickman, and welders*** | Stanley Waligora and Marvin Resnikoff, "Occupational Exposures to Radioactive Scale and Sludge: Coleman et al v. H.C. Price Co et al, December 2013" (Coleman et al v. H.C. Price Co et al, December 2013) ; Correspondence and conversations with nuclear forensics scientist Dr. Marco Kaltofen, 2019-2024

288 | ***were diagnosed with a number of cancers*** | Stanley Waligora and Marvin Resnikoff, "Occupational Exposures to Radioactive Scale and Sludge: Coleman et al v. H.C. Price Co et al, December 2013" (Coleman et al v. H.C. Price Co et al, December 2013)

288 | ***intended to analyze the exposures of nuclear weapons workers*** | "NIOSH-IREP" (U.S. Centers for Disease Control and Prevention, 2024)

288 | ***IREP showed with over 99 percent certainty that these men's cancers*** | Stanley Waligora and Marvin Resnikoff, "Occupational Exposures to Radioactive Scale and Sludge: Coleman et al v. H.C. Price Co et al, December 2013" (Coleman et al v. H.C. Price Co et al, December 2013) ; Correspondence and conversations with nuclear physicist Dr. Marvin Resnikoff, 2018-2023

288 | ***"These men," Stuart tells me in 2020, "are guinea pigs."*** | Correspondence and conversations with Louisiana attorney Stuart Smith, 2020-2021 ; Justin Nobel, "The Syrian Job: Uncovering the Oil Industry's Radioactive

Secret" DeSmog (Seattle, Washington, April 29 2020)
289 | ***lung cancer can take a decade, or several decades*** | John Howard, "Minimum Latency & Types or Categories of Cancer" (World Trade Center Health Program, October 17, 2012)
289 | ***learning curve on a case like this is tremendous,"*** | Correspondence and conversations with Louisiana attorney Stuart Smith, 2020-2021
289 | ***Paula Bliss's female-run firm*** | Correspondence and conversations with attorney Paula Bliss, 2022-2023
289 | ***"This is a civil action" for pipeline workers*** | "Complaint and Jury Demand in Case of Craig Hamelin and Michael McCarron, Individually and as representative of all others similarly situated, Plaintiffs, v. Kinder Morgan, Inc., Kidner Morgan Energy Partners, L.P., Tennessee Gas Pipeline Co., LLC, The Berkshire Gas Company, and Avangrid, Inc., Defendants, Docket No. 2176CV00024" (Trial Court Department, Berkshire Superior Court, Commonwealth of Massachusetts, January 29 2021)
289 | ***Kinder Morgan has not replied to my questions*** | Attempted correspondence with Kinder Morgan, 2022 (newsroom@kindermorgan.com August 11 2022 and March 29 2022)
289 | ***we think it is going to be this."*** | Paula Bliss, 2022-2023
290 | ***Lisa Johnson grew up in a military family*** | Correspondence and conversations with Pennsylvania attorney Lisa Johnson, 2022-20224
290 | ***"We're going to fight this until hell freezes over*** | Mica Rosenberg, "Chevron's U.S. win in Ecuador case looms over cases elsewhere" Reuters (London, England, March 7, 2014)
290 | ***have gathered outside the courthouse*** | Andy Sheehan, "Washington County family takes 2 corporations to court over fracking health concerns," CBS News (New York, New York, June 20, 2023)
290 |***fracking here for 20 years*** | Conversation with Cat Lodge of Environmental Integrity Project, 2023
291 | ***open up an entirely new legal front*** | Lisa Johnson

Chapter 15
293 | ***Kurt and Janice speak, as if their voices → And that same day he died."*** | Correspondence with Kurt and Janice Blanock, 2021-2024
295 | ***2019 investigative reporters at the* Pittsburgh Post-Gazette *revealed*** | David Templeton and Don Hopey, "CDC, state officials investigating multiple cases of rare cancer in southwestern Pa." Pittsburgh Post-Gazette (Pittsburgh, Pennsylvania, March 28, 2019) ; David Templeton and Don Hopey, "Human Toll: Are the 27 cases of Ewing sarcoma near Pittsburgh a cluster?" Pittsburgh Post-Gazette (Pittsburgh, Pennsylvania, May 14 2019)
295 | ***known as Canon-Mac*** | "Channel 11 report prompts health department investigation of rare cancer cases" Channel 11 WPXI (Pittsurgh, Pennsylvania, March 27, 2019)
295 | ***One of them was Luke Blanock. Another was Mitch Barton*** | David Templeton and Don Hopey, "CDC, state officials investigating multiple cases of rare cancer in southwestern Pa." Pittsburgh Post-Gazette (Pittsburgh, Pennsylvania, March 28, 2019) ; Correspondence and conversations with Janice and Kurt Blanock, 2021-2024 ; Karen Mansfield, "Another local man battling Ewing's sarcoma" Observer-Reporter (Pittsburgh, Pennsylvania, March 24, 2019)

295 | ***Curtis Valent, also of Cecil → and died on November 15, 2013, at the age of 27*** | David Templeton and Don Hopey, "CDC, state officials investigating multiple cases of rare cancer in southwestern Pa." Pittsburgh Post-Gazette (Pittsburgh, Pennsylvania, March 28, 2019) ; Eliza Griswold, "When the Kids Started Getting Sick," The New Yorker (New York, New York, March 2, 2021)
296 | ***wife Alison wrote on a patient support site*** | "David's Story" (Caring Bridge, June 30 2018)
296 | ***less common place for Ewing sarcoma to show up*** | Conversations and correspondence with Canadian epidemiologist Dr. Murray Finkelstein 2021 ; Irfan Affandi Hamid, Siti Asmat Md Arepen, Nor Eyzawiah Hassan and Mawaddah Azman, "A case report of rare isolated Ewing sarcoma of left maxillary sinus," The Egyptian Journal of Otolaryngology, Volume 36, Number 6 (2020)
296 | ***The Post-Gazette article described*** | David Templeton and Don Hopey, "CDC, state officials investigating multiple cases of rare cancer in southwestern Pa." Pittsburgh Post-Gazette (Pittsburgh, Pennsylvania, March 28, 2019)
296 | ***says the American Academy of Orthopaedic Surgeons*** | "Diseases & Conditions: Ewing's Sarcoma" (American Academy of Orthopaedic Surgeons, April 2019)
296-297 | ***225 of them are diagnosed with Ewing sarcoma*** | "Ewing Sarcoma in Adults" (John Hopkins School of Medicine)
297 | ***But certain information is firmly known → when bones are growing quickly*** | "Ewing Sarcoma in Adults" (John Hopkins School of Medicine, 2024) ; "Ewing Sarcoma" (St. Jude Children's Hospital, 2024) ; "Ewing Sarcoma" (Mayo Clinic, 2024) ; "Ewing Sarcoma Treatment (PDQ®)–Patient Version" (National Cancer Institute, September 13 2023)
297 | ***lot more turnover of cells," says Dr. Larysa Dyrszka*** | Correspondence and conversations with Larysa Dyrszka, 2019-2024
297 | ***publish an epic report entitled, Compendium of Scientific*** | "Press Release for Compendium of Scientific, Medical, and Media Findings Demonstrating Risks and Harms of Fracking and Associated Gas and Oil Infrastructure, Ninth Edition, October 19, 2023" (Concerned Health Professionals of NY, October 19 2023)
297 | ***The latest volume cites from over*** | "Compendium of Scientific, Medical, and Media Findings Demonstrating Risks and Harms of Fracking and Associated Gas and Oil Infrastructure, Ninth Edition" (Concerned Health Professionals of NY, Physicians for Social Responsibility and Science & Environmental Health Network, October 2023)
297-298 | ***children would naturally serve as the canary in the coal mine*** | Correspondence and conversations with Larysa Dyrszka, 2019-2024
298 | ***also helped establish a clinical cancer research unit*** | "James Ewing: 'The Chief' of cancer pathology" (Healio, October 25, 2008) ; "Founder: James Ewing" (American Association for Cancer Research)
298 | ***In 1919, he published,* Neoplastic Diseases** | "History of Medicine: Time Magazine's 'Cancer Man'" (Columbia Surgery, 2024) ; Richard A. Brand, "Biographical Sketch: James Stephen Ewing, MD (1844–1943)," Clinical Orthopaedics and Related Research, Volume 470, Number 3 (2012) ; James Ewing, Neoplastic Diseases: A Treatise on Tumors (Philadelphia, Pennsylvania: W.B. Saunders, 1922)
298 | ***1921 meeting of the New York Pathological Society, Ewing spoke*** | James Ewing, "Diffuse Endothelioma of Bone" Proceedings of the New York

Pathological Society, Volume 21 (1921)

298-299 | ***James Ewing was part of a group of cancer researchers → 9 grams worth*** | Matthew Tontonoz, "What Ever Happened to Coley's Toxins?" (Cancer Research Institute, April 2, 2015) ; Arty R. Zantinga and Max J. Coppes, "James Ewing (1866–1943): 'the chief'," Medical and Pediatric Oncology, Volume 21, Number 7 (1993) ; Matthew Tontonoz "Hot Times in 'Radium Hospital': The History of Radium Therapy at MSK" (Memorial Sloan Kettering Cancer Center, September 22, 2016)

299 | ***"Death occurred on December 23, 1920"*** | James Ewing, "Diffuse Endothelioma of Bone" Proceedings of the New York Pathological Society, Volume 21 (1921)

299 | ***appeared on the cover of* Time *magazine*** | "History of Medicine: Time Magazine's 'Cancer Man'" (Columbia Surgery, 2024) ; "Professor James Ewing, Time Magazine Cover from Jan. 12, 1931" (Time magazine, January 12 1931)

299 | ***Ewing, writes Kate Moore, in her book*** | Kate Moore, The Radium Girls: The Dark Story of America's Shining Women. (Naperville, Illinois: Sourcebooks, 2017)

299-300 | ***1931 article in* The American Journal of Cancer *→ inevitably escape the body out through the mouth*** | Harrison S. Martland, "The Occurrence of Malignancy in Radioactive Persons," The American Journal of Cancer, Volume XV, No 4 (1931)

301-302 | ***"The corruption here was pathetic → so what the hell are we eating?"*** | Correspondence and conversations with Ron Gulla, 2019-2024

302 | ***Dr. Nathaniel Warner, an environmental engineer → "brought the radioactivity into their hard shells."*** | Correspondence and conversations with Penn State geochemist Dr. Nathaniel Warner, 2019-2023 ; Thomas J. Geeza, David P. Gillikin, Bonnie McDevitt, Katherine Van Sice and Nathaniel R. Warner, "Accumulation of Marcellus Formation Oil and Gas Wastewater Metals in Freshwater Mussel Shells," Environmental Science & Technology, Volume 52, Number 18 (2018)

302 | ***literature is all over the place*** | Dr. Nathaniel Warner

303 | ***Allen's Waste Water Services had illegally dumped*** | "Greene County Man Accused Of Dumping Drilling Waste Water" CBS Pittsburgh (Pittsburgh, Pennsylvania, March 18 2011)

303 | ***discharging waste at night, in rainstorms*** | Aaron Skirboll, "Gas profiteers' shocking crimes: Allan Shipman was found guilty of illegal dumping, but he's part of a much bigger problem" Salon (San Francisco, California, August 18 2012)

303 | ***front of rusty brown contamination invaded*** | "Briny water flows into local streams" Observer-Reporter (Pittsburgh, Pennsylvania, February 12, 2013)

303 | ***also dumped waste into an old coal mine shaft*** | Aaron Skirboll, Gas profiteers'

303 | ***Greene County environmental leader told a reporter*** | Briny water, Observer-Reporter

303-304 | ***Fayette County, it also must have been open season → completely filled with drill cuttings*** | Alyssa Choiniere, "Investigation reveals oil and gas drilling waste dumped at local magistrate, Dairy Queen" Herald-Standard (Uniontown, Pennsylvania, March 29 2017)

304 | ***investigation in the early years of Pennsylvania's*** | Sabrina Shankman, "Pennsylvania's Gas Wells Booming -- But So Are Spills" ProPublica

(New York, New York, January 27, 2010)
304 | ***research team that assessed the brine spill in Blacktail Creek in the Bakken oilfield*** | Isabelle M. Cozzarelli, Douglas B. Kent, Martin Briggs, Mark A. Engle, Adam Benthem, Katherine J. Skalak, Adam C. Mumford, Jeanne Jaeschke, Aïda Farag, John W. Lane Jr and Denise M. Akob, "Geochemical and geophysical indicators of oil and gas wastewater can trace potential exposure pathways following releases to surface waters," Science of the Total Environment, Volume 755 (2021)
304 | ***Dawn Fuchs Coleman in a book she wrote*** | Dawn Fuchs Coleman, Get Your Game F.A.C.E. On: The Secret to Growing Your Company in Any Economy: The Secret to Growing Your Company In Any Economy (2020)
305 | ***I ask Weavertown*** | Attempted correspondence with Weavertown Environmental, 2023-2024 (tford@weavertown.com and pro-onerock@prosek.com, July 24 2023 and February 22 2024)
305 | ***were pitchers and one was a catcher*** | Bill Beckner Jr., "Westmoreland notebook: Mt. Pleasant to honor Giallonardo" Pittsburgh Tribune-Review (Pittsburgh, Pennsylvania, March 18 2021) ; Eliza Griswold, "When the Kids Started Getting Sick," The New Yorker (NY, NY, March 2 2021)
305 | ***Pribanic suggested the infield dirt the kids had played on*** | Conversations and correspondences with Public Herald co-founder Joshua Pribanic, 2019-2024
305 | ***Samples Pribanic brings to University of Pittsburgh geochemist*** | "Excel Spreadsheet with Radium Soil Samples" (Dr. Dan Bain's Lab at the University of Pittsburgh, August 20, 2020)
305 | ***"There is cause to conduct a full investigation*** | Joshua Pribanic
306 | ***I connect with Kate Blanock, Luke Blanock's sister*** | Correspondence with Luke Blanock's sister, geologist Kate Blanock, 2023-2024
306 | ***finding radium levels to be highest not in the infield clay, but the outfield*** | "Eberline Analytical Final Report of Analysis for Cecil Baseball Field Soil Samples, SDG 23-09070" (Eberline Analytical, September 2023)
306 | ***EPA's radium limits for topsoil at toxic waste dumps*** | EPA Facts about Radium, (EPA), https://semspub.epa.gov/work/HQ/176334.pdf
306 | ***according to a Department of Energy fact sheet*** | "Fact Sheet: Canonsburg, Pennsylvania, Disposal Site" (U.S. Department of Energy, Legacy Management, July 2021)
306 | ***according to one history, the plant also produced "radium fertilizer"*** | Joel O. Lubenau and Edward R. Landa, "Radium City: A History of America's First Nuclear Industry" (Senator John Heinz History Center, 2019)
306 | ***Government reports from the 1990s indicate*** | "Long-Term Surveillance Plan for the U.S. Department of Energy Canonsburg Uranium Mill Tailings Disposal Site Canonsburg, Pennsylvania" (U.S. Department of Energy, Office of Legacy Management, January 2008)
306 | ***samples drawn from the creek next to the former uranium mill*** | Conversations and correspondences with Public Herald co-founder Joshua Pribanic, 2019-2024 ; "Excel Spreadsheet with Radium Soil Samples" (Dr. Dan Bain's Lab at the University of Pittsburgh, August 20, 2020)
306-307 | ***It is not yet noon, and Ray Kemble → right into the river, schwoop!"*** | Correspondence and conversations with Ray Kemble, 2018-2024
307 | ***brine in Pennsylvania was initially discharged to pits → custom developed of bringing this waste to sewage plants*** | Paul Hart, "Challenges

and Merging Practices for the Treatment of Natural Gas Fluids" (Hart Resource Technologies, November 2, 2012) ; Correspondence with former Pennsylvania Department of Environmental Protection Director David Hess, 2020-2023

307-308 | ***even brine from conventional oil and gas wells*** | "U.S. Geological Survey National Produced Waters Geochemical Database, version 3.0" (U.S. Geological Survey, 2024)

308 | ***safe drinking water limit for radium*** | "Radionuclides Rule" (EPA, November 7, 2023)

308 | ***didn't require operators to check for radium □ It's the wild west!*** | Correspondence with former Pennsylvania Department of Environmental Protection Director David Hess, 2020-2023

308 | ***added stricter discharge limits for salts and some metals*** | John A. Veil, "DOE Award No.: FWP 49462, Final Report, Water Management Technologies Used by Marcellus Shale Gas Producers" (Argonne National Laboratory for U.S. Department of Energy, National Energy Technology Laboratory)

308 | ***still no rules for radium*** | David Hess

308-309 | ***Bill Burgos, along with a team of other researchers □ "Sediment layers corresponding to the years of maximum"*** | Correspondence and conversations with Penn State environmental engineer Dr. Bill Burgos, 2019-2024 ; William D. Burgos, Luis Castillo-Meza, Travis L. Tasker, Thomas J. Geeza, Patrick J. Drohan, Xiaofeng Liu, Joshua D. Landis, Jens Blotevogel, Molly McLaughlin, Thomas Borch, and Nathaniel R. Warner, "Watershed-Scale Impacts from Surface Water Disposal of Oil and Gas Wastewater in Western Pennsylvania," Environmental Science & Technology, Volume 51 (2018)

309 | ***levels were so high, the researchers reported in 2013*** | Nathaniel R. Warner, Cidney A. Christie, Robert B. Jackson and Avner Vengosh, "Impacts of Shale Gas Wastewater Disposal on Water Quality in Western Pennsylvania," Environmental Science & Technology, Volume 47 (2013)

310 | ***little-publicized 2018 report on oilfield wastewater treatment plants*** | "Detailed Study of the Centralized Waste Treatment Point Source Category for Facilities Managing Oil and Gas Extraction Wastes EPA-821-R-18-004" (EPA, Office of Water, Engineering and Analysis Division, May 2018)

310 | ***The Department of Energy also examined the issue*** | John A. Veil, "DOE Award No.: FWP 49462, Final Report, Water Management Technologies Used by Marcellus Shale Gas Producers" (Argonne National Laboratory for U.S. Department of Energy, National Energy Technology Laboratory)

310 | ***asked Argonne why not, and not received a reply*** | Attempted correspondence with Argonne National Laboratory officials, 2018-2024 (August 17 2018 Argonne researcher Karen P. Smith ; August 8 2022 Chief communications officer Leslie Krohn and general media contact media@anl.gov ; January 29 2024 Chief communications officer Leslie Krohn and general media contact media@anl.gov)

310 | ***Pennsylvania Department of Environmental Protection published an expansive report on oilfield radioactivity*** | Technologically Enhanced Naturally Occurring Radioactive Materials (TENORM) Study Report, (Pennsylvania Department of Environmental Protection, 2016)

311 | ***Brett Jennings, Chairman of the Hallstead-Great Bend → By afternoon, his plant was dead*** | Conversations and correspondence with Bret Jennings, 2022

311 | ***investigative reporter Joaquin Sapien reported*** | Joaquin Sapien, "With Natural Gas Drilling Boom, Pennsylvania Faces Flood of Wastewater" ProPublica (NY, NY, October 5, 2009)
311 | ***a former Pittsburgh Water & Sewer Authority water plant worker tells me*** | Correspondence with Pittsburgh Water & Sewer Authority water plant worker, 2022-2024
312 | ***beginnings were humble,"*** | "American Water Company History" (American Water website)
312 | ***345 billion gallons of water to more than ten million customers*** | "American Water Company History Timeline" (Zippia)
312 | ***"We work hard each and every*** | "American Water Company History" (American Water website)
312 | ***"Private Water Companies Join Forces With Fracking Interests"*** | Sarah Pavlus, "Private Water Companies Join Forces With Fracking Interests" Colorado Independent (April 23, 2012)
312 | ***In 2011 he told another investigative reporter*** | Anthony Brino, "Fracking at Drinking Water Source for 80,000 Pennsylvanians Raises Alarms" (Toronto, Canada, May 18, 2012)
313 | ***company's 2012 annual report*** | "American Water: 2012 Annual Report" (American Water, 2012)
313 | ***a March 2012 presentation to investors stated*** | Sarah Pavlus, "Private Water Companies Join Forces With Fracking Interests" Colorado Independent (April 23, 2012)
313 | ***company has three large drinking water intake*** | Correspondence and attempted correspondence with Pennsylvania American Water spokesperson Gary Lobaugh, 2021-2024 (June 21, 2021)
313-314 | ***says Dr. Mike Domach, a chemical engineer*** | Conversations and correspondence with Carnegie Mellon University chemical engineer Dr Michael Domach, 2022-2024
314 | ***a significant challenge to the barrier model*** | Dr Michael Domach
314 | ***contamination could even be tasted*** |"Pa. official: End nears for wastewater releases" Associated Press (New York, New York, April 24 2011)
314 | ***Joaquin Sapien reported in his 2009 article*** | Joaquin Sapien, "With Natural Gas Drilling Boom, Pennsylvania Faces Flood of Wastewater" ProPublica (New York, New York, October 5, 2009)
314 | ***complaining about a salty taste in their drinking water*** | "Pa. official: End nears for wastewater releases" Associated Press (New York, New York, April 24 2011)
315 | ***bromide combined with the chlorine used by water plants for treatment*** |"Pa. official: End nears for wastewater releases" Associated Press (New York, New York, April 24 2011)
315 | ***Dr. Jessica Wilson pointed out*** | J.M. Wilson and J.M. VanBriesen, "Oil and gas produced water management and surface drinking water sources," Environmental Practice, Volume 14 (2012)
315 | ***But the Carnegie Mellon research → pouring into the rivers."*** |"Pa. official: End nears for wastewater releases" Associated Press (New York, New York, April 24 2011)
316 | ***investigative reporter at the New York Times, turned his attention to America's fracking boom*** | Ian Urbina, "Drilling Down Series" New York

Times (New York, New York, 2011-2012)

316-317 | ***first story he published, on February 26, 2011 → eating, drinking or breathing, it can cause cancer."*** | Ian Urbina, "Drilling Down: Regulation Lax as Gas Wells' Tainted Water Hits Rivers" New York Times (New York, New York, February 26, 2011)

317 | ***both conducted water testing*** | Don Hopey, "No dangerous radiation found in Pa. water, but EPA urges more radiation checks" Pittsburgh Post-Gazette (Pittsburgh, Pennsylvania, March 8, 2011)

317-318 | ***"The DEP tested water from the Monongahela → stringent oversight program for the gas drilling industry."*** | Don Hopey, No dangerous radiation

318 | ***Pennsylvania American Water conducted tests → has not been impacted by radioactive materials."*** | "New Tests Confirm Marcellus Development Not Impacting Pa. Waterways" (Marcellus Shale Coaltion, May 18 2011)

318 | ***enforceable rules on radium in drinking water*** | "Radionuclides Rule" (US EPA, 2023)

318 | ***required to test for radium once every nine years*** | "Radionuclides Rule: A Quick Reference Guide" (US EPA, June 2001)

318 | ***"To do radium once every nine years is ridiculous," says the former water plant worker*** | Correspondence with Pittsburgh Water & Sewer Authority water plant worker, 2022-2024

319 | ***parts of the US have naturally high radium levels*** | C. Richard Cothern and Paul A Rebers, "Radon, Radium and Uranium in Drinking Water" (Chelsea, Michigan: Lewis Publishers, 1990)

319-320 | ***conflict of interest, Lobaugh tells me*** | Correspondence and attempted correspondence with Pennsylvania American Water spokesperson Gary Lobaugh, 2021-2024 (Correspondence: June 21, 2021 ; Attempted correspondence: August 8 2022, September 15 2023, February 25 2024)

320-321 | ***"When I started out with the field of pediatric epidemiology → want to stake their career on studying something rare."*** | Correspondence and conversations with Dr. Logan Spector, Director of the Division of Epidemiology and Clinical Research at the University of Minnesota, 2022-2023

321 | ***Canadian epidemiologist Dr. Murray Finkelstein → afternoon I reach him by phone*** | Murray M. Finkelstein, "Radium in drinking water and the risk of death from bone cancer among Ontario youths," Canadian Medical Association Journal, Volume 151, Number 5 (1994) ; Murray M. Finkelstein and Nancy Kreiger, "Radium in drinking water and risk of bone cancer in Ontario youths: a second study and combined analysis," Occupational and Environmental Medicine, Volume 53 (1996) ; Correspondence and conversations with Canadian epidemiologist Dr. Murray Finkelstein, 2021

322 | ***Linear No-Threshold model says*** | Moshe Yanovskiy, Yair Y. Shaki and Yehoshua Socol, "Ethics of Adoption and Use of the Linear No-Threshold Model" Dose Response, Vol 17, Number 1 (2019)

322 | ***"If you accept there is no threshold → vegetables would not be the ideal water museum*** | Correspondence and conversations with Canadian epidemiologist Dr. Murray Finkelstein, 2021 ; Murray M. Finkelstein, "Radium in drinking water and the risk of death from bone cancer among Ontario youths," Canadian Medical Association Journal, Volume 151, Number 5 (1994) ; Murray M.

Finkelstein and Nancy Kreiger, "Radium in drinking water and risk of bone cancer in Ontario youths: a second study and combined analysis," Occupational and Environmental Medicine, Volume 53 (1996)
324 | ***I connect with Stacey Magda*** | Correspondence and conversations with Stacey Magda and Ashley Funk of Mountain Watershed Association, 2019-2024
324 | ***Heaven Sensky of Center for Coalfield Justice*** | Correspondence and conversations with Heaven Sensky of Center for Coalfield Justice, 2019-2024
324-325 | ***P-trap samples to Dr. Marco Kaltofen → reading no different from background."*** | Correspondence and conversations with nuclear forensics scientist Dr. Marco Kaltofen, 2019-2024
325 | ***the 1988 book,* Zodiac** | Neal Stephenson, Zodiac (New York, New York: Grove Press, 1988)
325 | ***Regulators' Guide to the Management of Radioactive Residuals → Meaning these residuals could become so radioactive*** | "A Regulators' Guide to the Management of Radioactive Residuals from Drinking Water Treatment Technologies," (EPA, Office of Water, July 2005)
325 | ***setup a formal slot of time known as a file review*** | Correspondence with Edward Stokan and Marion Leturgey in the Pennsylvania Department of Environmental Protection's Southwest Regional Office, 2022-2023
325-326 | ***already formally requested of the Department of Environmental Protection*** | "Justin Nobel, Rolling Stone/DeSmog/Simon & Schuster, Correspondences and materials of Former Director of the Pennsylvania Department of Environmental Protection Bureau of Radiation Protection David Allard" (DEP Right-to-Know Law Record Request Form, March 2023)
326 | ***months later to tell me: "your request is denied"*** | "May 3 2023 Letter from Pennsylvania Department of Environmental Protection to Justin Nobel Re: Right-to-Know Request Tracking Number: 2023-0226 (CO)" (Pennsylvania Department of Environmental Protection, May 3 2023)
326 | ***So, I filed a second records request*** | "Justin Nobel, Rolling Stone/ DeSmog/Simon & Schuster, Correspondences and materials of Former and Current Director of the Pennsylvania Department of Environmental Protection Bureau of Radiation Protection" (DEP Right-to-Know Law Record Request Form, May 2023)
326 | ***This request was also denied*** | "June 15, 2023 Letter from Pennsylvania Department of Environmental Protection to Justin Nobel Re: Right-to-Know Request Tracking Number: 2023-0381 (CO)" (Pennsylvania Department of Environmental Protection, June 15, 2023)
326 | ***Documents filed by Pennsylvania American Water's E.H. Aldrich plant, on April 6, 2010*** | Justin Nobel File Review at Pennsylvania Department of Environmental Protection's Southwest Regional Office, April 20 2023 and May 22 2023 ("Department of Environmental Protection, General Information Form – Authorization Application, Pennsylvania American Water, E.H. Aldrich: Water Standards & Facility Regulation: Application Tracking Form, Permit #: PA0000272, PWS ID# 5020039" (December 2, 2009))
327 | ***I do not find the answer to that question in the files I am reviewing*** | Justin Nobel File Review at Pennsylvania Department of Environmental Protection's Southwest Regional Office, April 20 2023 and May 22 2023
327 | ***On November 6, 1996, Pennsylvania American Water sent a letter to the Pennsylvania Department of Environmental Protection → "is not considered waste and does not require any permits or tracking."*** |

Justin Nobel File Review at Pennsylvania Department of Environmental Protection's Southwest Regional Office, April 20 2023 and May 22 2023 (Letter Exchange Between Pennsylvania American Water and Pennsylvania Department of Environmental Protection Re: Pennsylvania-American Water Company Hays Mine and Aldrich Treatment Plant Dewasting Determination Request, November 26, 1996-January 8, 2019)
328 | ***I dial up the health physicist source → they got away with one"*** | Correspondence with staff health physicist source, 2020-2024
328 | ***case from the Charles Allen Water Filtration Plant in Englewood, Colorado*** | Rick Sallinger, "Water Treatment Plant Worker With Cancer Calls Health Department Letter 'Smoking Gun'" CBS Colorado (New York, New York, August 3, 2016)
328 | ***Gary Lobaugh, with Pennsylvania American Water, tells me*** | Correspondence and attempted correspondence with Pennsylvania American Water spokesperson Gary Lobaugh, 2021-2024 (Correspondence: June 21, 2021 and March 10, 2024 ; Attempted correspondence: August 8 2022, September 15 2023, February 25 2024)

Chapter 16
329 | ***in this place that Dr. Paul Templet → During the 1960s he worked as a chemist at a set of Shell oil*** | Correspondence and conversations with Dr. Paul Templet, 2018-2023
330 | ***we're in trouble," Roemer told a reporter*** | Wayne King, "Bad Times on the Bayou" New York Times Magazine (New York, New York, June 11, 1989)
330-331 | ***founded after Emancipation by people that had formerly been enslaved in the adjacent plantations*** | Idna G. Castellón, "Cancer Alley and the Fight Against Environmental Racism," Villanova Environmental Law Journal, Volume 15 (2021)
331 | ***experience was certainly eye opening" → to learn what the state's most pressing environmental issues*** | Correspondence and conversations with Dr. Paul Templet, 2018-2023
331 | ***the only time we had that kind of environmental leadership"*** | Correspondence and conversations with Louisiana environmental toxicologist Wilma Subra, 2018-2024
331 | ***Another member was Maureen O'Neill*** | Peggy Frankland and Susan Tucker, Women Pioneers of the Louisiana Environmental Movement (Jackson, Mississippi: University Press of Mississippi, 2013)
331-333 | ***Between growing up in Louisiana → Templet had discovered another concerning pathway of environmental contamination*** | Dr. Paul Templet
333 | ***Louisiana was discharging roughly 1.8 to 2 million barrels of oilfield brine daily*** | "Report to Congress, Management of Wastes from the Exploration, Development, and Production of Crude Oil, Natural Gas, and Geothermal Energy, Volume 1 of 3, Oil and Gas" (U.S. EPA, December 1987) ; "Report to Congress, Management of Wastes from the Exploration, Development, and Production of Crude Oil, Natural Gas, and Geothermal Energy, Volume 3 of 3, Appendices, A-Summary of State Oil and Gas Regulations, B-Glossary of Terms Volume 1, C-Damage Case Summaries" (U.S. EPA, December 1987)
333 | ***elevated radium in the tissue of the oysters*** | Kerry M. St. Pé, "An

Assessment of Produced Water Impacts to Low-Energy, Brackish Water Systems in Southeast Louisiana" (Louisiana Department of Environmental Quality, Water Pollution Control Division, July 1990)

334 | ***Department of Environmental Quality issued rules that halted*** | Dr. Paul Templet

334 | ***"On Sept. 20, 1989," the oil industry consultant Peter*** | Peter Gray, "Radioactive Materials Could Pose Problems For the Gas Industry" Oil & Gas Journal (Tulsa, Oklahoma, June 25, 1990)

334 | ***Texas and Mississippi began working on rules*** | P.R. Gray, "NORM Contamination in the Petroleum Industry" Journal of Petroleum Technology, Volume 45, Number 01 (1993)

334 | **New York Times *ran a front-page story on December 3***| Keith Schneider, "Radiation Danger Found in Oilfields Across the Nation" New York Times (New York, New York, December 3, 1990)

334 | ***Another New York Times story, published on Christmas*** | Keith Schneider, "2 Suits on Radium Cleanup Test Oil Industry's Liability" New York Times (NY, NY, December 24, 1990)

335 | ***Nevertheless, Templet didn't cave*** | Dr. Paul Templet

335 | ***Templet wrote a letter to the Occupational Safety and Health Administration → "very difficult questions concerning potential liabilities"*** | "Letter from Paul H. Templet, Ph.D., Secretary State of Louisiana Department of Environmental Quality to U.S. Occupational Safety & Health Administration Re: Radiation Associated with Oil and Natural Gas Production and Processing Facilities" (U.S. Occupational Safety & Health Administration, October 20 1988)

335 | ***they still have done nothing*** | Correspondences with U.S. Occupational Safety and Health Administration under the U.S. Department of Labor, 2018-2023 (Michael Trupo, August 23 2018)

335 | ***no federal agency has issued rules on oilfield radioactivity*** | Correspondence with staff health physicist source, 2020-2024

336 | ***It's the secret of the century*** | Dr. Paul Templet

nothing will ever be the same, the same, again

Milton Keynes UK
Ingram Content Group UK Ltd.
UKHW020717030524
442155UK00010B/70/J

9 798989 546237